GCSE
BIOLOGY

D0525156

Julian Ford-Robertson

Letts
EDUCATIONAL

First published 1979
Revised 1981, 1987, 1989, 1994
Reprinted 1991, 1993, 1995

Letts Educational
Aldine House
Aldine Place
London W12 8AW

Text: © Julian Ford-Robertson 1994
Design and illustrations: © BPP (Letts Educational) Ltd 1994

British Library Cataloguing in Publication Data
A CIP record for this book is available from the British Library.

ISBN 1 85758 300 0

Printed in Great Britain by WM Print Limited, Walsall, West Midlands WS2 9NE

Letts Educational is the trading name of BPP (Letts Educational) Ltd

Preface

Revise Biology is designed to meet the needs of the GCSE and SCE exams. It emphasizes the **experimental basis** for scientific knowledge, putting the facts deduced by experiment into a **framework of knowledge**. Advice on **revision** and **examination technique** is given along with **questions** on which students may gain practice. In the last chapter **ideas for experiments of your own** are given.

The latest update takes account of the most recent changes in the National Curriculum. Changes include sections on DNA structure and function, adaptations to extreme environments, the life histories and importance of liver fluke and *Entamoeba*, advances in medical technology and contraception, fossils and their significance, and sports injuries. Sections on birdflight, earthworm burrowing and woodlouse walking have been added. There are also many other minor improvements and additions.

Of particular help to students is an explanation of how Boards assess practical coursework – clues as to how to go about experimental work.

Changes have also been made in line with the recommendations made by the Institute of Biology (1989) on the classification of organisms and biological nomenclature. Finally, an extensive range of actual GCSE and SCE examination questions has been included. Throughout this book the term 'Man' has been used to refer to 'human beings', both male and female; no bias is implied on the basis of gender.

In the preparation of this book I have been greatly assisted by helpful criticism from C. G. Gayford, BSc, MEd (Science Education), PhD, PGCE, Lecturer in Education at the University of Reading; Wilf Stout, BSc, MA, MEd, CBiol, MIBiol; and B. Arnold, MSc, MIBiol, Lecturer in Biology at Aberdeen College of Education. I am also grateful for specialist advice from Mr P. H. L. Worth, Consultant Urologist, Dr J. Higgo of Imperial College, Mrs E. Skinner of the Cancer Research Campaign, Dr M. F. Cheyne, Resident Medical Officer at Haileybury College, Prof. D. E. Jacobs of the Royal Veterinary College, and Prof. G. Webbe of the London School of Hygiene and Tropical Medicine. To my wife and Susan Hunt who typed, to Stan Martin who illustrated and to Wayne Davies, Tim Jackson and Richard Carr who edited the work I owe a special debt; but numerous others – Alex my son, colleagues and friends – also lent valuable support.

I am grateful to the following Examination Groups for permission to use a selection of their GCSE and Standard Grade (SEB) questions in Biology: MEG, NEAB, NICCEA, SEG, ULEAC, WJEC and SEB. The answers to all questions are mine alone, and the Groups can accept no responsibility for them.

Julian Ford-Robertson
1994

Contents

Introduction

How to use this book

Revise Biology is written especially for those who need help in preparing for the GCSE or the Scottish Standard Grade examinations. It provides:
- advice on **what your syllabus requires**: a table of syllabus analysis.
- advice on **how to learn**: learning made easier.
- **what to learn** in readily revisable form: information, lavishly illustrated.
- advice on how to **show the examiner** that you know what he is asking for: an outline of good examination technique.
- **practice in answering** examination questions.

If you follow this sequence in the use of this book, you will have a good chance of success.

Using the table of analysis

Turn to p. 4 and select from the table your own Examination Group and syllabus. For each syllabus details are provided on:
(a) the number of theory papers and their length;
(b) the 'tiers' of entry and the 'levels' attainable.

Then turn to pages 6–11. This table will tell you what you need to know, topic by topic. This material has been divided into numbered units, not all of which need be studied for your own syllabus.

Select carefully the units you require by referring to the symbols:
- unit required for a syllabus
(●) unit required, but with reservations. These reservations may include such things as 'less detail than this is required' or 'this organism can be used as an example for a part of the syllabus, but is not specifically named'.

Where neither of these symbols appears against a topic, i.e. the space is *left blank*, you do not need to study that unit.

The Table of Analysis of Syllabus Content must be regarded only as a helpful guide. If you send for your Examination Group's syllabus and for copies of past examination papers (use the addresses on p. 5), you will be able to judge more easily what the special features of your syllabus are. Your teacher will also give you advice, particularly on units marked (●).

Before using the subject material, first take care to understand *how* you should revise (see 'Studying and revising', p. 12). Do not exceed your 'concentration time' (see p. 14).

Using the subject material

Work through only the units that you need to select (see above). Use every memory aid that you can (see 'Studying and revising'). Remember that 75% of the marks that decide your grade in GCSE (or equivalent) can come from **your efforts on paper in the examination room**.

The other 25% of your marks can come from practical work **in the laboratory** (Coursework Assessment). So remind yourself of the practical techniques that you should have used throughout the course. Chapter 22 is particularly important.

Examination technique for biology examinations

Turn to p. 234. The advice given ranges from tips on organizing what to take into the examination room to how to use your time well. Then build up your confidence by trying to answer the examination questions on p. 239 – all of them provided by the Examining Groups.

The National Curriculum and GCSE

Science

Science is a compulsory part of the National Curriculum and may be studied as either

1. **Science: Single Award** *or* **Science: Double Award** – both of which include Biology, Chemistry and Physics – or

2. **Science: Biology** *and* **Science: Chemistry** *and* **Science: Physics**, i.e. a suite of three subjects. This method has the advantage of giving those who are more scientifically interested wider opportunities in their subjects. It gives them three GCSE passes (instead of the two or one awarded in Science). It also prepares them better for Science A levels and the competition that ensues for University places.

Aims of the National Curriculum Biology course for GCSE

1. To enable students, through experiment and study, to be able to take a critical interest in biological science in a technological world, realizing the strengths and weaknesses of scientific methods but also their usefulness in everyday life.

2. To encourage those who are interested to go on to further studies in Biology.

3. To stimulate curiosity, interest and enjoyment in the study of Biology and to see its applications used safely in everyday life.

4. To promote care for the environment. However, this must take into account all sorts of different factors beyond those in the purely natural world.

5. To make students aware that purely scientific discoveries become influenced, in their application, by social, economic, technological, ethical and cultural influences.

6. To make students realize that 'a fact' today may not be a fact tomorrow because of new scientific evidence and interpretation.

How you get a Biology GCSE

There are two parts to getting a pass: Coursework (25%) and written Exams (75%). Within the total is a hidden 5% allocated to good English.

- **Coursework**, also known as Science 1, is compulsory for all science courses. This is the programme of practical investigation continuously assessed by teachers in the laboratory or through fieldwork, throughout the course.

- **Written exams** in Biology are known as Science 2 (Chemistry and Physics are Sciences 3 and 4, respectively). All questions are compulsory. The exams are taken at the end of the course.

- **Levels:** After the exams a level is awarded for each of Sciences 1–4 from 10 (highest) down to 4 (lowest).

- **Grades:** The levels are then translated into grades A★ to G, which are entered on the Certificate.

The relationship between Levels and Grades is shown in the Table opposite. Note that there is no direct correlation between grades C, D and E and levels 7 and 6.

Levels	Grades
10	A★
9	A
8	B
7	C
	D
6	E
5	F
4	G
3	U

- **Entry tiers:** Your teacher, on the basis of your performance, enters you for exams at one of three tiers. The six different Exam Boards have their own names for these tiers, but they amount to Upper, Middle and Lower ability range exams. A very good student would be entered for Upper tier exams. If students in fact do better or worse than the expected levels attainable on the exams for which they had been entered, there is provision to award levels higher or lower than expected. The range of Levels that can be awarded in each Tier of exams and the duration of those exams can be seen on p. 4.

- **English:** Marks are awarded for quality of spelling, punctuation, grammar and for the precise use of specialist terms.

The Scottish Certificate of Education (SCE)

The principles of the SCE are similar to those of GCSE.

Students are tested by teachers on their **Practical Abilities** during the course. At the end of the course, written examinations test **Knowledge and Understanding** and **Problem Solving**. A grade is awarded for each of these three 'elements' on the certificate, along with an overall grade.

- **Aims:** The aims of SCE are much the same as in GCSE but are expressed less verbosely. They add that pupils should appreciate the employment opportunities in biology and see its application to leisure pursuits. They also stress that 'positive attitudes' such as open-mindedness should be fostered but without sacrificing the ability to take decisions affecting the well-being of themselves, others and the environment.

- **Entry:** Biology is one of the few subjects that is only offered at Credit and General levels – there is no Foundation level. (All three levels do, however, exist for Science, which includes Biology, Chemistry and Physics.) Students can take either Credit or General level exams or, if teachers think it wise, both. If both are taken, the better of the two grades is awarded. Students can take Biology (or any other science subject) on its own.

- **Grades:** Credit level gives grades 1 and 2, General level gives grades 3 and 4 (with a possibility of grade 5 for work below the expected lowest mark. Grade 7 is reserved for those who have completed the course but fallen below the standard of grade 5. The overall grade 3 is equivalent to grade C in GCSE.

- **Syllabus:** There are seven topics
  The biosphere
  The world of plants
  Animal survival
  Investigation of cells
  The body in action
  Inheritance
  Biotechnology

There is no subdivision into 'core' and 'extension work'. For details, see the Table of Analysis of Syllabus Content (p. 6).

- **Practical abilities:** see p. 17.

Analysis of examinations

Find your examining group and syllabus in the following table. This will then give you details of the number of papers you will have to sit, their length and the levels of attainment available.

The actual details of the topics from this book that you will need to study for your syllabus are given on pages 5–11.

Paper analysis

Group & Syllabus	Length of exam(s)			Levels of attainment: targetted (other levels possible are shown in brackets)		
MEG Biology 1780 Nuffield 1785 } Salters 1790	**Further** 2¼ hrs	**Central** 2 hrs	**Basic** 1½ hrs	**Further** 10–9 (8, 7)	**Central** (9) 8–7 (6, 5)	**Basic** (7) 6–4 (3)
NEAB	**R** 2½ hrs	**Q** 2 hrs	**P** 1½ hrs	**R** 10–8 (7)	**Q** 8–6 (5)	**P** 6–4 (3)
NICCEA	**R** 1½ hrs +1½ hrs	**Q** 1 hr +1½ hrs	**P** 1 hr +1½ hrs	**R** 10–8 (7)	**Q** 8–6 (5)	**P** 6–4 (3)
SEG	**Higher** 1½ hrs core + 1 hr extension	**Intermed.** 1½ hrs core + 1 hr extension	**Foundation** 1½ hrs core + 1 hr extension	**Higher** 10–8 (7)	**Intermed.** (9) 8–6 (5)	**Foundation** (7) 6–4 (3)
ULEAC A 1026 } B 1028 }	**Higher** 1½ hrs core + 1½ hrs extension	**Intermed.** 1½ hrs core + 1½ hrs extension	**Foundation** 1½ hrs core + 1½ hrs extension	**Higher** 10–8 (7)	**Intermed.** (9) 8–6 (5)	**Foundation** (7) 6–4 (3)
WJEC	**R** 2½ hrs	**Q** 2 hrs	**P** 1½ hrs	**R** 10–8 (7)	**Q** 8–6 (5)	**P** 6–4 (3)
SEB	**Credit** 1½ hrs	**General** 1½ hrs Both papers may be taken		**Credit** 1, 2	**General** 3, 4 (5)	
IGCSE	**Extension** 1 hr + 1¼ hrs	**Core** ¾ hr + 1 hr		**Extension** A–E	**Core** C–G	

Examination Boards: Addresses

MEG   **Midland Examining Group**

1 Hills Road
Cambridge
CB1 2EU

Tel: 0223 553311

NEAB   **Northern Examinations and Assessment Board**

12 Harter Street
Manchester
M1 6HL

Tel: 061 953 1180

NICCEA   **Northern Ireland Council for the Curriculum Examinations and Assessment**

Beechill House
42 Beechill Road
Belfast
BT8 4RS

Tel: 0232 704666

SEB   **Scottish Examination Board**

Ironmills Road
Dalkeith
Midlothian
EH22 1LE

Tel: 031 663 6601

SEG   **Southern Examining Group**

Stag Hill House
Guildford
GU2 5XJ

Tel: 0483 506506

ULEAC   **University of London Examinations and Assessment Council**

Stewart House
32 Russell Square
London
WC1B 5DN

Tel: 071 331 4000

WJEC   **Welsh Joint Education Committee**

245 Western Avenue
Cardiff
CF5 2YX

Tel: 0222 561231

Table of analysis of syllabus content

GROUPS AND SYLLABUSES	MEG			NEAB	NICCEA	SEG	ULEAC		WJEC	SEB	IGCSE
	Biology 1780	Nuffield 1785	Salters 1790				A 1026	B 1028			
1 Life											
1.1 Characteristics of organisms	•	•	•	•	•	•	•	•	•	•	•
1.2 Cells in detail	•	•	•	•	•	•	•	•	•	•	(•)
1.3 How the nucleus 'controls' the cell	•	•	•	•	•	•	•	•	•	•	
1.4 DNA structure and function	•	•	•	•	•	•	•	•	•	•	
1.5 Enzymes and metabolism	•	•	•	•	•	•	•	•	•	•	•
1.6 Units of life beyond the cell	•	•	•	•	•	•	•	•	•		•
2 Classification											
2.1 Linnaeus and his classification system	•	•	•	•	•	•	•	•	•		•
2.2 Groups and subgroups	•	•	•	•	•	•	•	•	•		
2.3 Plant kingdom and simpler forms of life	•	•	•	•	•	•	•	•	•	•	•
2.4 Animal kingdom	•	•	•	•	•	•	•	•	•	(•)	•
2.5 Modern classification	•	•	•	•	•	•	•	•			
2.6 Multicell plants and animals compared				•		•			•		
3 Viruses, microorganisms, fungi and biotechnology											
3.1 Viruses	•	•	•	•	•	•	•	•	•		(•)
3.2 Bacteria	•	•	•	•	•	•	•	•	•	(•)	(•)
3.3 Importance of bacteria	•	•	•	•	•	•	•	•	•	•	
3.4 How viruses and bacteria reach people	•	•	•	•	•	•	•	•	•	•	
3.5 Control of harmful bacteria	•	(•)			•	•	(•)	(•)		•	
3.6 Growing bacteria	•	•	•	•	•	•	•	•	•	•	
3.7 Fungi – moulds and their culture	•	•	•	•	•	•	•	•	•	•	
3.8 Fungi – mushrooms and yeasts	•	•	•	•	•	•	•	•	•		
3.9 Importance of fungi	•	•	•	•	•	•	•	•	•	(•)	(•)
3.10 Algae		•	•	•	•		•	•	•	•	
3.11 Protozoa		•	•		•	(•)			•		
3.12 Biotechnology	(•)	•	•	•	•	•	(•)	(•)	(•)	•	(•)
4 Foods and feeding											
4.1 Food	•	•	•	•	•	•	•	•	•	•	•
4.2 Holophytic, holozoic and saprophytic nutrition compared	•	•	•	•	•	•	•	•	•		
4.3 Mineral salts for mammals and flowering plants	•	•	•	•	•	•	•	•	•		(•)
4.4 Carbohydrates, fats and proteins	•	•	•	•	•	•	•	•	•	•	•
4.5 Vitamins	•	•	•	•	•	•	•	•	•		(•)
4.6 Diet, health and additives	•	•	•	•	•	•	•	•	•	(•)	•
5 Green plant nutrition											
5.1 Photosynthesis	•	•	•	•	•	•	•	•	•	•	•
5.2 Factors necessary for photosynthesis	•	•	•	•	•	•	•	•	•	•	•

GROUP AND SYLLABUSES	MEG Biology 1780	MEG Nuffield 1785	MEG Salters 1790	NEAB	NICCEA	SEG	ULEAC A 1026	ULEAC B 1028	WJEC	SEB	IGCSE
5.3 Limiting factors	•	•	•	•	•	•	•	•	•	•	•
5.4 Rate of photosynthesis	•	•	•	•	•	•	•	•	•	•	•
5.5 Leaf structure and photosynthesis	•	•	•	•	•	•	•	•	•	•	
5.6 Gaseous exchange in leaves	•	•	•	•	•	•	•	•	•	•	
5.7 Amino acid synthesis	•	•	•	•	•	•	•	•	•		
5.8 Mineral salt uptake by roots	•	•	•	•	•	•	•	•	•		
6 Animal nutrition											
6.1 Feeding methods of animals						•					
6.2 Digestion and its consequences	•	•	•	•	•	•	•	•	•	•	
6.3 Experiments with digestive enzymes	•	•	•	•	•	•	•	•	•	•	•
6.4 Mammal teeth	•	•	•	•	•	•	•	•	•	•	•
6.5 Mammal alimentary canal	•	•	•	•	•	•	•	•	•	•	•
6.6 Dental health		•	•	•	•		•	•	•	•	
6.7 Herbivores and carnivores: teeth and jaws		•	•			•				•	
6.8 Absorption of food at a villus	•	•	•	•	•	•	•	•	•	•	•
6.9 Storage of food	•	•	•	•	•	•	•	•	•	•	
6.10 The liver	(•)	(•)		•	•	•	(•)	•	•	(•)	•
7 Water uptake and loss in plants and animals											
7.1 Importance of water	•	•	•	•	•	•	•	•	•	•	
7.2 Diffusion and active transport	•	•	•	•	•	•	•	•	•	•	•
7.3 Osmosis	•	•	•	•	•	•	•	•	•	•	•
7.4 Osmosis in cells	•	•	•	•	•	•	•	•	•	•	•
7.5 Water uptake and loss in flowering plants	•	•	•	•	•	•	•	•	•		
7.6 Guard cells and stomata	•	•	•	•	•	•	(•)	(•)	•	(•)	◉
7.7 Transpiration	•	•	•	•	•	•	•	•	•	•	•
7.8 Transport of organic food	•	•	•	•	•	•	•	•	•	•	•
7.9 Tissues in the stem and root	•	•	•	•	•	•	•	•	•		
7.10 Water uptake and loss in animals		•	•	(•)							
8 The blood and lymphatic systems											
8.1 Blood systems	•	•	•	•	•	•	•	•	•	•	•
8.2 Mammal blood and other body fluids	•	•	•	•	•	•	•	•	•	•	•
8.3 Blood vessels and blood circulation	•	•	•	•	•	•	•	•	•	•	•
8.4 The heart	•	•	•	•	•	•	•	•	•	•	•
8.5 Changes in blood around the circulatory system	•	•	•	•	•	•	•	•	•	•	(•)
8.6 Lymphatic system	•	•	•	•	•	•	•	•	•	(•)	•
9 Respiration											
9.1 Breathing, gaseous exchange and cellular respiration	•	•	•	•	•	•	•	•	•	•	•
9.2 Cellular respiration (aerobic and anaerobic)	•	•	•	•	•	•	•	•	•	•	•
9.3 Anaerobic respiration	•	•	•	•	•	•	•	•	•	•	•
9.4 Aerobic respiration	•	•	•	•	•	•	•	•	•	•	•
9.5 Rate of respiration		(•)	(•)			•	(•)	(•)		(•)	•
9.6 Gaseous exchange	•	•	•	•	•	•	•	•	•	•	•

GROUPS AND SYLLABUSES	MEG Biology 1780	MEG Nuffield 1785	MEG Salters 1790	NEAB	NICCEA	SEG	ULEAC A 1026	ULEAC B 1028	WJEC	SEB	IGCSE
9.7 Organisms respiring in water and air	•	•					(•)	(•)			
9.8 Mammal respiration	•	•	•	•	•	•	•	•	•	•	•
9.9 Gas changes during breathing	•	•	•	•	•	•	•	•	•	•	•
9.10 The respiratory pathway	•	•	•	•	•	•	•	•	•	•	•
9.11 Smoking or health	•	•	•	•	•	•	•	•	•		(•)
9.12 Gaseous exchange in flowering plants	•	•	•	•	•	•	•	•	•		•
9.13 Uses for energy from respiration	•	•	•	•	•	•	•	•			•
9.14 ATP (adenosine triphosphate)	•	•	•			•					
9.15 Measuring energy values of foods	•	•	•	•	•	•	•	•	•	•	
10 Excretion, temperature regulation and homeostasis											
10.1 Wastes and means of excretion	•	•	•	•	•	•	•	•	•	•	•
10.2 Mammal urinary system	•	•	•	•	•	•	•	•	•		•
10.3 The nephron	•	•	•	•	•	•	•	•		•	
10.4 Water conservation	•	•	•	•	•	•	•	•	•	•	
10.5 Abnormal kidney function	•	•	•	•	•	•	•	•	•	•	(•)
10.6 Body temperature in organisms	(•)	(•)	(•)	(•)	(•)	(•)	(•)	(•)		(•)	
10.7 Mammal temperature control	•	•	•	•	•	•	•	•	•		•
10.8 Adaptations to extreme conditions: polar bear, camel and cactus	(•)	•	(•)	(•)	(•)	(•)	(•)	(•)			
10.9 Homeostasis	•	•	•	•	•	•	•	•	•		•
10.10 Skin functions	•	•	•	•	•	•	•	•	•		
11 Sensitivity											
11.1 Sensitivity in plants and animals	•	•	•	•	•	•	•	•	•	•	•
11.2 Mammal sense organs	•	•	•	•	•	•	•	•	•	(•)	•
11.3 The eye	•	•	•	•	•	•	•	•	•	•	•
11.4 The ear	•	•	•	•	•	•	•	•	•	•	
12 Coordination and response											
12.1 Information, messages and action	•	•	•	•	•	•	•	•	•	•	•
12.2 Mammal nervous system	•	•	•	•	•	•	•	•	•	•	•
12.3 Nervous impulses	•	•	•			(•)	•	•		(•)	
12.4 Reflex action	•	•	•	•	•	•	•	•	•	•	•
12.5 Learned behaviour	•	•	•	•	•	•	•	•	•		
12.6 Instinctive behaviour		•	•								
12.7 The brain	•	•	•	•	•	•	•	•	•	(•)	
12.8 Misused drugs	•	•	•	•	•	•	•	•	•		(•)
12.9 Alcohol – ethanol	•	•	•	•	•	•	•	•	•		•
12.10 Endocrine system	•	•	•	•	•	•	•	•	•		(•)
12.11 Nervous and hormonal systems compared	•			•	•	•	(•)	(•)	•		•
12.12 Feedback	•	•	•	•	•	•	•	•	•		•
12.13 Taxis	•					•				•	•
12.14 Tropisms	•	•	•	•	•	•	•	•	•		•
12.15 Geotropism	•	•	•								•
12.16 Photoperiodism		•								•	

GROUPS AND SYLLABUSES	MEG Biology 1780	MEG Nuffield 1785	MEG Salters 1790	NEAB	NICCEA	SEG	ULEAC A 1026	ULEAC B 1028	WJEC	SEB	IGCSE
13 Support and locomotion											
13.1 Principles of support		•	(•)	(•)	(•)	(•)	(•)	(•)	(•)	•	
13.2 Support in plants	•	•	•	•	•	•	•	•	•		
13.3 Support and locomotion in animals		•								•	
13.4 Principles of movement	•	•	•	•	•	•	•	•	•	•	
13.5 Mammal tissues for support and locomotion	•	•	•	•	•	•	•	•	•	•	
13.6 Mammal skeleton	•	•	•	•	•	•	•	•	•	(•)	
13.7 Limbs and limb girdles of Man	(•)	(•)	(•)	(•)	(•)	(•)	•	(•)	(•)	•	
13.8 Joints	•	•	•	•	•	•	•	•	•	•	
13.9 Movement of an arm	•	•	•	•	•	•	•	•	•	•	•
13.10 Functions of mammal skeletons	•	•	•	•	•	•	•	•	•		
13.11 Sports injuries		•	(•)	(•)							
13.12 Hydraulic skeleton and earthworm movement	•										
13.13 Exoskeleton and woodlouse movement	•										
14 Reproduction: mainly plants											
14.1 Asexual and sexual reproduction compared	•	•	•	•	•	•	•	•	•	•	•
14.2 Asexual methods of reproduction	•	•	•	•	•	•	•	•	•	•	•
14.3 Surviving winter – perennation	(•)	(•)	•	(•)	(•)	(•)	(•)	(•)	(•)	(•)	(•)
14.4 Vegetative propagation	•	•	•	•	•	•	•	•	•	•	
14.5 Flowers	•	•	•	•	•	•	•	•	•	•	•
14.6 Self- and cross-pollination	•	•	•	•	•	•	•	•	•	•	
14.7 Wind and insect pollination	•	•	•	•	•	•	•	•	•	•	•
14.8 Fertilization and its consequences	•	•	•	•	•	•	•	•	•	•	
14.9 From flower to seed	•	•	•	•	•	•	•	•	•	•	
14.10 Fruits and seed dispersal	•	•	•	•	•	•	•	•	•	•	(•)
15 Reproduction: humans											
15.1 Sexual reproduction in humans	•	•	•	•	•	•	•	•	•	•	•
15.2 Placenta	•	•	•	•	•	•	•	•	•	•	•
15.3 Menstrual cycle	•	•	•	•	•	•	•	•	•		
15.4 Contraception	•	•	•	•	•	•	•	•	•		•
15.5 Sexually transmitted diseases (STD)	•	•	•	•	•	•	•	•	•		
15.6 Abortion and amniocentesis	•	•	•	•	•	•	•	•			
16 Growth of cells and populations											
16.1 Principles of growth	•	•	•	•	•	•	•	•	•	•	
16.2 Factors affecting growth	•	•	•	•	•	•	•	•	•	•	
16.3 Human growth	•	•	•	•	•	•	•	•	•		
16.4 Seed structure and germination	•	•	•	•	•	•	•	•	•		
16.5 Conditions necessary for germination	•	•	•	•	•	•	•	•	•	•	•
16.6 Growth measurement and its difficulties		•								•	
16.7 Growth of populations	•	•	•	•	•	•	•	•	•	•	
16.8 Human population	•	•	•	•	•	•	•	•			•
16.9 Population structure by age and sex	•										
16.10 Cancer	(•)	•	(•)	•	(•)	(•)	•	(•)	•		

GROUPS AND SYLLABUSES	MEG Biology 1780	MEG Nuffield 1785	MEG Salters 1790	NEAB	NICCEA	SEG	ULEAC A 1026	ULEAC B 1028	WJEC	SEB	IGCSE
17 Genes, chromosomes and heredity											
17.1 The nucleus, chromosomes and genes	●	●	●	●	●	●	●	●	●	●	●
17.2 Genes and characteristics	●	●	●	●	●	●	●	●	●	●	●
17.3 Human blood groups: codominance	●	●	●	●	●	●	●	●	●		●
17.4 Mendel's experiments	●	●	●	●	●	●	●	●	●	●	
17.5 Hints on tackling genetic problems	●	●	●	●	●	●	●	●	●	●	
17.6 Test cross test	●	●	●	●	●	●	●	●	●	●	
17.7 Ratios of phenotypes	●	●	●	●	●	●	●	●	●	●	
17.8 Sex determination in mammals	●	●	●	●	●	●	●	●	●	●	
17.9 Sex linkage	●	●	●	●	●	●	●	●	●		
17.10 Mitosis and meiosis in the life cycle	●	●	●	●	●	●	●	●	●	●	●
17.11 How chromosomes move apart at cell division	●	●	●	●	●	●	●	●	●	●	
17.12 Mitosis and meiosis compared	●	●	●	●	●	●	●	●	●	●	
17.13 Meiosis shuffles genes	●	●	●	(●)		(●)	●		(●)		
17.14 Variation in populations	●	●	●	●	●	●	●	●	●	●	●
17.15 Mutation	●	●	●	●	●	●	●	●	●	●	
17.16 Genetic engineering	●	●	●	●	●	●	●	●	●	●	
18 Evolution											
18.1 Selection of the 'best' from a variety	●	●	●	●	●	●	●	●	●		●
18.2 Examples of natural selection	●	●	●	●	●	●	●	●	●		●
18.3 Evolution by natural selection	●	●	●	●	●	●	●	●	●		●
18.4 Charles Darwin (1809–82)	●	●	●	●	●	●	●	●	●		
18.5 Artificial selection	●	●	●	●	●	●	●	●	●	●	●
18.6 Evidence for evolution: fossils	●	●	●	●	●	●	●	●			
18.7 Other theories of evolution			●			●					
19 Ecology											
19.1 The biosphere – its limits and organization	●	●	●	●	●	●	●	●	●	●	
19.2 Food chains, food webs and food cycles	●	●	●	●	●	●	●	●	●	●	●
19.3 Feeding relationships between species	●	●	●	●	●	●	●	●	●	●	
19.4 Stable and unstable ecosystems	●	●		●		●			●	(●)	
19.5 Pond ecosystem			(●)			(●)	●			(●)	
19.6 Woodland ecosystem	(●)	(●)	(●)		●	(●)	●			(●)	
19.7 Soil ecosystem	●	●	●		●	(●)	●				
19.8 Keys	●	●	●	●	●	●	●	●	●	●	●
19.9 Soil components	●		●								
19.10 Nitrogen cycle	●	●	●	●	●	●	●	●	●	●	●
19.11 Carbon cycle	●	●	●	●	●	●	●	●	●	(●)	●
19.12 Earthworms and soil	●	●	●							(●)	
19.13 Water cycle							●				●
20 Man and his environment											
20.1 Ploughing	●	●	●							●	
20.2 Liming and fertilizing	●	●	●	●	●	(●)				●	
20.3 Crop rotation	●	●	●	●	●	●	●	●	●	(●)	

GROUPS AND SYLLABUSES	MEG			NEAB	NICCEA	SEG	ULEAC		WJEC	SEB	IGCSE
	Biology 1780	Nuffield 1785	Salters 1790				A 1026	B 1028			
20.4 Pest control	•	•	•	•	•	•	•	•	•	•	
20.5 Human population crisis (problems)	•	•	•	•	•	•	•	•	•		•
20.6 Pollution	•	•	•	•	•	•	•	•	•	•	•
20.7 Depletion of resources	•	•	•	•	•	•	•	•	•	•	•
20.8 Human population crisis (solutions)	•	•	•	•	•	•	•	•	•	•	•
20.9 Types of disease in Man	•	•	•	•	•	•	•	•	•		
20.10 Natural defences of the body against pathogens	•	•	•	•	•	•	•	•	•		
20.11 Notable contributors to health and hygiene	•	•			(•)	•	•	•			
20.12 Options for a human future	•	•			•	•	•	•		•	•
21 A variety of life											
21.1 Algae	(•)	(•)		(•)	(•)				(•)	(•)	
21.2 Mosses and ferns	•	•	•	•	•	•	•	•	•		
21.3 Flowering plants	•	•	•	•	•	•	•	•	•		
21.4 Annelids	(•)	(•)			(•)			(•)			
21.5 Molluscs		(•)		(•)	(•)		(•)	(•)	(•)		
21.6 Crustacea	(•)	(•)				(•)					
21.7 Insects	•	(•)	•	(•)	(•)	•	(•)	•	(•)		
21.8 Locust	•					•					
21.9 Housefly and blowfly	•					•	•				
21.10 Large cabbage white butterfly								(•)			
21.11 Honey-bee						•					
21.12 Mosquito	•	•			•	(•)	•				
21.13 Malaria and other mosquito-borne diseases	•	•				•	•				
21.14 Importance of insects to Man		(•)					(•)	(•)			
21.15 Liver fluke and bilharzia		(•)			(•)	•					
21.16 Bony fish	•	(•)		(•)	(•)	(•)	(•)	•	(•)	(•)	(•)
21.17 Amphibia	(•)	(•)		(•)	(•)		(•)		(•)		(•)
21.18 Birds	(•)	(•)		(•)	(•)	•	(•)	(•)	(•)		(•)
21.19 Mammals	(•)	•	(•)	(•)	(•)		(•)	(•)	(•)		(•)
22 Biology as a science											
22.1 Scientific method	•	•	•	•	•	•	•	•	•	•	•
22.2 Reporting your own experiments	•	•	•	•	•	•	•	•	•	•	•
22.3 Scientific units of measurement	(•)	(•)	(•)	(•)	(•)	(•)	(•)	(•)	(•)	(•)	(•)
22.4 Elements, compounds and mixtures	•	•	•	•	•	•	•	•	•	•	•
22.5 Energy	•	•	•	•	•	•	•	•	•	•	•
22.6 Surface area to volume ratio	•	•	•	•	•	•	•	•	•	(•)	•
22.7 Handling measurements and making them meaningful	•	•	•	•	•	•	•	•	•	(•)	•
22.8 Drawings	•	•	•	•	•	•	•	•	•	•	•
22.9 Ideas for experiments of your own	•	•	•	•	•	•	•	•	•	•	•

Revision and coursework

Studying and revising

Successful students are those who can organize their work. In particular, they must be able to work effectively on their own. If you are to be successful you need determination to succeed, a work plan fitted to a time schedule and determination to keep to that schedule. Unfortunately, few students are told *how* to devise that plan and carry it out – that is where this book comes in.

This section contains some advice that will help you to succeed in school. It also gives reasons for this advice. The rest of the book concerns itself with presenting biological facts, and how to deduce them by experiment, in a form that makes it easy to revise.

The first three steps in the learning process (see Fig. A) are planned by your teacher, who knows the sort of examination you will be sitting (stage 5) and plans accordingly. Where so many students fail, needlessly, is at stage 4 (revision) – because they do not know how to go about it. **Revision** is what this book is all about – leave out stage 4 in the diagram below and you have F for failure.

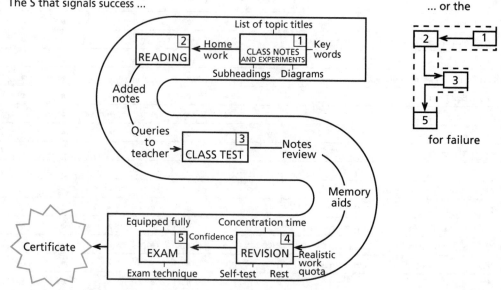

Fig. A The 'S' for success ... or the 'F' for failure

The learning process: patterns in the mind

In science you learn from experiments – your own or those reported by others. It is well known that students tend to remember far better the 'facts' they have learned by doing experiments themselves. Unfortunately there is not enough time to learn everything this way, so that the rest has to be learned by reading, listening and seeing visual aids.

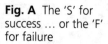

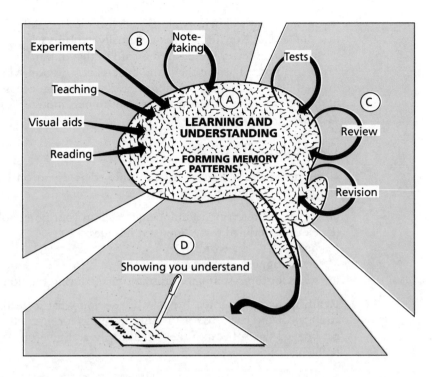

Fig. B From learning to showing you understand

Why is learning through reading and listening harder than learning by experiment? Why are good annotated diagrams often so much easier to learn than line upon line of words? Why is a good teacher such a help in learning?

Experiments: Doing these needs personal involvement and the use of several senses. Then, at the end of the experiment, one must arrive at a conclusion – which requires some reasoning. In a word, the whole process requires *understanding* – understanding the **aim** of the experiment, the **method** to be used and how to record the **results** in a meaningful way. And the final step, the **conclusion**, requires reasoning from what you have already understood.

During this process you will notice that you have built up a pattern of knowledge – like a jig-saw – lacking just one piece to complete it (the conclusion). In other words, **learning is a process requiring patterns to be built up in the mind**: relate what you have just learned to what you already know and the facts will stick – because you *understand*.

Reading: In contrast to experimenting, when reading you are using only one of your senses – sight – and you are not *involved*, as you are in an experiment, unless you make a mental effort. Nor do you feel the same sense of discovery. Worst of all, the information is presented as a series of facts. In well-written books the facts *are* written to form patterns; but it is you, the reader, who has to concentrate hard enough to pick them out. If you can do this, you have learned to learn by reading. This is initially much harder to do than learning by experiment.

Pictures and diagrams: One method of learning from books goes halfway towards experimental learning. Do you enjoy strip cartoons? At any rate you will agree that they are easy reading and convey much more than the few words appearing with the pictures. Pictures and diagrams, like words, require eyes alone to see them. But, unlike words, pictures build up patterns in the brain more readily and understanding is more immediate. So, well-constructed diagrams are an invaluable learning aid. If you learn the art of diagram-drawing you will reinforce both your memory and your understanding. Ultimately you should be able to construct your own original topic-summary diagrams, and there is a definite stage in the learning process when you should do this (see 'Retaining facts').

Teachers: Have you ever thought about the role of teachers in the learning process? They attempt to activate more senses in you than just your hearing. By showing films and slides, by drawing diagrams or asking your opinions and by giving you definite learning objectives, they try to keep you personally involved. It is for you to respond –

if you are going to learn. Amidst it all you must carefully latch onto the *pattern* of facts that the teacher explains. A teacher usually explains what the *whole* lesson is to be about during the first few minutes. Listen hard to that outline and the rest of the lesson will be easier to absorb. The outline is the basic skeleton upon which the teacher will build up the flesh and features of the subject, as the lesson proceeds. If you miss the description of the skeleton, the subject may turn out to be a monster for you!

Capturing facts

Class notes: Your teacher has probably advised you on how to make these. For easy revision it is essential that they include:

(*a*) a topic list referring to numbered pages in your notebook;
(*b*) clear, underlined topic titles and subtitles;
(*c*) underlined 'key words';
(*d*) clear diagrams with titles;
(*e*) space for topic-summary diagrams made during revision.

Reading texts: Your teacher may advise you what to read. Realize too that a text has an index at the back; use it to look up things for yourself. At this stage many students get bogged down because they read slowly and give up. If you are someone with this problem, try this:

The cat sat on the mat.

Because of the way you were taught to read, for example 'c–a–t' or 'cat', you have been 'brainwashed' into thinking that you can only read one word at a time. Now bring your head back further from the page. Notice that now you can have more than one word in focus at a time – without having to move your eyes at all. With practice you will find that not only 'cat' is in focus but also 'The' and perhaps even 'sat' as well. It does need practice but soon you will find that the whole of 'The cat sat on' is in focus at one glance and that you can take it *all* in. Four words instead of one at each glance – four times your original reading speed!

Time how long it takes you to read a page now. Repeat the test after each week of practising the new method. Some people can read 800 words per minute with ease, understanding as they go. No wonder this method is called speed-reading! Reading the text should be done after you have been taught the topic – say during homework. Your reading:

(*a*) reinforces in your mind the facts recorded in class notes;
(*b*) allows you to add extra bits to your notes;
(*c*) should clear up misunderstandings.

Ask your teacher if you still do not understand something.

Class tests: These are designed to help you to recall facts and to reason from them. In this process you and the teacher are on the *same* side; together you will succeed. The teacher is *not* putting you to the torture. Tests:

(*a*) help you to assess your progress (should you work harder?);
(*b*) help the teacher to clear up your difficulties (adjust your notes?);
(*c*) help you to remember facts better;
(*d*) give you exam practice.

Retaining facts

Revision: This is the vital last stage in the learning process, the stage when you are finally on your own.

All of us have different '**concentration times**'. How long is yours? Go to a quiet working place indoors, without distractions, and note the time. Read a part of your textbook that is new to you, making a determined effort to take in all you read. When your mind begins to wander, look again at your watch; you are at the end of your concentration time. It should be around 20–40 minutes and will differ according to the amount of sleep you have had, what else is on your mind, and even on the subject matter. Never revise for longer than your concentration time. If you do, you will waste your time. You may still be reading but you will not understand. So **rest** for five minutes.

After the rest, surprisingly enough, the facts you read in the textbook will come back to you more easily still. During the rest, your brain was 'organizing' the facts you took in. Note-taking would have assisted this organizing process. Unfortunately most of these facts go into what is called your 'short-term memory'. Within 48 hours you will retain as little as 10% of what you thought you knew so well. Don't be depressed. You can push these facts into your 'long-term memory', which is essential for examination purposes, by **reviewing**.

Reviewing: This is a *quick* reread of your notes, taking only a few minutes. If your notes are disorganized you will not gain much. But with clear summaries, such as you will find in this book, you should dramatically increase the number of facts going into your long-term memory. Do this rereading after a week and then again two weeks later after having learned the topic for the first time in class.

Revision is just an extension of reviewing. If you have followed the learning plan so far, there will be relatively little to do. During revision whole chunks of your notes will not need to be read because subtitles and key words alone will trigger off a mass of facts already in your long-term memory. For the rest of the plan, follow these principles:

(i)   Months ahead of the examinations plan how much to revise each week.
(ii) Have a regular time for work and stick to it. Avoid distractions: no TV or pets.
(iii) With your concentration time in mind, plan a *realistic* amount of work for each 20–40 minute session. You must get up from your task with a sense of achievement, i.e. that you have completed what you set out to do. Otherwise you will get depressed 'at the hopelessness of it all'.
(iv) Take those 5-minute breaks. But do not exceed them.
(v)   Use the memory aids and summary diagrams in this book to help you.

Memory aids:

(i) Repetition   (ii) Mnemonics   (iii) Pattern-diagrams

(i)   **Repetition:** By chanting something over and over again you can learn it 'parrot-fashion'. Many people learn their times-tables or poetry in this way. The method has its uses. But though you can remember in this way you do not necessarily *understand*.

(ii) **Mnemonics:** These are words, sentences or little rhymes chosen from everyday language to help you to remember technical words that you find difficult to memorize. This book provides you with a few examples; but you may be able to do better. Make your own mnemonics funny, outrageously absurd – even rude – if you are going to remember them. Dull mnemonics are difficult to remember. The words you choose must be sufficiently similar to the technical words to remind you of them. For example:

'How can I remember the characteristics of living things – which I *do* understand but may not be able to remember fully in an exam?' Try **Germs in our seas** and turn to Unit 1.1. This example uses initial letters of the key words only. You will find another mnemonic in Unit 2.2.

(iii) **Pattern-diagrams:** these are important or 'key' words written down and joined up with lines according to their connections with each other. You have already seen two examples (Figs. A and B). When you have finished revising a topic always try to summarize it in this way. You will be surprised how easy it is. And why? Because your mind thinks in patterns and not in lists. When you come to the examination you will be able to remember your pattern-diagrams and even create new ones when planning your answers to essay questions.

Coursework (GCSE)

Coursework accounts for 25% of the GCSE marks (NICCEA is 24%).

1. The coursework you do in the laboratory or in fieldwork must be *your own work* to count. If it is the result of teamwork and a team report, it is unlikely to be allowed. If you have been helped significantly by a teacher you are unlikely to get full marks.

2. To be assessed you must do a *complete experiment* starting with an idea (hypothesis) which is tested and gives results from which one may reach a conclusion.

3. However, only one part or 'strand' (see below) of this experiment need be counted towards your total Coursework mark. If it is your best work *all three of the strands* may be counted.

4. Only your *best bits of work* count towards your final mark.

5. All your coursework is assessed by your teachers, who give you marks. To be fair, all the Biology teachers in your school then meet to compare their marking to make sure that they are giving the same marks for the same level of work. Finally, your Exam Board then looks at samples of work from all the schools taking their exams to make sure that all schools are marking to the *same standard*.

Strands

Most Exam Boards have three 'strands' (skills in experimental work) that they test. These are: (1) **Planning**, (2) **Carrying out** and (3) **Concluding** from the experiment. The NICCEA have included a fourth strand: (4) **Use of Information Technology**.

These strands are explained below in such a way as to guide you from the easiest levels to the most difficult – and to achieve level 10 is definitely hard. The higher you can realistically aim, the better you will be as an experimental scientist.

1 *Planning*

- Experiments have to start with ideas (hypotheses). Your idea should predict a result (which your experiment will test and not necessarily find correct). Better still, your predictions should be based on scientific knowledge and be quantitative, e.g. not just 'it will react faster if it is warmer' but 'it will react twice as fast if the temperature is raised by 10 °C'. You must take into account other factors that might affect the results.

- At the highest level (10) deeper scientific knowledge such as reference to laws, theories or models governing the subject may be used to set up the hypothesis.

2 *Carrying out*

- You will have to observe and measure what is changing in the experiment using suitable instruments. Your teacher will observe you in action to see that you are doing this safely and accurately, e.g. that you are stirring a mixture that is heating while taking its temperature with a thermometer and are using safety glasses while observing from a safe distance.

- You must set up a 'fair test' in your experiment, i.e. a 'controlled' experiment, with at least a part of it giving an 'expected' result to compare with the results in the test you are conducting (see Unit 22.1).

- You should measure to as fine a degree of accuracy as you can, choosing the most suitable instruments available at your level in the school.

- You should be able to take account of two or more variables in an experiment, changing them or measuring them as accurately as possible, e.g. the temperature *and* light intensity affecting the rate of photosynthesis of a water weed using a thermometer and a light meter.

- You could judge which of two or more variables is most effective, e.g. in the example above is it light or temperature (or CO_2 concentration) that has the greatest effect?

- At the highest level (10) you could criticize your own methods of doing the experiment to satisfy yourself that the results obtained are sufficiently good to criticize or to support existing laws, theories or models.

3 *Concluding*

- You must compare your results with what you expected to find, according to your hypothesis.

- You should be able to explain how and why you got your results, i.e. understand them.

- You should be able to consider different interpretations of your results to come to conclusions.

- Your experiment will not have been perfect and you should be able to explain its limitations and the effect these might have on your conclusions.

- At level 9 you must be able to show that, despite your best efforts, there is a degree of uncertainty about your measurements and observations that may affect what otherwise seem to be good conclusions. For example, biological material is notoriously variable (age, sex and season all affect how it responds to the same experimental conditions) and maybe the number of times you repeated your experiment or the number of individuals you used could have been improved?

- At level 10 you must analyse your data sufficiently to evaluate the law, theory or model that you started with in your hypothesis.

Students can find the full detail of Coursework in their own particular syllabuses. The jargon is daunting however and is meant for teachers. If you also find the briefer descriptions above difficult to understand, get help from your teacher. The effort will be worthwhile because tasks are always easier when you understand *what* you are expected to do and *how* to achieve them.

4 *Use of Information Technology (IT)*

Although this is unique to NICCEA and the full detail can be read in their syllabus, it is worth pointing out that the National Curriculum encourages the use of IT to spread to as many parts of the Curriculum as possible, i.e. to ensure that students use their computer literacy extensively. The main abilities required are:

- Ability to present information in graphical form, record it as a database and extract information from provided databases.

- Ability to use a set of procedures that can command a number of sensors to take measurements at intervals and to use such information to show the relationship between them.

- Ability to use IT devices to monitor and control experiments, e.g. to keep biological conditions at an optimum for brewing in a fermenter.

- Ability to use computer models.

- Ability to produce an extended report on a problem-solving project using databases, graphics and spreadsheets.

- At level 10, to evaluate how effective IT has been in comparison with other possible methods of achieving the same aims.

Practical abilities (SCE)

There are two categories of ability tested: (1) **Carrying out Techniques** and (2) **Designing and Carrying out Investigations**.

1 *Carrying out Techniques*

This specifies ten tasks, which include sampling techniques in an ecosystem, measuring two abiotic factors and using a biological key for identifying specimens; preparing a wet mount on a microscope slide, using a simple microscope and drawing a biological specimen; performing the chemical tests for starch and reducing sugar; and setting up a choice chamber.

Repetition of the task to achieve full competence is permitted.

2 *Designing and Carrying out Investigations*

During the course students are helped by teachers to appreciate four skill areas subdivided into 14 objectives. The assessment is on the *best two* complete investigations which are entirely the student's own work. Help given by teachers affects the marking. The four skill areas are:

1. **Generative skills** (G): identifying a problem, forming a hypothesis and stating an aim and a broad idea for action.

2. **Experimentation skills** (E): identifying the variables, setting up a controlled experiment, safely, and measuring accurately and repeatedly.

3. **Evaluation skills** (Ev): making valid conclusions, relevant to the hypothesis, including, perhaps, that the results were inconclusive.

4. **Recording and reporting skills** (RR): description of the experiment by diagram and by words and of how measurements were taken and variables controlled.

For fuller details on Practical Abilities consult your syllabus or teacher.

Chapter 1
Life

1.1 Characteristics of organisms

Living things are called **organisms**. Two large groups of organisms are the **plants**, e.g. grass, and the **animals** (see Units 2.3 and 2.4). All organisms perform *all* the seven 'vital functions' (growth, excretion, respiration, movement, sensitivity, nutrition, reproduction) at some time during their existence and their bodies are made of cells. Some organisms remain, for a time, **dormant** (inactive), e.g. as seeds, spores or cysts. These bodies appear not to perform vital functions but they can be activated by suitable stimulation to do so, e.g. by germinating.

Eight characteristics of organisms (*Mnemonic:* GERMS NR Cs 'germs in our seas')
Growth
Excretion
Respiration
Movement
Sensitivity
Nutrition
Reproduction
Cells

G **Growth:** cells divide and then get larger again by adding more living material (made from their food) until they repeat the process. (See Unit 16.1.)

E **Excretion:** removal of waste products from **metabolism** (all the chemical reactions within the body). (See Chapter 10.)

N.B. Do not confuse this with 'egestion' (removal of **indigestible** matter – which has thus never entered cells to be metabolized) (Fig. 1.1).

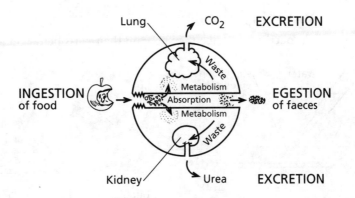

Fig. 1.1 The distinction between excretion and egestion

R **Respiration:** release of energy within cells from food so as to power other vital functions. In most organisms this requires oxygen and releases carbon dioxide and heat. (See Chapter 9.)

M **Movement:** an animal moves its whole body, using limbs or their equivalent. A plant 'moves' only by *growing* parts of itself towards or away from influences important to it. (See Units 12.13 and 12.14.)

S **Sensitivity and response:** influences (**stimuli**) in the surroundings (**environment**) stimulate certain areas of an organism so that they send messages to other parts which respond, e.g. by movement, growth or secretion. (See Chapter 11.)

N **Nutrition:** intake of food materials from the environment for building up and maintaining living matter. (See Unit 4.2.)

R **Reproduction:** formation of more individuals either from one parent (**asexually**) or two (**sexually**). (See Unit 14.1.)

All organisms eventually die. **Death** is when metabolism ceases completely.

C **Cells:** the simplest units of life. All cells, when young, have at the very least three parts: *a membrane* enclosing jelly-like *cytoplasm*, in which lies a *nucleus* which controls their life. (See Unit 1.2.) These three parts make up *protoplasm* (living matter). The cell wall secreted outside the protoplasm, by plant cells only, is non-living. Cells cannot live without supplies of energy, food, water and O_2 and a suitable environmental temperature and pH.

Cells from animals and plants show differences, as seen in Fig. 1.2.

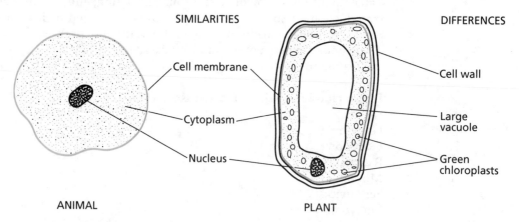

Fig. 1.2 Generalized animal and green plant cells as viewed through a light microscope

Other cells you should know about are root hair, sperm, ovum and neurone – use the index.

1.2 Cells in detail

Observing

Cells need to be stained to show up their parts better under the light microscope.

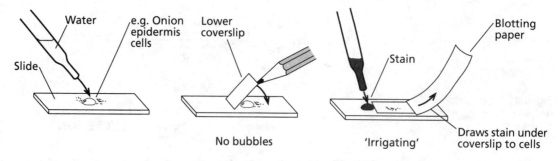

Fig. 1.3 Mounting and staining cells for microscopic examination

The *coverslip* delays water drying up around cells and permits viewing under high power without distortion under the light microscope.

Organelles

Only certain organelles (parts of the cell with special functions) can be seen under the light microscope's magnification. Even smaller organelles can be examined with an electron microscope.

1 Cell wall
Made of cellulose.
Freely permeable (porous) to all kinds of molecules.
Supports and protects the cell.
Supports non-woody plant organs, e.g. leaves, by water pressure within vacuole distending the cell wall.
Osmoregulates by resisting entry of excess water into cell. (See Fig. 7.6C.)

2 Cell membrane
Exterior of all protoplasm.
Very thin layer of protein and oil.
Freely permeable to water and gases only.
Selectively permeable to other molecules (e.g. allows foods in but keeps unwanted molecules out).

3 Vacuoles
Spaces for various functions, e.g. food storage, osmoregulation.
Plant cell vacuoles contain 'cell sap' (a weak solution of sugar and salts) inside a membrane.

4 Cytoplasmic matrix
Supports organelles.
Consistency of raw egg-white.
Up to 80% water; remainder mainly protein.
Often contains grains of stored food: starch (plants); glycogen (animals).

5 Nucleus
Stores and passes on cell 'information'.
Contains many long strands of DNA (invisible by light microscope).
When a cell divides, the DNA coils up to form chromosomes (visible). (See Unit 17.1.)
Segments of DNA are called **genes**.
Genes are responsible for characteristics of organisms, e.g. blood group and eye colour. (See Unit 1.3.)

6 Chloroplasts (for photosynthesis)
Large bodies containing chlorophyll (green).
Chlorophyll converts sunlight energy into chemical energy (ATP).
ATP is used to combine CO_2 with H_2O making glucose – which stores the energy in its bonds.

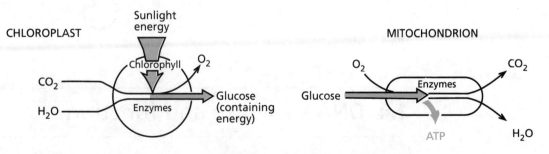

Fig. 1.4 The roles of chloroplasts and mitochondria in transforming energy

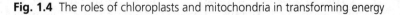

7 Mitochondria (for cell respiration)
Just specks (2 μm) under the light microscope.

Absorb O_2 and glucose.

Break down glucose to CO_2 and H_2O. This releases energy from glucose bonds to form ATP.

ATP is chemical energy a cell can use – for *any* vital function (see Unit 9.14).

⑧ **Ribosomes** (protein factories)

Invisible (20 nm) without the electron microscope.

Minute bodies in thousands in cytoplasm.

Assemble amino acids into proteins, each different according to purpose. (See Unit 4.4.) Instructions for assembly from nucleus.

1.3 How the nucleus 'controls' the cell

Every gene is a recipe for a different protein.

Required recipes are 'copied' and passed to ribosomes.

Ribosomes assemble amino acids in a special order – according to recipe – to make proteins.

Thus DNA makes RNA and RNA makes proteins (Fig. 1.5)

These different proteins are either

① *secreted* by gland cells, e.g. digestive enzymes, hormones, or

② *retained* within cells for metabolism, e.g. enzymes for photosynthesis, respiration; haemoglobin in erythrocytes.

In both cases the proteins determine what each cell can do. So the nucleus, through the proteins it determines, controls what cells can do.

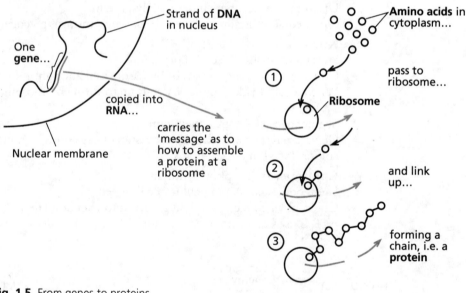

Fig. 1.5 From genes to proteins

1.4 DNA structure and function

DNA is a huge ladder-like molecule made up of sugar ■, phosphate ● and four organic bases called **A**denine, **G**uanine, **C**ytosine and **T**hymine (Fig. 1.6). The bases will only join up in the pairs A to T and G to C.

The two halves of the ladder can also *un-zip* between the pairs of bases. They do this:
(a) **At mitosis**: each half ladder forms the other half on itself. So *two* ladders, which are identical, result. This is the reason why a chromosome that splits in mitosis forms two identical chromosomes (see Unit 17.12).

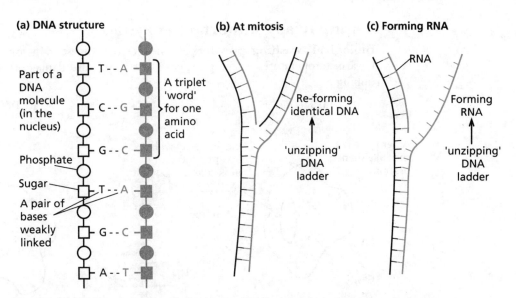

Fig. 1.6 (a) DNA structure; (b) duplicating itself; (c) passing its 'message' to ribosomes

(b) **When genes make proteins**: each half ladder forms a related substance, RNA (very similar to DNA) on it. This then detaches, passing to the ribosomes (see Fig. 1.5). RNA carries the sequence of bases that were in the DNA. Each three letter 'word' (triplet), e.g. AGC, attracts a particular amino acid to the ribosome.

The *sequence* of the hundreds of triplets is what determines the kind of protein formed at the ribosomes – each protein has its own unique DNA sequence.

Thus a length of DNA with its own unique sequence is a gene; and a gene is what is used to make its own, unique, protein by linking a particular sequence of amino acids together at a ribosome.

The 'ladder' structure of DNA is in fact turned into a spiral (double helix) thread, with 10 base pairs per complete 360° turn. This has little to do with the function of DNA but it was a crucial fact, discovered by Franklin, Wilkins, Watson and Crick, in determining its structure.

1.5 Enzymes and metabolism

Enzymes are

1. **catalysts** – substances that speed up chemical reactions. These reactions do not change the catalyst, so even small amounts of enzyme can do a big job.

2. **protein** – whose chemical shape (see Fig. 1.7) is special to the substance it works on.

3. **specific** – starch alone fits into the special shape of the enzyme salivary amylase, not protein or anything else, so starch alone is digested by it.

4. **temperature sensitive** – boiling destroys enzymes (by altering their shape); cooling only slows down their action. Best (i.e. 'optimum') for mammals is blood temperature.

5. **pH sensitive** – each enzyme has its own preferred (optimum) pH, e.g. optimum pH for pepsin is pH 2 (acid); for salivary amylase pH 6.8 (almost neutral); for lipase pH 9 (alkaline). (See Fig. 6.5.)

Enzymes catalyse all chemical reactions of the body (metabolism). Without enzymes, reactions would not go fast enough for life to exist.

Metabolism includes:

Anabolism: building up complex molecules, e.g. in photosynthesis, food storage.

Catabolism: breaking down complex molecules, e.g. in respiration, digestion. It occurs both within cells (e.g. respiration) and outside them (digestion).

Commercially important enzymes

'Biological' washing powders – enzymes that digest stains on clothing. They work at warm temperatures – saving expense of boiling, and damage to clothes by boiling or rubbing.

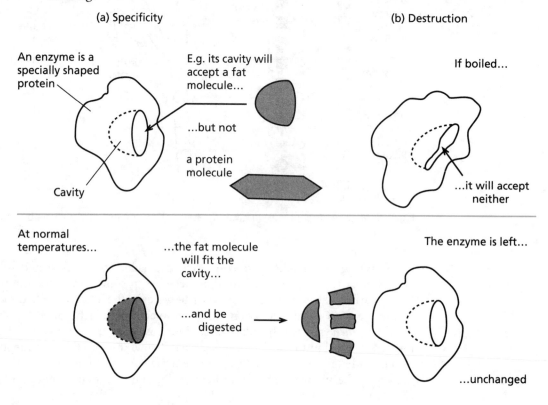

Fig. 1.7 Two features of enzymes dependent on their chemical shape: the 'lock and key' hypothesis

'Malting' in beer making – amylases formed in germinating barley digest starch in the grain to malt sugar (maltose). This sugar is then fermented by yeast – whose enzymes cannot use starch – during brewing (see Fig. 3.12).

Every useful biological product – food, flavourings, antibiotics, vaccines, etc. – is a product of the metabolism of some organism or another. So, in reality, *every* enzyme involved in making these products is important commercially.

1.6 Units of life beyond the cell

Just as inorganic molecules are built up into organic molecules, which in turn are built into organelles (see Unit 1.2), so cells are subunits of organisms. There is a great variety of types of cell. (See Units 5.5, leaf cells; 7.9, xylem and phloem; 8.2, blood cells; 12.2, neurones; 13.5, bone; 15.1, gametes.)

Tissues are groups of cells, usually of the same type, specialized to carry out certain functions, e.g. muscle for movement, nerves for sending 'messages', xylem for transport and support.

Organs are made up of tissues coordinated to perform certain functions, e.g. eye, leaf, kidney.

Organ systems are groups of organs which combine to perform their functions, e.g. gut, endocrine system, nervous system. The nervous system consists of brain, spinal cord and nerves.

Organisms, depending on their complexity, may each be just one cell, e.g. a bacterium or *Amoeba*, or millions of cells with a variety of functional units as above, e.g.

an oak tree or Man. An organism which reproduces sexually is not much use on its own, unless it self-fertilizes. The basic unit of reproduction is thus usually a **breeding pair**. From this arise **populations** – as small as herds or as large as hundreds of herds occupying an island or a continent. All the populations of this type of organism form a **species** (see Fig. 1.8). Populations of different species living in balance in nature are called **communities**. Communities form part of **ecosystems** in the **biosphere**. (See Unit 19.1.)

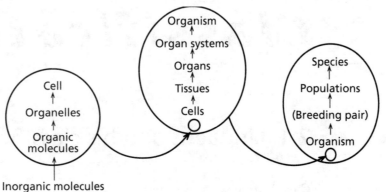

Fig. 1.8 Units of life

Summary

1 Organisms have seven vital functions in common; and they are made of cells.

2 Animal cells are made up of a nucleus, cytoplasm and a cell membrane.

3 In addition, plant cells have a cell wall of cellulose, a large central vacuole and, if green, chloroplasts.

4 Chloroplasts are the organelles of photosynthesis.

5 Mitochondria are the organelles of aerobic respiration.

6 Ribosomes assemble amino acids to make proteins.

7 DNA is the chemical of genes and controls the making of proteins.

8 Enzymes are the protein catalysts of life, controlling every biochemical reaction of metabolism.

9 Cells of one type make up a tissue; various tissues make up organs and organ systems. Put together, these form organisms.

Chapter 2
Classification

2.1 Linnaeus and his classification system

Carl Linnaeus of Sweden in 1735 introduced the basis of modern **taxonomy** (classification). All species are given two names in Latin – the **binomial system** of naming:

1. genus name, written first, which starts with a *capital* letter, e.g. *Homo* (Man);

2. species name, written second, which starts with a *small* letter, e.g. *sapiens* (modern).

The binomial ought to be printed in italics but is underlined when handwritten or typed by scientists, e.g. <u>Panthera tigris</u> (tiger).

Species: a group of organisms capable of breeding to produce fertile offspring. They are very similar, but do show variety.

Genus: a group of organisms with a large number of similarities but whose different subgroups (species) are usually unable to interbreed successfully.

2.2 Groups and subgroups

Just as species are subgroups of genera, so Linnaeus grouped genera into larger and larger groups. Each group included as many *similarities* as possible. The largest group is a kingdom, the smallest a species. The lion can be classified as follows:

Kingdom	Animalia	– animals, as opposed to plants.
Phylum	Vertebrata	– animals with backbones (fish, amphibia, reptiles, birds and mammals).
Class	Mammalia	– hairy, warm blooded, suckle young on milk.
Order	Carnivora	– mainly flesh-eating group (cats, dogs, bears, seals).
Family	Felidae	– cats, large and small.
Genus	*Panthera*	– certain cats (includes tiger, *P. tigris;* leopard, *P. pardus*).
Species	*leo*	– lion only.

Mnemonic: **K**adet, **P.C.**, **OF**ficer, **G**eneral in**S**pector (promotion in the police force).

Advantages of the system

- **Universal:** Japanese, Bantu or Russian biologists all understand that *Panthera catus* means 'house cat' without having to resort to a dictionary.

- **Shorthand information:** one word, e.g. mammal, conveys a mass of information to all biologists. (See Unit 21.9.)

- **Reflects evolutionary relationships:** e.g. the five classes of vertebrate are very different (see Unit 2.4), yet all have a common body plan. The basic plan (in Fish) (see Fig. 2.1(b)) was improved upon, allowing land colonization (Amphibia), its exploitation (Reptiles and Mammals), and even conquering of the air (Birds). The classification of vertebrates thus probably reflects the evolutionary process.

2.3 Plant kingdom and simpler forms of life

Classification of the main members of the plant kingdom, bacteria, fungi and protoctista can be seen in Fig. 2.1(a).

2.4 Animal kingdom

Classification of the main members of the animal kingdom can be seen in Fig. 2.1(b).

2.5 Modern classification

Most biologists favour the **Five Kingdom** classification.

Viruses are not included in this scheme since they lack many properties of living things: not cells, a very small piece of DNA or RNA inside a protein coat; parasitic inside cells when active. (See Unit 3.1.)

1 **Kingdom Prokaryotae**: bacteria – single, very small cell, no true nucleus (since no membrane around the DNA in the cytoplasm) but have cell wall. (See Unit 3.2.)

Organisms in the other four kingdoms have much larger cells and true nuclei:

2 **Kingdom Protoctista**: algae and protozoa (see Fig. 2.1(a)) and slime moulds.

3 **Kingdom Fungi**: (see Fig. 2.1(a)) usually made up of filaments of cells (hyphae); have no chlorophyll; absorb food they have digested from outside through cell walls.

4 **Kingdom Plantae**: all green plants in Fig. 2.1(a) except algae; they photosynthesize; have cellulose cell walls.

5 **Kingdom Animalia**: animals, i.e. organisms with no cell walls or chlorophyll in their cells; have nerve and muscle cells.

Almost all Examining Groups at GCSE level and the A-level Boards have now given the Five Kingdom classification their support. However no one will, at present, be marked wrong for using such terms as bacteria, algae and protozoa.

Fig. 2.1(a)

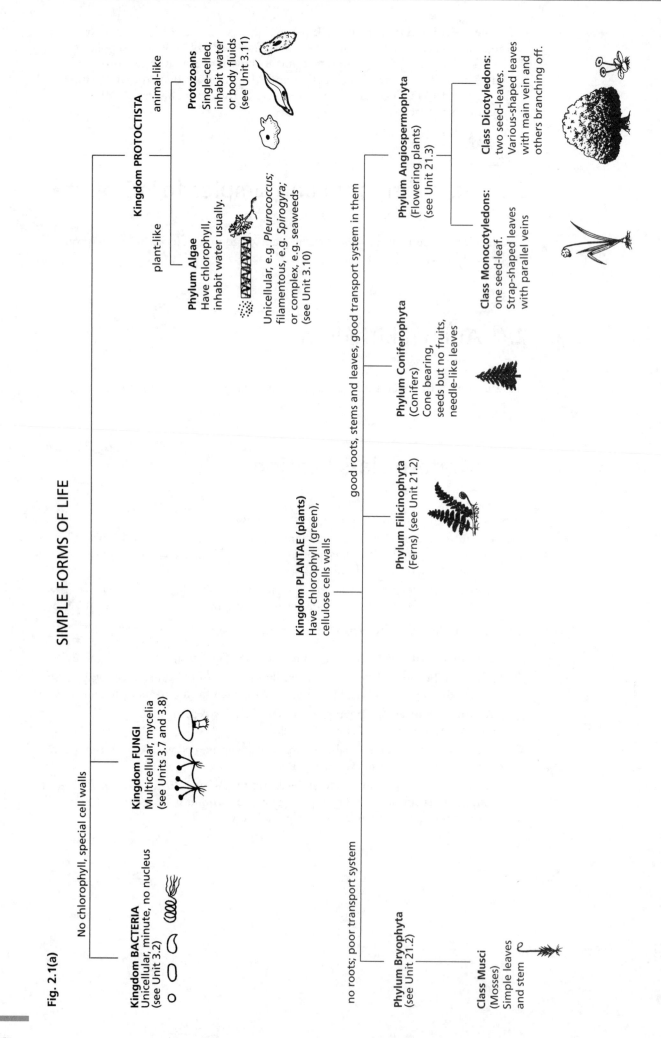

SIMPLE FORMS OF LIFE

No chlorophyll, special cell walls

Kingdom BACTERIA
Unicellular, minute, no nucleus
(see Unit 3.2)

Kingdom FUNGI
Multicellular, mycelia
(see Units 3.7 and 3.8)

Kingdom PROTOCTISTA

plant-like

animal-like

Phylum Algae
Have chlorophyll,
inhabit water usually.

Unicellular, e.g. *Pleurococcus*;
filamentous, e.g. *Spirogyra*;
or complex, e.g. seaweeds
(see Unit 3.10)

Protozoans
Single-celled,
inhabit water
or body fluids
(see Unit 3.11)

Kingdom PLANTAE (plants)
Have chlorophyll (green),
cellulose cells walls

good roots, stems and leaves, good transport system in them

Phylum Angiospermophyta
(Flowering plants)
(see Unit 21.3)

Class Dicotyledons:
two seed-leaves.
Various-shaped leaves
with main vein and
others branching off.

Class Monocotyledons:
one seed-leaf.
Strap-shaped leaves
with parallel veins

Phylum Coniferophyta
(Conifers)
Cone bearing,
seeds but no fruits,
needle-like leaves

Phylum Filicinophyta
(Ferns) (see Unit 21.2)

no roots; poor transport system

Phylum Bryophyta
(see Unit 21.2)

Class Musci
(Mosses)
Simple leaves
and stem

Fig. 2.1(b)

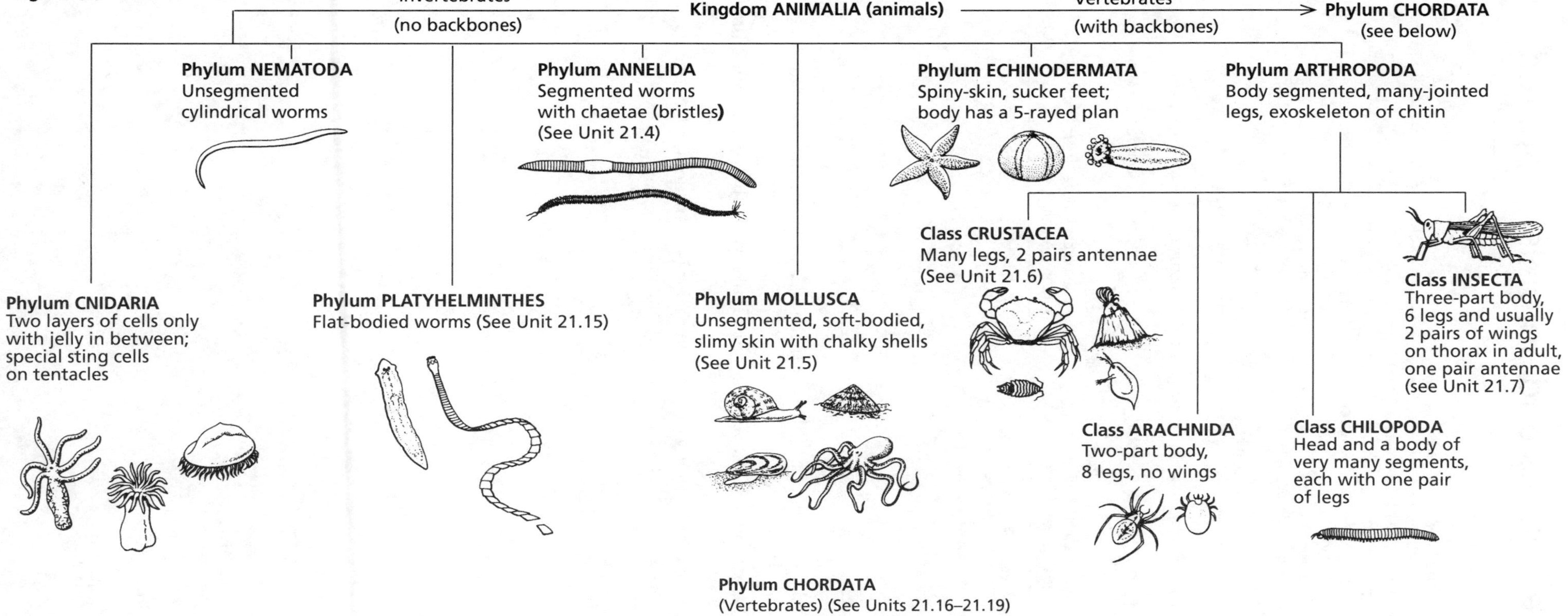

Kingdom ANIMALIA (animals)

Invertebrates (no backbones) — Vertebrates (with backbones)

Phylum CNIDARIA Two layers of cells only with jelly in between; special sting cells on tentacles

Phylum NEMATODA Unsegmented cylindrical worms

Phylum PLATYHELMINTHES Flat-bodied worms (See Unit 21.15)

Phylum ANNELIDA Segmented worms with chaetae (bristles) (See Unit 21.4)

Phylum MOLLUSCA Unsegmented, soft-bodied, slimy skin with chalky shells (See Unit 21.5)

Phylum ECHINODERMATA Spiny-skin, sucker feet; body has a 5-rayed plan

Phylum ARTHROPODA Body segmented, many-jointed legs, exoskeleton of chitin

Class CRUSTACEA Many legs, 2 pairs antennae (See Unit 21.6)

Class ARACHNIDA Two-part body, 8 legs, no wings

Class INSECTA Three-part body, 6 legs and usually 2 pairs of wings on thorax in adult, one pair antennae (see Unit 21.7)

Class CHILOPODA Head and a body of very many segments, each with one pair of legs

→ **Phylum CHORDATA** (see below)

Phylum CHORDATA (Vertebrates) (See Units 21.16–21.19)

	Class PISCES (Fish)	Class AMPHIBIA	Class REPTILIA	Class AVES (Birds)	Class MAMMALIA
Outer covering	Slimy, bony scales	Slimy, smooth	Dry, leathery scales	Dry, feathers	Dry, hair
Reproduction: fertilization	Externally in water		Internally on land		
eggs laid	Thousands, some yolk	Hundreds, some yolk	100 or fewer, lots of yolk, soft leathery shell	Tens or fewer, lots of yolk, hard chalky shell	Don't lay; food from placenta
parental care	Rare	Rare	Of eggs in some	Of eggs and young in nest	Of embryo in uterus; and of young; fed milk and protected
Special features	Gills for gaseous exchange. Fins for limbs	Fish-like larva (tadpole). Adult with 4 legs for land		Toothless jaws – beaks. Fore-limbs are wings	Milk from female mammary glands; ears external
Temperature control	Ectothermic – temperature varies with their surroundings			Endothermic – temperature constant and warm	

2.6 Multicell plants and animals compared

Table 2.1 Comparison of multicell plants and animals

	Plants	Animals
Growth	*Branching* – large surface area to absorb nutrients and sunlight	*Compact* – except for limbs for seeking food
Excretion	*Oxygen* and carbon dioxide	Carbon dioxide
	Other wastes, e.g. by dropping leaves	*Nitrogen* wastes in urine
Reproduction	*Asexual:* frequent	*Asexual:* only simple animals
	Sexual reproduction usual	
Movement	No muscles, cell walls rigid – *Anchored*	Use muscles, skeleton – *Mobile*
Sensitivity	No obvious sense organs	*Eyes, ears,* etc. obvious
and response	Response *slow*, using *hormones* to affect growth	Response *fast*, using *nerves* to affect behaviour
Nutrition	*Autotrophic* – inorganic food: synthesized	*Heterotrophic* – organic food: digested
Respiration	*Starch* food store	*Glycogen* food store
	Respiration usually aerobic	
	Anaerobic: produces *ethanol*	Anaerobic: produces *lactic acid*
Cells	*Cell wall, large vacuole, chloroplasts*	All three organelles absent

Note use of mnemonic: 'Germs in our seas' (Unit 1.1) as a checklist.

Summary

1   Linnaeus invented a method of classifying organisms and the binomial system for naming them, using latin words.

2   Today, we classify organisms into five kingdoms: Prokaryotes (bacteria); Protoctista; Fungi, Plants and Animals.

3   Plants and Animals are significantly different in their vital functions, a fact that stems from their markedly different methods of nutrition.

Chapter 3
Viruses, microorganisms, fungi and biotechnology

3.1 Viruses

Size: between 30 and 300 nm (1/100 size of bacteria) – visible only with electron microscope.

Structure: protein coat around a DNA or RNA strand (a few genes) (Fig. 3.1).

Living?: no; are not cells, having no metabolism of their own. (See Unit 1.1.)

All are *parasites*, killing host cells as they reproduce within them, using the cell's energy and materials. This causes disease, e.g. rabies.

Disease transmission

1 by water, e.g. polio;

2 by droplet (sneezing), e.g. colds, 'flu;

3 by vector (carrier of disease), e.g. mosquito transmits yellow fever and greenfly transmits the TMV (Fig. 3.1).

Useful: for biological control of rabbits – myxomatosis virus.

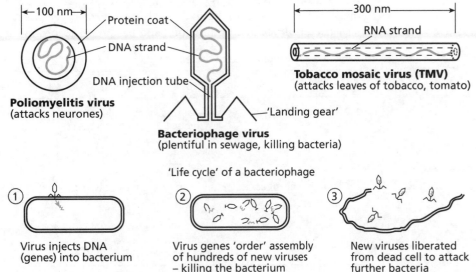

Fig. 3.1 Viruses

←100 nm→
Protein coat
DNA strand
DNA injection tube
Poliomyelitis virus
(attacks neurones)

←300 nm→
RNA strand
Tobacco mosaic virus (TMV)
(attacks leaves of tobacco, tomato)

'Landing gear'
Bacteriophage virus
(plentiful in sewage, killing bacteria)

'Life cycle' of a bacteriophage

1 Virus injects DNA (genes) into bacterium

2 Virus genes 'order' assembly of hundreds of new viruses – killing the bacterium

3 New viruses liberated from dead cell to attack further bacteria

3.2 Bacteria

Size: between 0.1 and 10 μm (1/100 size of mammal cheek cell).
Structure: cell is unique in *not* having:

- nuclear membrane around its single loop chromosome, so there is no nucleus;
- mitochondria (cell membrane has the same function).

Cell is unlike a green plant cell in having *no*:

- chloroplasts (therefore bacteria are either saprophytes or parasites) (see Unit 4.2);
- cellulose in cell walls (made of nitrogenous compounds instead) (Fig. 3.2).

Reproduction

- asexually: by binary fission, every 20 minutes in suitable conditions.
- sexually: use a tube to transfer DNA from one bacterium to another.

Bacteria do *not* reproduce by forming spores. Some bacilli, only, form spores (endospores) for *survival* when conditions become unfavourable.

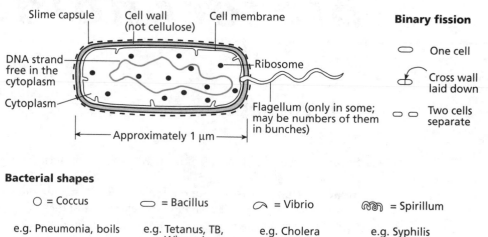

Fig. 3.2 Bacteria

3.3 Importance of bacteria

Bacteria obtain both energy and materials from their food as we do. In doing so, their metabolism can help or harm Man. In some cases (see nos. 1a, 3a and 3b below), the *same* bacterium can be both helpful and harmful – according to what it is acting upon.

Table 3.1 The importance of bacteria to Man

Activity	Helpful	Harmful
1 Decomposing	(a) *Dead organisms*, litter, manure into simple nutrients for green plants to use, e.g. CO_2, salts (b) *sewage*, so preventing water pollution	*Food*, e.g. putrefying meat, fish
2 Circulating nitrogen	(a) *Fixing nitrogen*, so increasing soil fertility (see Unit 19.10) (b) Converting ammonia (toxic) into nitrate for green plants, i.e. *nitrification*	*Denitrifying* the soil by converting nitrate to nitrogen gas, so reducing soil fertility

Table 3.1 *(continued)*

Activity	Helpful	Harmful
3 In industry	(a) *Dairy products**: making yoghurt, butter, cheese	*Souring* milk
	(b) *Wineries:* making vinegar	Souring wine
	(c) Making biogas *fuel* (methane)	*Damaging oil* lubricating engines
4 Affecting health	(a) Producing *antibiotics*, e.g. *Streptomyces* gives over 50 of them	Causing *disease* in Man and his animals (see Unit 3.2)
	(b) Producing human *hormones* by genetic engineering (see Unit 17.16)	Causing *food poisoning*, e.g. *Salmonella*

* Special bacteria turn milk sour, to form **yoghurt**, or cream sour, to make a lumpy product which when churned becomes unsalted **butter**.

To make **cheese**: (a) milk is soured, (b) rennin (Unit 6.5) is added to clot it forming solid (curds) and juice (whey) which is removed, (c) the curds are 'ripened' by adding special bacteria or fungi which feed on it, giving it characteristic flavours.

3.4 How viruses (V) and bacteria (B) reach people

Table 3.2

Method	Examples
1 By air	Inhaling minute droplets of infected mucus expelled during sneezing, coughing and even talking. Crowds, poor ventilation and not using handkerchiefs assist infection, e.g. 'flu, colds, measles (V); pneumonia, tuberculosis, whooping cough (B)
2 By water	Especially if contaminated by faeces, e.g. poliomyelitis (V); cholera, dysentery (B)
3 By mud	Introduced deeply into wounds, e.g. tetanus, gangrene (B)
4 Sexually (own species)	During copulation, e.g. genital herpes (V); gonorrhea, syphilis (B); AIDS (V) (see Unit 15.5)
5 By vectors (other species)	Mosquitoes inject yellow fever (V) into blood; houseflies vomit dysentery, cholera (B) onto our food from faeces (see Unit 21.9)

In general, viruses and bacteria enter via natural openings of the body which secrete mucus (mucous membranes); or they enter forcibly (nos. 3 and 5), by-passing the natural barrier of the skin.

Infected food and water are particularly common means of entry, e.g. when water is not purified, sewage disposal is poor and personal hygiene is of a low standard (see below).

Hospital hygiene must be particularly good to prevent the great range of available infections from spreading to others in wards and on operating tables (see Unit 20.11).

Drug addicts using non-sterile needles add to their misery with infections such as hepatitis, AIDS and blood poisoning.

3.5 Control of harmful bacteria

If the basic requirements of bacteria are removed, they die (Table 3.3).

Table 3.3 Control of harmful bacteria

Requirements of bacteria	Control measure, with examples
1 Moisture	**Dried foods:** peas, raisins, milk, meat – keep for ever **Salting:** e.g. ham, or *syruping*, e.g. peaches, plasmolyses (see Unit 7.4) bacteria
2 Organic food	**Hygiene:** removal of bacterial foods by washing body, clothes, food utensils; by disposing of refuse, excreta and hospital dressings; cleaning homes
3 Suitable temperature (warmth)	**Temperature treatment** (a) *refrigeration:* deep-freeze (−18 °C) suspends life; fridge (+4 °C) slows rotting to acceptable level; (b) *boiling:* kills most, but not spores; (c) *pressure-cooking* ('sterilizing' or 'autoclaving') for 10 min at 100 kN/m^2 (15 lb/in^2) kills all, including spores; (d) *pasteurization* (of milk): heat to 77 °C for seconds and rapidly cool to 4 °C Enclosing food from (b)–(d), by bottling, canning and vacuum packing, prevents access of bacteria to it
4 Suitable chemical environment	**Chemicals** are also used to kill bacteria: (a) *chlorine* in drinking water and swimming baths; (b) *disinfectants* in loos; (c) *medical use* of antiseptics, antibiotics, antibodies and drugs in or on Man's body (see Unit 20.11); (d) *vinegar* for pickling food (pH too acid for bacteria)
5 No ultraviolet light	**Irradiate with ultraviolet light** (thin sliced food, surgical instruments) and plan sunny homes (sunlight contains UV light)

3.6 Growing bacteria

Culturing bacteria safely

Golden rules:

1. Do not culture bacteria except under teacher supervision.
2. Do not incubate them unless within taped petri dishes or stoppered test tubes, clearly marked with their source.
3. Dispose of unwanted cultures by autoclaving.
4. Take care not to eat during such classes, nor to inhale air close to cultures.
5. Bacterial 'loops' (of wire), used to transfer bacteria, must be 'flamed' in a Bunsen burner after use.

Bacteria transferred by flamed, cooled (sterile) loop...

...streaked onto sterile agar and food...

...marked with source and date; incubated upside down, e.g. in oven

Source of bacteria, e.g. soil, milk

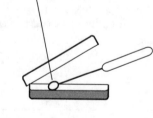

Tape

Fig. 3.3 Method for culturing bacteria on agar jelly

Plan view of streaking

Plan view of colonies growing after 24 hours

Testing antibiotics

- Particular colonies may be transferred by means of a 'swab' of sterile wet cotton wool on a stick, and 'painted' onto fresh agar to spread it evenly.
- Discs of filter paper, soaked in antibiotic, are placed on the culture before incubation, but not on the control.
- Clear zones indicate no bacterial growth, i.e. antibiotic effective (Fig. 3.4).
  A doctor may take a swab from an infection to discover, using the method above, which antibiotic is the best for curing it.

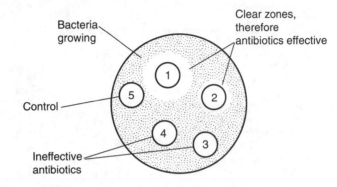

Fig. 3.4 Testing antibiotics

3.7 Fungi – moulds and their culture

Fungi consist of multicellular filaments called hyphae. Cells forming hyphae lack chloroplasts, cellulose and complete cross-walls – in contrast to green plants.
Nutrition: saprophytic or parasitic (see Unit 19.3).
Distribute themselves by spores, formed asexually.

Moulds

Rhizopus (mould on bread) and *Mucor* (mould on dung) are both 'pin-moulds' (Fig. 3.5).
Structure: the cytoplasm, with many nuclei in it, lines the cell wall – a continuous tube (of chitin) with no partitions forming separate cells. Inside the cytoplasm is a continuous vacuole. Threads of fungus (hyphae) make up a mycelium.
Nutrition: saprophytic (see Unit 4.2). Rootlet hyphae branch through the food, secreting digestive enzymes and absorbing the soluble products.

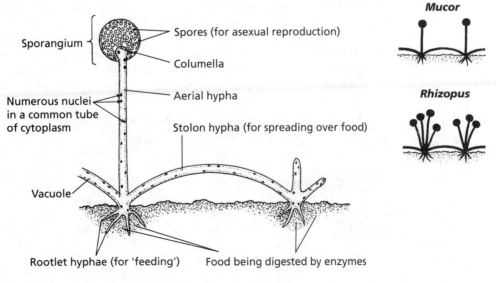

Fig. 3.5 Structure of a mould fungus

Reproduction:

① **asexually** by hundreds of spores from each sporangium. In *Mucor*, the sporangium wall dissolves in moisture and spores are distributed in a slime-drop by rain or animals. In *Rhizopus*, the wall cracks open when dry and wind distributes dry spores.

② **sexually** using special hyphae from two different strains to bring together gamete-nuclei. These gametes fuse and a tough zygospore is formed to survive unfavourable conditions, e.g. drought or the winter.

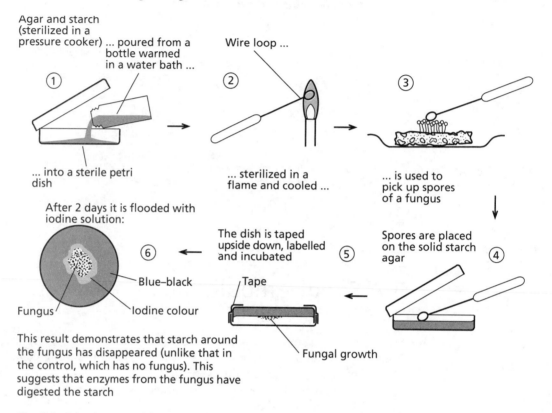

Agar and starch (sterilized in a pressure cooker) ... poured from a bottle warmed in a water bath ...

① ... into a sterile petri dish

Wire loop ...

② ... sterilized in a flame and cooled ...

③ ... is used to pick up spores of a fungus

④ Spores are placed on the solid starch agar

⑤ The dish is taped upside down, labelled and incubated

Tape

Fungal growth

⑥ After 2 days it is flooded with iodine solution:

Blue–black

Fungus

Iodine colour

This result demonstrates that starch around the fungus has disappeared (unlike that in the control, which has no fungus). This suggests that enzymes from the fungus have digested the starch

Fig. 3.6 Culturing a mould and testing for saprophytic nutrition

3.8 Fungi – mushrooms and yeasts

Mushrooms and toadstools exist unseen as a mycelium within soil, dead wood, etc. In damp cool conditions (e.g. October), hundreds of hyphae grow solidly up together, out of the soil, to form a toadstool (Fig. 3.7). On the underside this sheds millions of spores from 'gills' or pores. Such fungi are usually saprophytic; others are parasites and mutualists (see Unit 19.3). Growing mushrooms on waste straw avoids stubble burning – which pollutes the air – and provides useful garden mulch at the end.

Yeasts are exceptional among the Fungi in being single celled – no hyphae (Fig. 3.8). Natural yeasts on fruit skins ferment them to produce wine. Special yeasts are cultivated by Man for brewing, SCP, etc.

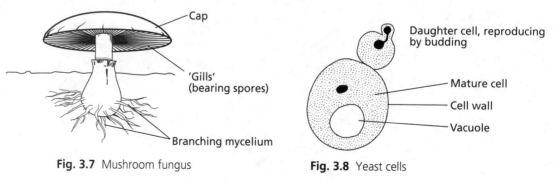

Cap

'Gills' (bearing spores)

Branching mycelium

Daughter cell, reproducing by budding

Mature cell

Cell wall

Vacuole

Fig. 3.7 Mushroom fungus

Fig. 3.8 Yeast cells

3.9 Importance of fungi

Helpful

1 **Decay fungi** (decomposers) release nutrients for green plants from dead organisms.
2 **Yeasts**, respiring anaerobically, provide:
(*a*) alcohol for brewers and wine-makers: this may be distilled to make spirits, e.g. gin;
(*b*) CO_2 for bakers (yeast acts on sugar in dough, making it rise)
$$C_6H_{12}O_6 \rightarrow 2C_2H_5OH + 2CO_2$$
(*c*) the yeast cells themselves also yield extracts (e.g. 'Marmite'), rich in vitamin B;
(*d*) 'gasohol' is ethanol brewed from sugar cane in Brazil and distilled to fuel over a million cars there.
3 **Antibiotic producers**, e.g. *Penicillium* produces pencillin.
4 **Food**
(*a*) natural, e.g. mushrooms, chanterelle, truffles.
(*b*) certain yeasts, grown in fermenter vessels containing solutions of ammonium and other salts which is bubbled through with natural gas, are harvested to give 'single cell protein' (**SCP**), very cheaply. Fed to cattle for quick growth.
(*c*) the mould *Fusarium graminearum* provides a high quality **mycoprotein** food for humans, marketed as 'Quorn' (see Unit 3.12).

Harmful

1 **Decay fungi** spoil food, e.g. *Rhizopus*, *Penicillium* on bread, cakes and jam.
2 **Plant diseases**, e.g. potato blight, caused millions to die in the Irish potato famine; 'rust' fungi damage cereal crops seriously; dutch elm disease killed millions of elm trees.
3 **Dry rot** fungus destroys house timbers.
4 **Minor animal diseases**, e.g. 'athlete's foot' and 'ringworm' (both attack the skin). Control of athlete's foot involves *washing* feet thoroughly (especially between toes), *drying* thoroughly and dusting with *antifungal powder*, e.g. Mycil (also inside shoes). Socks should be washed daily. Infection is via *wet* surfaces, e.g. bath mats, towels, socks, changing rooms. Drying kills the fungus, as does Terbinasine, applied as a cream for a week.

3.10 Algae

The Algae are green plants with no roots, stems or leaves (Fig. 3.9).
Their cells are little specialized – apart from gametes.
Nutrition is holophytic (see Unit 4.2).

Importance of algae

- **Diatoms** (unicellular algae) are the main plant component of plankton (phytoplankton). They
  (*a*) provide the majority of the world's O_2;
  (*b*) are at the base of most marine food chains.
- Some **seaweeds** are eaten, e.g. 'Irish moss'.
- **Extracts:** 'agar' for bacterial culture methods; 'alginates' for ice-cream.

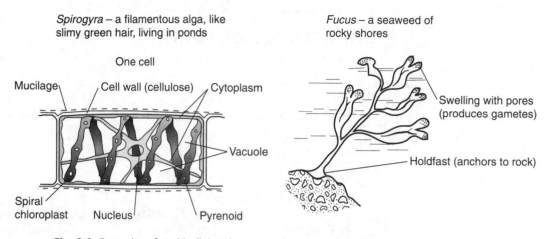

Spirogyra – a filamentous alga, like slimy green hair, living in ponds

Fucus – a seaweed of rocky shores

Fig. 3.9 Examples of multicellular algae. See also *Cladophora* (Unit 21.1)

3.11 Protozoa

The Protozoa are single-celled animals. Organelles for movement include pseudopodia (for flowing along), flagella and cilia (for swimming).

Nutrition is holozoic or parasitic.

Amoeba is a large freshwater protozoan (up to 1 mm in diameter) (Fig. 3.10).

Locomotion: cytoplasm in the centre (plasmasol) flows forward forming a pseudopodium. At the front the plasmasol fountains out, solidifying to a jelly-like tube (plasmagel) through which the centre flows. The plasmagel re-liquefies at the rear end, flowing into the centre.

Nutrition: holozoic (see Unit 4.2). Pursues prey (algae, bacteria, other protozoa) by following the trail of chemicals they exude (chemotaxis, see Unit 12.13). The prey is ingested using pseudopodia; digested in a food vacuole; indigestible matter, e.g. cellulose, is egested.

Osmoregulation: water entering continually by osmosis is channelled to the contractile vacuole. When full, this bursts, squirting water out. The process uses energy.

Respiration: gaseous exchange (O_2 in, CO_2 out) occurs over the whole surface area (see Unit 9.7).

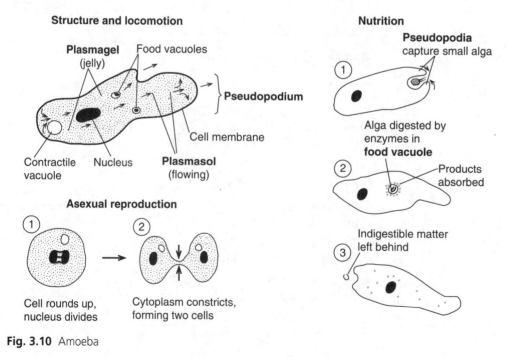

Fig. 3.10 Amoeba

Reproduction: asexually by binary fission; no sexual method.
Sensitivity: moves towards food; away from strong light, harmful chemicals and sharp objects.

Importance of protozoa

- **Malaria parasite** (*Plasmodium*), transmitted by mosquito, kills millions of people by fever in tropics when not protected by drugs like quinacrine (see Unit 21.13).
- **Sleeping sickness parasite** (*Trypanosoma*), transmitted by tsetse fly, kills millions of people, cattle and pigs in Africa. No drug protection against some types.
- **Dysentery parasite** (*Entamoeba*), transmitted by housefly and contaminated drinking water, causes dysentery (intestinal bleeding and upsets) and liver abscesses. Control of the housefly (Unit 21.9), sanitation to prevent flies picking up *Entamoeba* cysts from faeces and preventing water contamination are control methods. Drugs can cure the infection in Man.

3.12 Biotechnology

Biotechnology is the application of biological processes of microorganisms to manufacturing industries, service industries and to the maintenance of a pollution-free environment. Biotechnology is not new. Man has used microorganisms to produce his bread, wine, cheese, yoghurt and even biogas fuel for a long time. More recently he has disposed of sewage, produced antibiotics and obtained protein-rich foods using microorganisms.

The most recent advances result from understanding cell processes (dependent on enzymes), and from putting useful genes into microorganisms (genetic engineering) to do special jobs.

Biotechnology could transform our lives by providing efficient, low-cost solutions to many of the future problems of an overcrowded world, including shortage of energy and food.

Biotechnology requires cooperation between scientists:

1. **Biologists** – to find and grow microorganisms and to test the properties of potentially useful ones.
2. **Biochemists** – to study the metabolism of microorganisms and to genetically engineer them (see Unit 17.16).
3. **Engineers** – to design fermenters that provide the right growth conditions, flows of nutrients and products, and separation of the two at the end.
4. **Electronics scientists** – to provide sensitive feedback systems which automatically maintain the chosen conditions for growth.

Examples of the newer aspects of biotechnology are given below:

Food – single cell protein (SCP)

Table 3.4 SCP and its sources

Microbial foods	Examples	Notes
Glucose, salts, ammonia	RHM Mycoprotein – from fungi (marketed as 'Quorn')	Human food
Industrial wastes, e.g. molasses, whey, waste wood	Finnish Pekilo – from fungi	10 000 tonnes/year for animals – turns waste into profit, reduces pollution

Advantages of SCP

1. First class protein (see Unit 4.6), and contains fibre.
2. Can be produced in vast quantities quickly (mass-doubling time can be less than 1 hour).
3. Uses little space – compare farms.
4. Easily stored as dry powder – compare meat.
5. Free of biohazards, e.g. pesticides, hormones, food additives – if handled properly.
6. Can turn costly waste into a valuable product, e.g. Pekilo.

Note: SCP *algae* have long been cultivated, e.g. *Senedesmus* and *Chlorella* in Japan; *Spirulina* in Africa.

Energy

Man has traditionally burned recent **biomass** (wood, dung), which is renewable, and fossil biomass (coal, oil, natural gas), which is not. He is using both far too fast for this to continue long. (See also Unit 20.8, no. 7)

Wind, water and solar power are unlikely to supply the whole of world energy requirements.

Nuclear energy is expensive, can provide serious pollution hazards through release of radioactive materials (see Unit 20.6) and can only produce electrical energy. This currently cannot be easily stored to fuel automobiles, ships and aeroplanes.

Microorganisms may in the future play a larger role in producing the fuels **ethanol**, **methane** and **methanol** – to substitute for petrol, diesel and liquefied natural gas in vehicles. The chosen microorganisms cannot avoid depending on photosynthesis – which fixes ten times the world's present energy requirements. Ideally the microbes' food should be wastes, e.g. wood, bark, paper. But cultivation of 'fuel plants', e.g. sugar cane and maize (which fix twice as much solar energy as 'ordinary' green plants), for microorganisms to use as food is attractive, especially in the developing countries.

'Gasohol' (ethanol brewed from sugar) fuels over a million vehicles in Brazil; methanol (at present produced chemically) fuels over 5000 vehicles in oil-rich California. Neither fuel provides the pollution hazards of petrol (see Unit 20.6). Vegetable oils (sunflower, rape) are now being used by experimental buses. Methane cannot be liquefied cheaply enough for vehicle use, but it can be used direct from 'digesters' in sewage farms to power their pumps and lighting. Small digesters provide many Indian villagers with methane for heating.

Sewage disposal

1. **Removes pathogens** from infected people, e.g. those suffering from cholera, typhoid and bacillary dysentery.
2. **Lowers biological oxygen demand** (BOD) which would kill organisms, especially fish, if raw sewage reached rivers or lakes. The bacteria and fungi in them would decompose the faeces, using up the oxygen needed by aquatic life.
3. **Removes mineral salts** which would cause algal 'blooms' that turn the water green (see eutrophication, Unit 20.6).

Faeces, urine and water from washing comprise sewage. Sewage farms use bacteria and fungi to decompose organic matter. Some use anaerobic digesters to obtain methane to use as a fuel. The aerobic sprinkler and activated sludge methods are more efficient. Both rely on a food web of invertebrates, which feed on the bacteria and fungi, and on algae which thrive on the CO_2 and mineral salts produced by decomposers. The remaining mineral salts are removed either chemically or by vegetation in large ponds before water is returned to rivers.

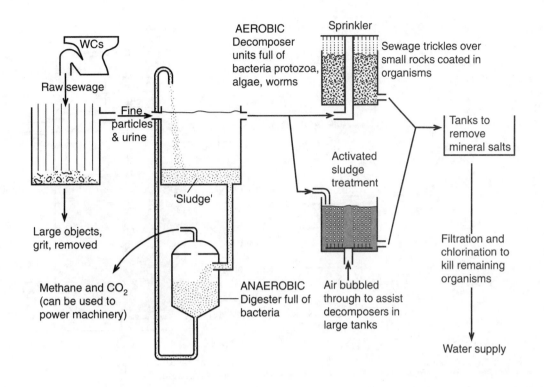

Fig. 3.11 Methods of sewage treatment

Enzymes

Enzymes (see Unit 1.5) have great advantages over inorganic catalysts.

1 Enormous variety of them, for every purpose.

2 Continuously produced (no shortages or great cost: compare platinum).

3 Work at low temperatures (not costly in energy).

4 Do a precise job, e.g. digesting the lignin of wood, leaving its cellulose intact for useful SCP microorganisms to use – as in the Pekilo process.

Enzymes *secreted* by microorganisms are easier to collect than those kept within their cells. Once extracted they store easily.

Enzymes are used either in solution, or trapped in polymer beads (where they are less easily destroyed) and can be used over and over again after each harvest of product. Many traditional processes can now be completed more quickly and with better control over the quality of the product using enzymes from microorganisms.

Table 3.5 The use of enzymes

Process	Enzymes from microorganisms used	Purpose
Washing clothes	Proteases	'Biological' washing powders remove stains, e.g. blood
Washing dishes	Amylases	Dishwasher powders remove starch smears on plates
Cheese making	Rennin Lipases	Curdles milk Speed up ripening of Danish blue cheese
Leather making	Proteases	Make leather supple (replace use of enzymes in dog dung!) and remove hair from hides
Brewing	Carbohydrases Proteases	Split starch into maltose and proteins into amino acids in malt (Fig. 3.12)

It is likely that in the future chemicals may be produced by a series of fermenters, each containing a single enzyme. By this means the final product can be produced, step by step, and be easily controlled.

Principles of fermenter technology

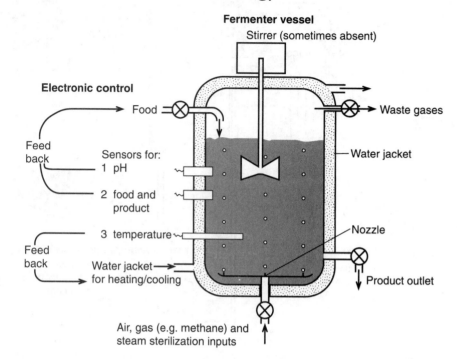

Fig. 3.12 A generalized fermenter

To achieve the desired pure product as cheaply and safely as possible the fermenting agent (microorganism or enzyme) must be studied carefully to achieve the best possible production levels. There are three main needs:

1. **Sterilization:** vessel must be sterilized by 'pressure cooking' the interior before use. During fermentation, food, air and other gases must also be sterile. The entry of unwanted organisms could spoil the product or poison or kill the consumer of it.

2. **Efficient contact** between the fermenting agent and the food and gases it needs. This maximizes production:

   (a) Stirrers or gases bubbling through the 'brew' continually supply the fermenting agents with fresh molecules to work on.

   (b) Organisms (e.g. yeast) or enzymes can be trapped ('immobilized') in jelly or acetate film, providing a huge surface area for reactions in the food flowing over them. This method also avoids the need to separate the product from the organisms at the end of the process.

3. **Temperature, pH, food and oxygen control:**

   (a) In 'batch' processes, each of these tends to change as fermentation proceeds. Initially the fermenter may need warming; later, when bacteria have multiplied, so much heat may be generated that cooling may be necessary. Biosensors coupled to electronic control systems automatically adjust fermenter contents where necessary.

   (b) In 'continuous' processes the sensors are particularly important in determining the rate of flow of food in and of product out.

Barley germination	$\longrightarrow$	Drying	$\longrightarrow$	Grinding	'Malt' $\longrightarrow$	Mashing
Cellulose, starch and protein of its food store (endosperm) broken down by enzymes		to 4% water without destroying enzymes		to give a large surface area for enzymes to work on		Water at 66 °C added. Further digestion for 2 hours $\downarrow$

		Fermenting		$\leftarrow$ Cooled to 15 °C.		Flavouring
Ale $\leftarrow$ 15 °C		Yeast added to ferment sugars to ethanol and CO_2		Hops removed		Hops added. Boiling destroys enzymes and prevents spoilage
Lager $\leftarrow$ 10 °C						

Fig. 3.13 Brewing beer (simplified)

Beer brewing in the UK is a **batch process**, i.e. the fermenter is totally cleared of microorganisms and products before a new supply of microorganisms and raw materials are introduced. 'Continuous processing' in beer brewing has been abandoned as it gives unwanted flavours.

A **continuous process** is one where raw materials flow into the fermenter and products and surplus microorganisms are continually harvested, bit by bit. The SCP 'Mycoprotein' is produced in this way. The fermenter is never emptied totally. Some continuous processes use enzymes stuck to ('immobilized' on) beads in the fermenter. Small amounts of enzyme do vast amounts of work without the need to keep whole microorganisms alive.

Health products

1 **Antibiotics** are extracted by solvents from certain bacteria and fungi, e.g. penicillin from *Penicillium*.

2 **Hormones**, e.g. insulin. The human gene for making insulin is inserted by genetic engineering (see Unit 17.16) into a bacterium. The engineered bacterium grows rapidly in a fermenter, producing insulin (see Unit 12.10).

Advantages:
   (a) less costly than extracting insulin from tonnes of slaughterhouse pancreases;
   (b) avoids allergic reactions to the animal product.

3 **Antibodies**. A single lymphocyte cell (see Table 8.1) which is producing a wanted antibody is selected. It is made to fuse with a cancer cell (which can be grown easily outside the body in a fermenter). The single fused cell multiplies rapidly, secreting the ('monoclonal') antibodies. These can be separated out to give a vaccine.

Advantages:
   (a) much more productive than the original method: collecting antibodies from the blood of animals injected with human pathogens;
   (b) avoids allergic reactions.

4 **Vitamins:** bacteria and fungi are usually rich in vitamins for humans – they can be individually extracted. A crude extract from yeast, rich in B vitamins, is 'Marmite'.

Pesticides

A number of microorganisms causing diseases of *particular* insect pests are in commercial production. These insecticides do not kill *all* insects as the now banned chemicals DDT and dieldrin did.

Mining

As minerals run out it will become important to recover metals even from low-grade ores and 'tailings' of previous mining operations. Already use is made of bacteria that change copper, zinc, lead, cobalt and uranium into soluble salts. These salts can be washed out from ores containing as little as 0.01% of the metal. This makes extraction profitable.

Summary

1 Viruses fall outside the description 'organisms', yet are immensely important parasites of cells.

2 Bacteria are uniquely tiny and simple cells, without a proper nucleus.

3 Bacteria are important in decay and disease.

4 Man has also harnessed bacteria to his own use in making many dairy products, fuel and antibiotics.

5 By genetic engineering, bacteria are used to make many useful products unnatural to them, e.g. hormones, enzymes.

6   Man has learned to control harmful bacteria by denying them the five vital conditions essential to their lives.

7   Fungi are also important in decay and disease and Man has learned to harness and control them.

8   Algae, though simple green organisms, are important, particularly in the sea, as they produce food and oxygen for the world.

9   Protozoa are simple animal-like cells, some of which are extremely important disease organisms.

10   Biotechnology is a fast-growing science, harnessing and manipulating microorganisms to our use.

Chapter 4
Foods and feeding

4.1 Food

Food (material for building up protoplasm) is of two types:

1. **Inorganic:** (simple molecules common to nonliving matter) e.g. carbon dioxide, mineral salts and water.

2. **Organic:** (complex, carbon-containing compounds) e.g. carbohydrates, fats, proteins and vitamins. These classes of molecules are characteristic of living matter.

4.2 Holophytic, holozoic and saprophytic nutrition compared

There are two fundamentally different methods of nutrition:

1. **Autotrophic** organisms (plants containing green chlorophyll) need *only inorganic food* from which they synthesize organic molecules, using *energy trapped from sunlight* to drive the reactions.

2. **Heterotrophic** organisms (animals, fungi, bacteria) have to feed on ready made *organic food*. From this they derive their *energy, released by respiration*. They also need some inorganic food.

Organic food can be obtained from living organisms (**holozoic** nutrition) or from dead matter (**saprophytic** nutrition). (For other variations see Unit 6.1.)

Table 4.1 Comparison of types of nutrition

	Autotrophic	Heterotrophic	
	Holophytic	Holozoic	Saprophytic
Examples of organisms	Typical green plants, e.g. *Spirogyra* (Unit 3.10) and flowering plants	Typical animals, e.g. *Amoeba* (Unit 3.11) and mammals	Bacteria and fungi of decay, e.g. *Mucor* (Unit 3.7) and mushrooms
Type of food	Inorganic only: CO_2, H_2O and mineral salts	Organic, H_2O and mineral salts	Dead organic, H_2O and mineral salts
How the food is used	**1** CO_2 and water are combined in **photosynthesis** to make carbohydrates **2** carbohydrates are modified and also often combined with salts to **form other organic molecules**, e.g. protein	Food organisms are killed; *ingested* into a **gut**; *digested* by enzymes secreted **internally**; soluble products *absorbed*; indigestible waste *egested* (eliminated)	Dead organisms or excreta are digested by enzymes secreted **externally** onto them; soluble products absorbed
Source of energy for vital functions	**Sunlight** – trapped by chlorophyll during photosynthesis	Cannot trap sunlight energy since they lack chlorophyll. Rely on **respiration** of organic molecules (the bonds of which contain energy)	

Thus the kinds of organisms practising these three forms of nutrition provide food for each other:

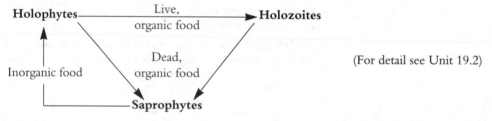

(For detail see Unit 19.2)

The principles outlined in Table 4.1 are best studied in detail by reference to simple organisms such as those named (see Units 3.7–3.11). Complex organisms, however, have complex requirements and uses for the molecules they absorb. This is taken into account below.

INORGANIC FOOD

1 Water (see Unit 7.1).
2 Mineral salts

4.3 Mineral salts for mammals and flowering plants

Table 4.2 Mammal requirements (especially Man)

Element	Good sources	Uses	Deficiency effects
Ca (Calcium)	Cheese; milk; bread (chalk added by law)	Bones and teeth are about $\frac{2}{3}$ calcium phosphate	Brittle bones and teeth
P (Phosphorus)	Milk	Bones and teeth; ATP – the energy molecule (Unit 9.14); DNA – genes and their functions (Unit 1.4)	As above
Fe (Iron)	Liver, egg yolk	Part of haemoglobin, the oxygen-carrying molecule	Anaemia (lack of red blood cells)
I (Iodine)	Sea foods Table salt (iodized by law)	Part of thyroxine, the hormone controlling metabolic rate (Unit 12.10)	Goitre – thyroid swelling in adults
F (Fluorine)	Toothpaste or tap water that have been fluoridated	Ensures hard tooth enamel, therefore less tooth decay (caries)	Dental caries more likely (Unit 6.6)
Na (Sodium)	Table salt (NaCl)	A correct balance of these is required, particularly for proper function of nerves and muscles	
K (Potassium)	Plant food		

Table 4.3 Flowering plant requirements (see Unit 5.8)

Element	Sources	Uses	Deficiency effects
N (Nitrogen)	Nitrates	Protein and DNA synthesis	Poor growth – little protoplasm made
S (Sulphur)	Sulphates		
Ca (Calcium)	Lime ($CaCO_3$)	'Gum' (middle lamella) between adjacent cell walls	Faulty cell division
Fe (Iron)	Iron salts	Enzymes for making chlorophyll	Pale leaves (chlorosis)
Mg (Magnesium)	Magnesium salts	Part of chlorophyll molecule molecule	
P (Phosphorus)	Phosphates	ATP (energy molecule) in photosynthesis and respiration; DNA synthesis	Poor growth – little energy for synthesis of protoplasm
K (Potassium)	Potassium salts	Functions not clear	Poor growth – dehydration

Trace elements include zinc (**Zn**), copper (**Cu**) and manganese (**Mn**). Required in very minute quantities for healthy growth (larger quantities are often poisonous).

Although green plants absorb mineral salts as ions, Man does not always give them to crops by way of inorganic fertilizers (see Unit 20.2). Organic fertilizers, such as dung, also yield salts, once they have been broken down by bacteria and fungi (see Units 3.3, 3.9, 19.10).

ORGANIC FOOD

1 **Carbohydrates, fats and proteins**
2 **Vitamins**

4.4 Carbohydrates, fats and proteins

Table 4.4 Carbohydrates, fats and proteins

	Carbohydrates	Fats (solids), oils (liquid)	Proteins
Elements	C, H, O Ratio of H:O is 2:1 (as in H_2O)	C, H, O Ratio of H:O is very high, i.e. very little O	C, H, O, N, often S
Examples	Glucose $C_6H_{12}O_6$ Starch $(C_6H_{10}O_5)_n$	Mutton fat $C_{57}H_{110}O_6$	Haemoglobin, amylase, insulin $C_{254}H_{377}N_{65}O_{75}S_6$
Units	Monosaccharides (simple sugars, like glucose)	Glycerol + fatty acids	Amino acids
	These are the smallest units into which these three classes of food can be broken down by digestion (hydrolysis). The units can be reassembled into larger molecules again by condensation, e.g. when food needs to be stored (see Unit 6.2)		
Larger molecules	Disaccharides (2 units), e.g. sucrose, maltose Polysaccharides (thousands of units), e.g. starch, glycogen, cellulose		Dipeptides (two linked amino acids) Polypeptides (many)
Chemical tests	1 Blue **Benedict's** solution + **reducing sugar** → (brought to the boil) orange precipitate 2 Brown **iodine** solution + **starch** → (must be cold) blue-black 3 **Clinistix** + **glucose** → (cold) mauve or purple	1 The clear filtrate obtained from mixing **absolute ethanol** with crushed food, when added to an equal quantity of water, gives a white emulsion. 2 **Translucency:** when warmed on paper, makes paper permanently translucent ('grease spot')	1 Colourless 40% **NaOH** + protein extract, add 2 drops blue **$CuSO_4$** → mauve Biuret colour (**Biuret test**) 2 **Albustix** and some proteins → (cold) green or (usually) blue-green
Functions	**Energy supply** when respired: 17 kJ/g. Used first. Stored as starch (green plants) and glycogen (animals, fungi). Transported as sugars **Structural:** cellulose cell walls **Origin of other organic molecules:** e.g. sugar + nitrate → amino acid	**Energy supply** when respired: 39 kJ/g. Used after carbohydrates. Important in flying, migrating and hibernating animals. (More energy per unit mass than glycogen) **Heat insulation:** subcutaneous fat in mammals **Waterproofing:** of skin, fur, feathers **Buoyancy:** e.g. fish larvae in the sea	**Energy supply** when respired: 18 kJ/g. Important in carnivores, otherwise only respired extensively in starvation **Movement:** muscles contract; tendons connect muscles to bones; ligaments connect bone to bone at joints – all are protein **Catalysts:** enzymes make reactions of metabolism possible (see Unit 1.5) **Hormones** regulate metabolism (see Unit 12.10). Many, e.g. insulin, are protein

4.5 Vitamins

Vitamins: organic substances (of a variety of kinds) required in *minute* amounts to maintain health of heterotrophs. Autotrophs make all they need.

Lack of a vitamin in the diet results in a *deficiency disease*, e.g. scurvy. A vitamin for one organism is not necessarily a vitamin for another, e.g. Man suffers scurvy from lack of vitamin C but rats do not because they synthesize their own.

Vitamins A and D are *fat soluble*, ingested in fats and oils.
Vitamins B and C are *water soluble* and present in other materials.

Table 4.5 Vitamins

Vitamins	Good sources	Functions	Deficiency diseases
A	Vegetables, butter, egg yolk. Liver oils, e.g. cod-liver oil, contain both A and D	**1** Healthy epithelia **2** Part of 'visual purple' in rod cells of retina (Unit 11.3)	Susceptibility to *invasion by disease organisms* *Poor night vision*
D 'sunshine vitamin'	Butter, egg yolk. (Can be synthesized in the skin from oils irradiated by ultraviolet light)	Regulation of calcium and phosphate absorption from gut and their deposition in bone	*Rickets:* poor bone formation, weak and often deformed, e.g. 'bow legs' in children
B₁ *(thiamine)*	Wholemeal bread		*Beri beri:* weak muscles, paralysis
B₂ *(riboflavin)*	Liver Yeast Marmite	Different roles in metabolism, especially respiration	Sore mouth cavity, tongue
B₃ *(nicotinic acid)*	Wholemeal bread		*Pellagra:* blistered skin, diarrhoea
B₁₂ *(cobalamine)*	Liver; extracted now from a mould, *Streptomyces*	Aids formation of red blood cells	*Pernicious anaemia:* lack of red blood cells
C	Citrus fruits, blackcurrants; fresh vegetables and milk	Healing of wounds; strong skin and capillaries	*Scurvy:* capillary bleeding; poor healing of wounds

Test for vitamin C: blue **DCPIP** solution is turned colourless by **vitamin C** solution (and by other reducing agents in foods as preservatives). DCPIP may turn red if acid foods are added but bleaching still occurs with vitamin C.

How much vitamin C in a food?
Find out the volume of liquidized food needed to decolourize a volume of DCPIP solution of known strength. Do the titration again with a standard vitamin C solution instead of food. By comparing the two volumes, the vitamin content of the liquid can be calculated.

4.6 Diet, health and additives

A **balanced diet** is one that maintains health. It must provide enough of the following:

1. **Energy** from carbohydrates and fats when respired.
2. **Materials for growth and repair:**
   from proteins to make muscles, enzymes;
   from mineral salts to make bones, red blood cells.
3. **Vitamins** to help run metabolism.
4. **Water** to transport materials; provide a medium in which they react (see Unit 7.1).
5. **Fibre** (roughage) to help peristalsis.

Starvation refers to massive lack of food of all kinds.
Malnutrition refers to lack or excess of particular parts of the diet, e.g. *obesity* (fatness) results from excessive intake of energy foods – linked to heart disease. *Anorexia* (wasting away) results from not eating enough energy foods. See also mineral salt and vitamin deficiency diseases (Units 4.3, 4.5).
Balanced diets differ according to *age* (the young require more protein and calcium), *occupation* (energy requirements and water intake to replace sweat differ), *climate* (less energy needed to keep body warm in tropics than in the Arctic) and *sex* (pregnant women need more iron and calcium for the baby's blood and bones).

Milk: Human milk supplies babies with enough water, protein, sugar (lactose), fat, minerals and vitamins. Cows' milk has much more protein ($\times$3) and salts ($\times$4) and less sugar. Young babies will vomit cows' milk if it has not been diluted and had sugar added. Some babies are allergic to cows' milk protein.

Quantity and quality of food is important for health:

1 Protein: made of 20 different amino acids, linked into chains. Of these 20, Man cannot make 8 and so must get them from food. Animal protein and SCP (see p. 39) are rich in all of them: 'first class protein'. Plant protein is usually poor, deficient in some amino acids: 'second class protein'.

Kwashiorkor (wasting of limbs, puffiness of tissues and pot-belly full of fluid) results from lack of first class protein, e.g. in maize-eating Africans.

2 Fats: two kinds – saturated (plentiful in animal fats) and unsaturated (plentiful in plant oils). High intake of animal fats, e.g. butter, seems linked with *heart disease* (p. 82). Margarines made from plant oils seem safer.

3 Additives: The food industry adds substances to foods to make them more attractive and tasty and to make them last longer. Most additives (other than flavourings) are given an 'E number', e.g. E140 is chlorophyll. Some further examples are given in Table 4.6.

Table 4.6 Some examples of additives

Colourings	E110 Sunset yellow E142 Green S	To colour orange squash To keep tinned peas green
Preservatives	E211 Sodium benzoate	To kill microorganisms reaching soft drinks, margarine, sausages
Antioxidants	E321 BHT	To prevent changes in taste or colour by oxidation in crisps, breakfast cereals
Emulsifiers, stabilizers	E400 Alginic acid	To give 'body' to ice cream, instant desserts

Unfortunately, some additives may cause some children to become *hyperactive* – they develop sleeplessness and behaviour problems and may also suffer from asthma and eczema (e.g. E110, E211, E321 – see Table 4.6). Another minority of people develop *allergies* to certain additives, e.g. to MSG (monosodium glutamate), a flavour enhancer used in pork pies, sausages and Chinese foods.

Since January 1986, the European Community agreed that all substances added to packaged food, including water, must be listed on the packet.

Summary

1   Food can be simple (inorganic) or complex, containing carbon (organic).

2   Autotrophs (green plants) need only inorganic food, synthesizing it into organic compounds using sunlight energy trapped by chlorophyll.

3   Heterotrophs rely on organic compounds to provide their energy (by respiration).

4   Heterotrophs have two different ways of dealing with organic food – the animal (holozoic) way and the decay (saprophytic) way.

5   Water, carbon dioxide and various mineral salts are the food of plants (see also summary to Chapter 5).

6   Animals also need water, but a different range of mineral salts. However, their main requirements are carbohydrates, fats and proteins, with small amounts of vitamins.

7   Human diets are 'balanced' if they keep the person healthy.

8   The ideal diet changes with age, activity and climate.

9   Additives are human additions to diet for purposes of food preservation, flavouring and colour, and they sometimes have harmful effects.

Chapter 5
Green plant nutrition

HOLOPHYTIC NUTRITION

Unique features: uses only inorganic food molecules to photosynthesize sugars and synthesize amino acids.

5.1 Photosynthesis

Photosynthesis makes sugars and the by-product oxygen from CO_2 and water, using the energy of sunlight, trapped by chlorophyll. Occurs in chloroplasts (see Unit 1.2). The simplest equation for photosynthesis is:

$$6CO_2 + 6H_2O \xrightarrow[\textbf{chlorophyll}]{\textbf{sunlight energy}} C_6H_{12}O_6 + 6O_2$$

carbon   water   glucose   oxygen
dioxide   (energy-rich)

In reality photosynthesis has *two* distinct stages:

1 photolysis – water is split to give (*a*) oxygen gas (by-product) } only in the *light*
(*b*) hydrogen for reducing CO_2

2 reduction – of CO_2 by hydrogen to form sugars, e.g. glucose; needs energy (ATP) and enzymes. *Evidence:* if heavy isotope of oxygen, ^{18}O, is used to 'label' water fed to plants, all the O_2 given off is ^{18}O and none is normal oxygen, ^{16}O. If the CO_2, and not the water, fed to the plants is labelled with ^{18}O, *none* of the O_2 given off is ^{18}O. Therefore all the O_2 by-product comes from water and not from CO_2.

To take account of this, the **overall equation** for photosynthesis must be:

$$6CO_2 + 12H_2O \xrightarrow[\text{chlorophyll}]{\text{sunlight energy}} C_6H_{12}O_6 + 6O_2 + 6H_2O$$

glucose
(storing sun energy)

This proves the need for water in photosynthesis – impossible to prove in any other way.

Fate of glucose:
(*a*) Converted to sucrose – for *transport* elsewhere.
(*b*) Converted to starch – for *storage* in leaf (transported away as sucrose by night). (Basis for leaf starch test.)
(*c*) Used in *respiration*, or *amino acid synthesis* (see Unit 5.7), or fat synthesis.
(*d*) Converted to cellulose – making *cell walls* at growing points.

Fate of oxygen:
Diffuses out of leaves to air or water surrounding them.
Evidence that it is oxygen: See Fig. 5.1.

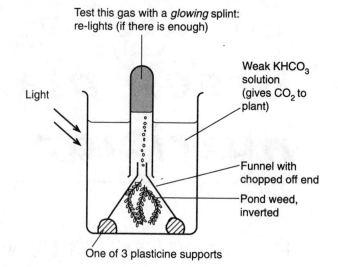

Fig. 5.1 Collecting and testing the gas from a pond weed

5.2 Factors necessary for photosynthesis

Evidence
Plant must be *de-starched* before any experiment by keeping it in the dark for 48 hours.
A leaf must now be tested for starch (as a control). The presence of starch in the leaves
at the end of the experiment is evidence of photosynthesis.

1 The starch test for leaves (Fig. 5.2)

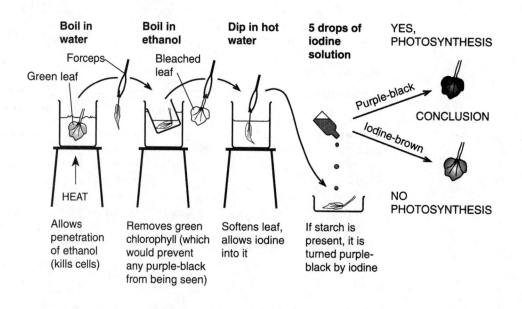

Fig. 5.2 Testing leaves for starch

2 Test the need for: ① Sunlight, ② Carbon dioxide, ③ Chlorophyll (Fig. 5.3)

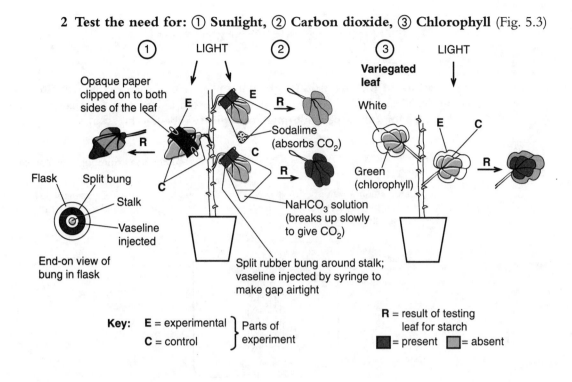

Fig. 5.3 Testing the need for ① sunlight, ② carbon dioxide, ③ chlorophyll in photosynthesis

5.3 Limiting factors

In a physiological process (such as photosynthesis) any factor which is in short supply, so that it reduces the rate of the process from its possible maximum, is said to be the limiting factor. Thus with plants photosynthesizing outdoors, *light* is limiting at dusk; *carbon dioxide* (CO_2) during most of the day; *water* probably never. *Temperature* can also be limiting (too cold – reactions too slow; too hot – destroys enzymes). *Factors closing stomata* are limiting by reducing flow of CO_2 into leaf. *Lack of magnesium (Mg)* in soil limits the amount of chlorophyll made in the leaf (see Fig. 5.4). Crops grown in commercial greenhouses avoid natural limiting factors: extra lighting, controlled warmth and air enriched with extra CO_2.

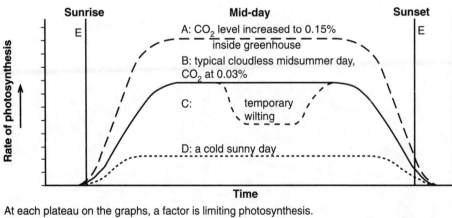

At each plateau on the graphs, a factor is limiting photosynthesis.
A and B: probably CO_2 in air
C: CO_2 reaching chloroplasts
D: temperature
E: at dawn and dusk: light

Fig. 5.4 Limiting factors for photosynthesis

5.4 Rate of photosynthesis

Rate of photosynthesis in a water plant, e.g. *Elodea*, can be estimated by counting the *number of bubbles* per unit time coming from a cut stem. Alternatively, trap bubbles and measure *volume* per unit time in a capillary tube (see Fig. 5.5).

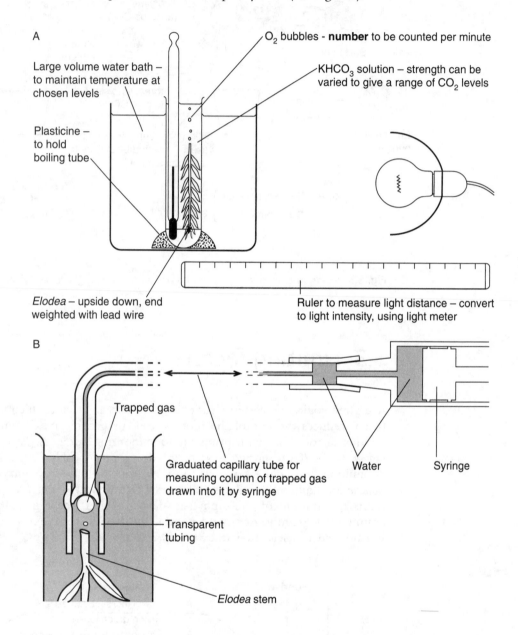

A

O_2 bubbles - **number** to be counted per minute

Large volume water bath – to maintain temperature at chosen levels

$KHCO_3$ solution – strength can be varied to give a range of CO_2 levels

Plasticine – to hold boiling tube

Elodea – upside down, end weighted with lead wire

Ruler to measure light distance – convert to light intensity, using light meter

B

Trapped gas

Graduated capillary tube for measuring column of trapped gas drawn into it by syringe

Water

Syringe

Transparent tubing

Elodea stem

Fig. 5.5 Measuring the rate of photosynthesis in a water plant, A – by counting the number of bubbles released per minute, B – by measuring the volume of gas evolved per minute

5.5 Leaf structure and photosynthesis

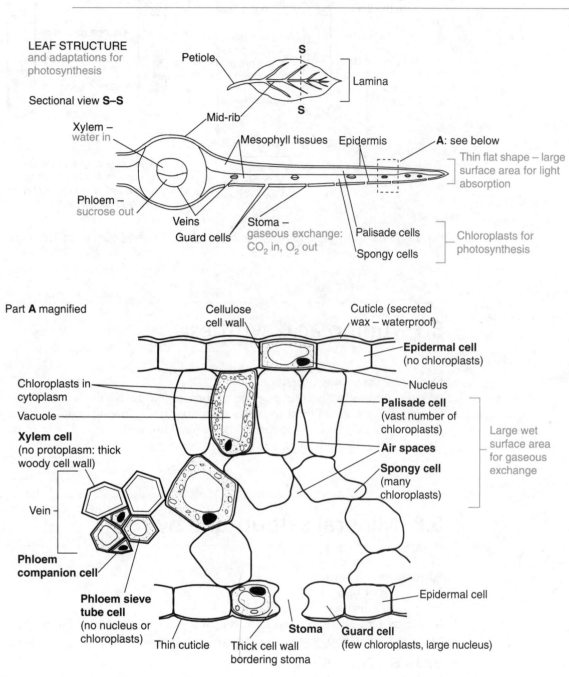

Fig 5.6 Leaf structure

5.6 Gaseous exchange in leaves

By night, leaves only respire: CO_2 out, O_2 in.

By day, they photosynthesize: CO_2 in, O_2 out. However, they also respire. But more sugars are made (by photosynthesis) than are broken down (by respiration).

At dawn and dusk (very little light) the two processes break even – the *compensation point*. This point can be determined by using the apparatus shown in Fig. 5.7, changing the distance of the light from the plant until the indicator remains orange – as in a corked control tube.

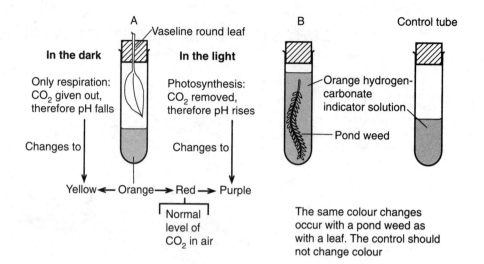

Fig. 5.7 Determining gaseous exchange: A in a leaf, B in a water plant using hydrogencarbonate indicator

5.7 Amino acid synthesis

Dependent on photosynthesis.
Nitrates combine with sugar products to form amino acids.
Green plants alone can do this, at root and shoot tips (growing regions).
Amino acids are converted to form protein (see Unit 6.2).
Chlorophyll is a protein with a magnesium compound linked to it.

5.8 Mineral salt uptake by roots

Absorption of salts
Mainly at root tips.
Partly at root hair region (see Fig. 16.1).
Mainly by active transport and thus oxygen is needed. Partly by diffusion (see Unit 7.2).
Quite independent of water uptake by osmosis (see Unit 7.3).

Evidence of need for salts
Plants are grown with roots in salt solutions ('water culture').
Control solution contains all salts needed (see Table 4.3).
Test solutions each omit one element, e.g. −N = omit nitrates; −S = omit sulphates.
Solutions aerated to allow efficient salt uptake.

In the experiment in Fig. 5.8, growth of test plants can be compared against control plants: harvest them, dry in oven at 110 °C, weigh. To avoid the possibility that some seedlings grow more vigorously than others because of *genetic* differences, the plants should be from the same clone, e.g. cuttings of the same plant.

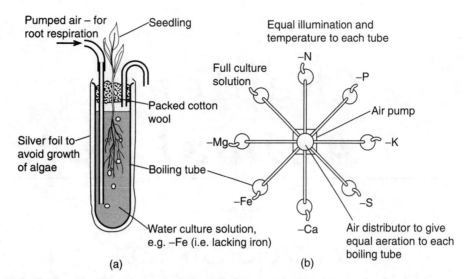

Fig. 5.8 Water culture experiment to determine the mineral salt requirements of a plant: (a) side view of one tube, (b) plan view of experiment

Summary

1 Green plants need carbon dioxide and water to make carbohydrate (initially sugars) and the by-product oxygen.

2 Sugars can be made into starch (for storage), cellulose (for cell walls) or be used in respiration (to provide energy).

3 Sugars can also be made into oils, or into amino acids and then proteins, with the help of mineral salts (especially nitrates).

4 Other substances can be made from sugars with the help of mineral salts, e.g. chlorophyll (needing magnesium) and DNA (needing phosphates and nitrates).

5 Various experiments on potted and other plants show the need for carbon dioxide, chlorophyll and light in photosynthesis, but only the use of oxygen isotopes can show that water is necessary too.

6 Any of the three factors above can become a limiting factor to photosynthesis – when its scarcity prevents a higher rate of photosynthesis. Water is usually not a limiting factor.

7 The starch test (iodine turns starch blue-black) is used to show whether photosynthesis has taken place in a leaf.

8 Hydrogencarbonate indicator solution can be used to show changes in the rate of both photosynthesis and respiration in living organisms, changing from red in ordinary air to yellow if carbon dioxide is being produced (respiration) and to purple if it is being removed (photosynthesis).

9 The leaf is a structure well adapted to photosynthesis by its shape, internal anatomy and the presence of chlorophyll.

Chapter 6
Animal nutrition

HOLOZOIC NUTRITION

6.1 Feeding methods of animals

Animals obtain food in one of three ways:

1 As solids:
food-organisms that have to be chewed (Fig. 6.1) small enough to be ingested.
Herbivores – eat plants
Carnivores – eat animals
Omnivores – eat plants and animals

2 As solids in suspension: tiny food-organisms in water that must be strained out of it – plankton (plants and animals).
Filter feeders, e.g. mosquito larva (Fig. 21.18)

3 As liquids:
(a) juices extracted from living hosts, without killing them.
Parasites (see Unit 19.3)
(b) liquid nutriment produced by digesting dead food externally and then sucking it up.
Saprozoites, e.g. housefly (Fig. 6.1)

Adaptations necessary for each feeding method

1 **Herbivores:** food does not run away, but large quantities must be gathered since food is relatively poor in quality. Herbivores include locusts, snails, deer and sheep.

2 **Carnivores:** have to capture and overcome prey, e.g. by cunning (dogs), traps (spiders' webs), poisons (cobras) and sharp weapons (claws, teeth) (see Fig. 6.6).

3 **Omnivores:** adaptations for feeding are intermediate between those of herbivores and carnivores, e.g. human teeth. Often very successful animals since they vary their food according to availability, e.g. cockroaches, rats, pigs and Man.

4 **Filter feeders:** require sieves, e.g. *Daphnia*, Fig. 21.10. Baleen whales trap 'krill' (shrimps) on frayed edges of whale-bone plates hanging down in mouth cavity, open to the sea as they swim.

5 **Parasites: endoparasites** bathe in nutritious liquids, e.g. blood or digested food in gut of host, absorbing food directly through 'skin' – no gut, e.g. *Trypanosoma*, tapeworms.

Ectoparasites pierce their host to suck out nutritious liquids, e.g. mosquito, flea (blood) (see Fig. 21.19). Aphids (greenfly) pierce phloem: pressure of sap forces it into insect (and some out as 'honey-dew').

⑥ **Saprozoites:** need no jaws, only tubes for saliva (down) and liquid food (up), with pumps (see Fig. 6.1).

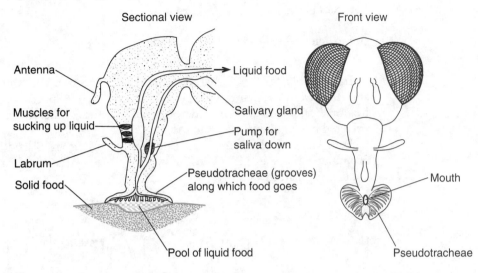

Fig. 6.1 Mouthparts of a housefly – for sucking up liquid food (digested externally)

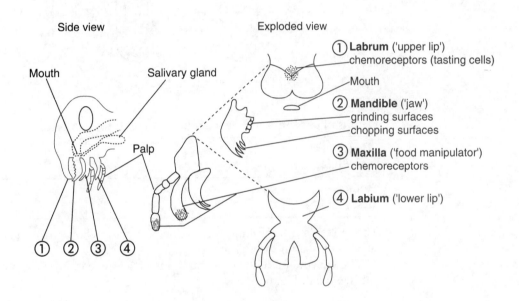

Fig. 6.2 Mouthparts of a chewing insect, e.g. locust (herbivore), cockroach (omnivore), ground beetle (carnivore)

6.2 Digestion and its consequences

All animals **ingest** food via the mouth into a gut (or equivalents). Exceptions: parasites which bathe in food. In the gut, food is **digested** in two ways:

(a) *physically* – by chewing or grinding (important in herbivores), stomach churning and peristalsis. This increases the surface area of food, making it easier for (b) below.

(b) *chemically* – by enzymes (see Unit 1.5) which hydrolyse large molecules into their small basic units (see Unit 4.4). Without this, large insoluble food molecules would not be small enough to be **absorbed** through the membranes of gut cells: e.g.

$$\text{starch} + \text{water} \xrightarrow[\text{enzymes}]{\text{carbohydrase}} \text{monosaccharides}$$
$$\text{fat} + \text{water} \xrightarrow[\text{enzymes}]{\text{lipase}} \text{fatty acids} + \text{glycerol}$$
$$\text{protein} + \text{water} \xrightarrow[\text{enzymes}]{\text{protease}} \text{amino acids}$$

⎫
⎬ these molecules are now soluble and small enough for absorption
⎭

Absorbed food is then **assimilated** (used or stored) into the body. Storage occurs when enzymes condense the small units of foods into large molecules (reverse of hydrolysis). For example:

amino acids $\xrightarrow[\text{enzymes}]{\text{condensing}}$ protein + water

Indigestible food is **egested** (eliminated) through the anus or equivalent. Most animals have no enzymes to digest cellulose – hence special adaptations of herbivores. Mammal *faeces* include egested roughage, bacteria, mucus, dead cells and water, and excreted bile pigments (see Fig. 6.12).

Four sacs of Visking containing different solutions are placed in distilled water. After 30 minutes the water is tested for starch and for reducing sugar. (The saliva must not contain sugar from sweets.)

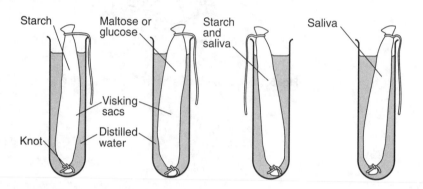

Fig. 6.3 A model of digestion and absorption

Results of tests on water outside the Visking in the 4 tubes:

Benedict's test (Table 4.4)	–	+	+	–
Iodine test (Table 4.4)	–	–	–	–

The model 'gut' is Visking membrane, known to allow small molecules (sugar) but not large ones (starch) through its pores.

The enzyme in saliva turns starch into maltose. Maltose is turned into glucose in the gut (see 'villi', Fig. 6.9).

Conclusions: 1 Sugars, but not starch, pass through Visking pores
2 Saliva turns starch into sugar

6.3 Experiments with digestive enzymes

Each enzyme works best at a certain temperature and pH (these are its 'optimum' conditions). Outside these conditions enzymes may cease to work or may even be destroyed.

Example 1: Investigating the effect of temperature on digestion of starch by salivary amylase

Method:
1 Add 5 cm³ of 1% starch solution to each of 5 boiling tubes and 1 cm³ of saliva diluted with water to 4 test-tubes as shown in Fig. 6.4(a).
2 Leave the starch and the enzyme for at least 2 minutes, to gain the temperature of the water bath.

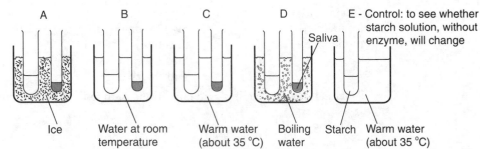

Fig. 6.4(a)

3 Pour the saliva into the boiling tube next to it, so mixing it with the starch. Note the time immediately.

4 Using a separate dropper for each tube, test one drop from each boiling tube with iodine, as shown in Fig. 6.4(b).

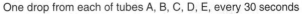

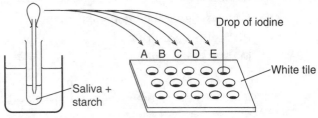

Fig. 6.4(b)

5 Note the time when each drop no longer turns the iodine blue-black (i.e. starch is digested). Do not test for longer than 15 minutes.
Possible results:

A – still blue-black after 15 minutes   D – still blue-black after 15 minutes
B – changes to brown at 8 minutes   E – still blue-black after 15 minutes
C – changes to brown at 2 minutes

6 Now put the boiling tubes from A and D into the warm water bath C and test them with iodine after 5 minutes (once only).
Results:

A – brown colour   D – blue-black

Conclusions:

1 Digestion proceeds faster at warm temperatures than at cold (A, B, C).
2 At low temperatures, the enzyme is inactive but not destroyed (A, step **6**).
3 At water's boiling point, the enzyme is destroyed (D, step **6**).

Example 2: Investigating the effect of pH on digestion of egg albumen (protein) by pepsin

Method:

1 Put in each of 6 tubes a 5 mm cube of cooked egg white and a thymol crystal (to prevent bacteria digesting the egg). Then add 2 cm^3 of 0.1M solutions to affect the pH as shown in Fig. 6.5.

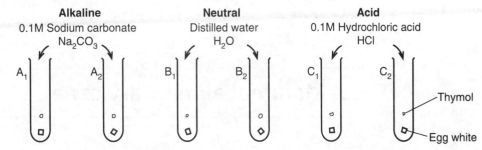

Fig. 6.5

2 Add 2 cm^3 pepsin solution to A_1, B_1 and C_1, but not to A_2, B_2 and C_2 (which are controls used to see whether Na_2CO_3, water and HCl alone digest egg white).

3 Incubate the tubes in a warm place (about 35 °C) for 24 hours and then look at the cubes.

Results:

Not digested:
in tubes A_1, A_2, B_2, C_2
Sharp edges

Slightly digested:
in tube B_1
Smaller cube
with fuzzy edges

Totally digested:
in tube C_1
Cube absent

Conclusion: pepsin requires acid conditions to digest cooked albumen.

6.4 Mammal teeth

Mammals are the only vertebrate group with *differentiated* teeth (four types with special uses):

1. **I**ncisors – for biting off food
2. **C**anines – for stabbing, holding prey
3. **Pre**molars – for grinding
4. **M**olars – for grinding

First set of teeth are shed ('milk teeth'): 20, made up of 8 **I**, 4 **C**, 8 **Pm** in Man.
Adult set includes 'wisdoms' (back molars): 32, made up of 20 larger replacements and 12 **M**.
Structure of teeth: layers of modified bone nourished from pulp cavity and shaped according to function (Fig. 6.6).

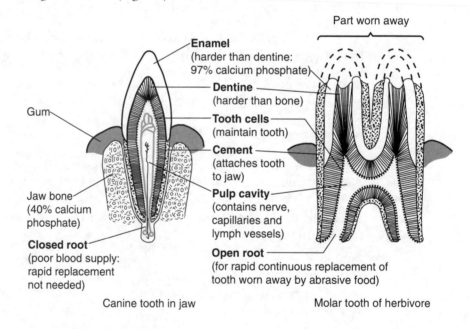

Fig. 6.6 Vertical section through two kinds of teeth

6.5 Mammal alimentary canal

The normal passage of food is illustrated in Fig. 6.7.

Abnormal passage of food:

1. **Vomiting:** strong contraction of stomach fountains the food, containing toxins, too much salt, etc., out of mouth.
2. **Diarrhoea:** irritation of villi causes too much mucus and intestinal juice secretion. Sweeps out harmful microorganisms, e.g. cholera in liquid faeces.

The resulting dehydration of the body can kill, especially the very young or old. **Oral rehydration therapy** involves dissolving the right amount of salts and glucose in the right volume of water and drinking it. Drinking water alone, in quantity, can kill.

3 **Constipation:** waste can be solidified too much by colon: hard faeces can cause bleeding. Roughage (fibre) in diet helps prevent this.

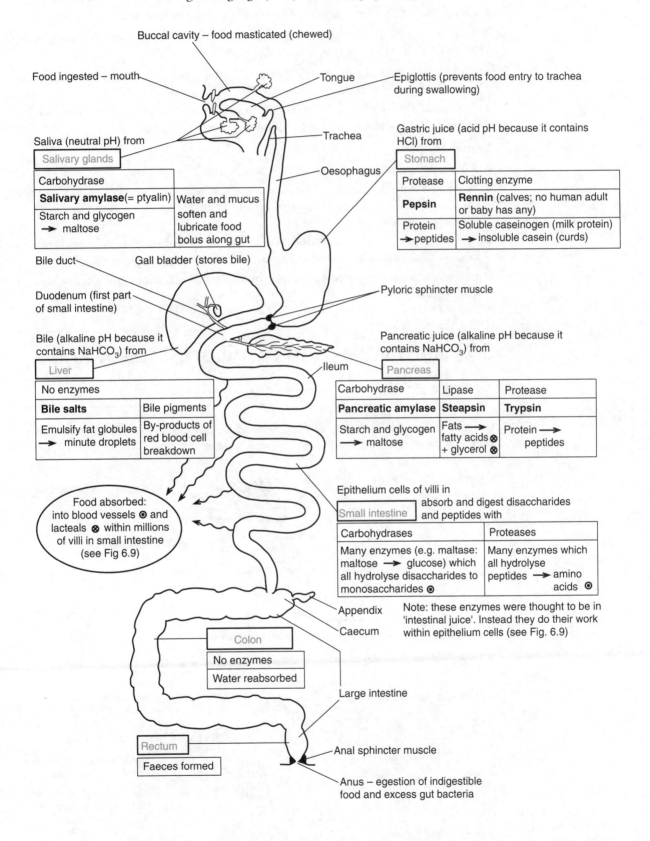

Fig. 6.7 Treatment of food from mouth to anus in mammals (based on Man)

6.6 Dental health

1 Growing healthy teeth need:

- food rich in *calcium* (Unit 4.3) and *vitamin D* to help in its absorption (Unit 4.5);
- *fluoride* from fluoridated water or toothpaste to harden enamel.

2 Maintaining healthy teeth requires controlling the bacteria around teeth by *dental hygiene*. There are two main dental diseases.

- *Caries* (holes in teeth) results from bacteria turning sugars into acids. Acids dissolve enamel, allowing bacteria to rot dentine.
- *Periodontal disease* (teeth fall out) results from bacteria entering space between tooth and unhealthy gums. They rot fibres holding teeth in socket.

Dental Hygiene

- *Rinse mouth with water* to remove sugars, after meals (or sweets).
- *Brush teeth* with fluoride toothpaste, especially before sleep, to remove food particles and bacteria. These form 'plaque' – a coating stuck to teeth – if left. Disclosing tablets stain it red.
- *Massage gums* by eating crisp foods and as part of tooth-brushing to keep them healthy. This prevents exposure of neck and root of tooth to bacteria.
- *Orthodontic treatment* improves hygiene by uncrowding teeth, making them easier to keep clean.

6.7 Herbivores and carnivores: teeth and jaws

Carnivores need only to swallow lumps of food; protease enzymes can do the rest. **Herbivores** must grind food to give a large surface area for cellulases to act upon (Unit 6.8).

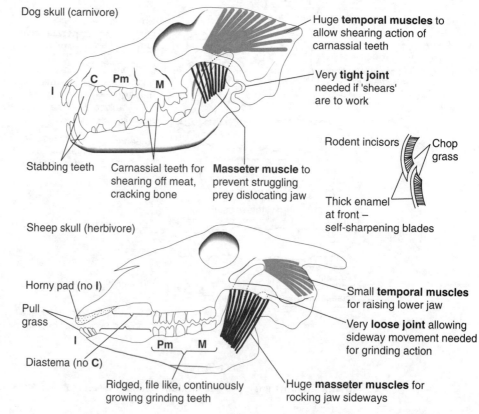

Fig. 6.8 Comparison of herbivore and carnivore jaws and teeth

6.8 Absorption of food at a villus

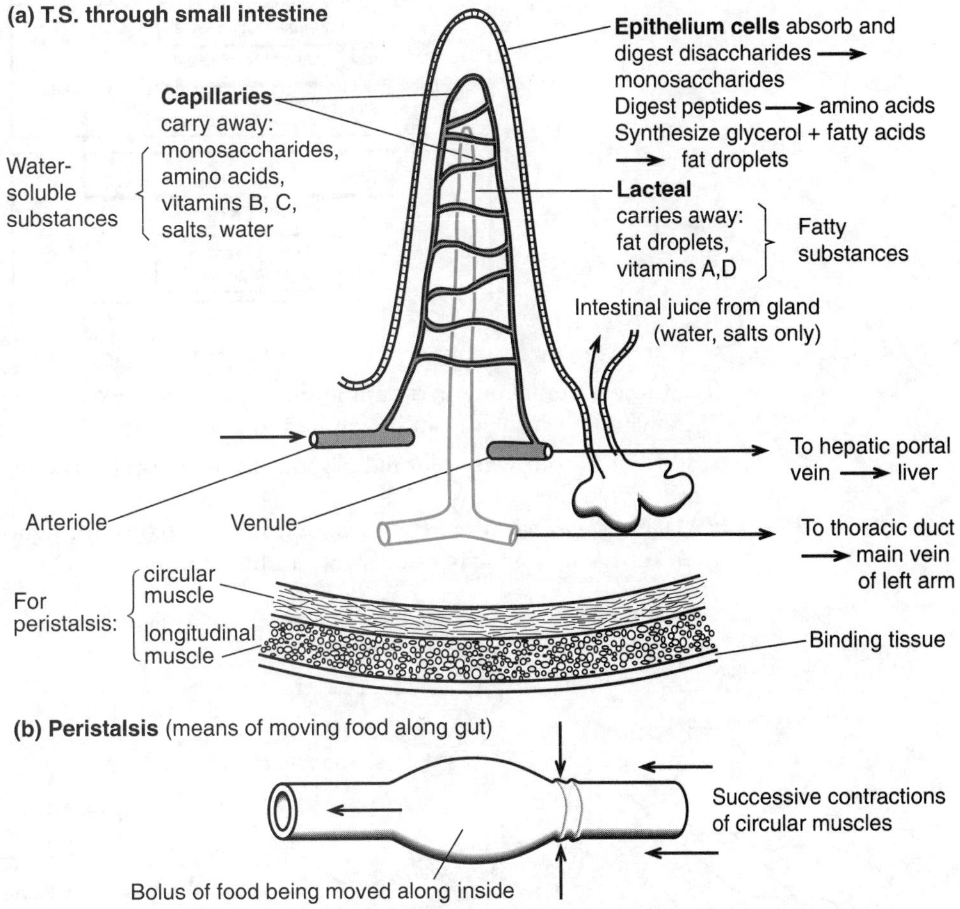

(a) T.S. through small intestine

Epithelium cells absorb and digest disaccharides ⟶ monosaccharides
Digest peptides ⟶ amino acids
Synthesize glycerol + fatty acids ⟶ fat droplets

Lacteal carries away: fat droplets, vitamins A,D ⎫ Fatty substances ⎭

Capillaries carry away: monosaccharides, amino acids, vitamins B, C, salts, water

Water-soluble substances ⎧ ⎨ ⎩

Intestinal juice from gland (water, salts only)

To hepatic portal vein ⟶ liver

To thoracic duct ⟶ main vein of left arm

Arteriole

Venule

For peristalsis: ⎧ circular muscle ⎨ longitudinal muscle ⎩

Binding tissue

(b) Peristalsis (means of moving food along gut)

Successive contractions of circular muscles

Bolus of food being moved along inside

Fig. 6.9 (a) Enlarged longitudinal section of a villus (millions lining the small intestine); (b) Peristalsis

6.9 Storage of food

❶ Monosaccharides, e.g. glucose: turned into glycogen for storage in liver and muscles; excess converted to fats stored under skin.

❷ Fatty substances: stored in liver (including vitamins A, D) and under skin.

❸ Amino acids: used immediately in growth and repair. *Not* stored; excess deaminated in liver.

6.10 The liver

A large organ, concerned with homeostasis by metabolizing food and poisons and removing unwanted cells. Stores foods and blood. Receives blood from two sources (Fig. 6.10); discharges bile.

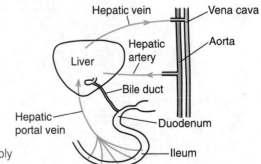

Hepatic vein
Vena cava
Hepatic artery
Aorta
Liver
Bile duct
Hepatic portal vein
Duodenum
Ileum

Fig. 6.10 The liver and its blood supply

- Stores *glucose* as glycogen, turning it back to glucose when needed. This is under the control of three hormones which keep the *blood level* of glucose constant. (See Fig. 6.11 and also Unit 12.12.)

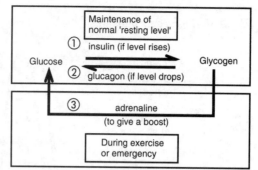

Fig. 6.11 An example of homeostasis (see Unit 10.9)

- Deaminates *excess amino acids* to give two parts:

(*a*) nitrogen-containing part (amine) becomes urea – excreted by kidneys;
(*b*) remainder (the acid) can be respired to give energy.

- Stores *iron* from worn-out red blood cells, which it breaks down, excreting *bile pigments* in the process.
- Makes *poisons* harmless, e.g. ethanol drunk or toxins from gut bacteria.
- Makes *bile salts* which emulsify fats in the intestine.

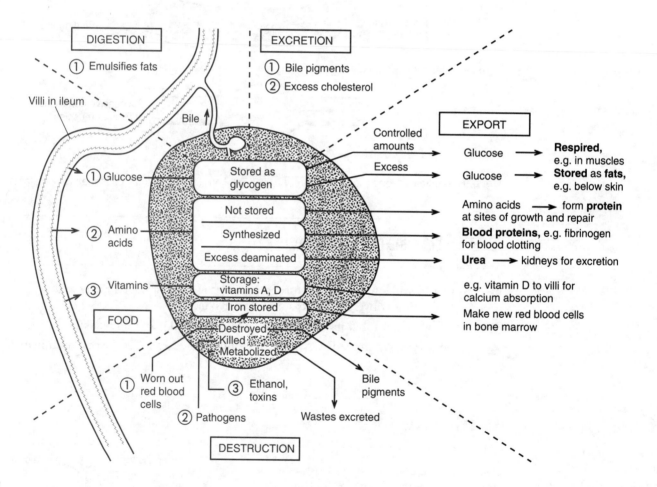

Fig. 6.12 The liver's five roles

Summary

1   Animals have a variety of ways of dealing with their solid, liquid and suspended food, to capture it in feeding.

2   Feeding is followed by digestion inside a gut.

3   Digestion is the breaking down of food to molecules small enough to be absorbed through the gut wall.

4   Enzymes catalyse these breakdowns. They are affected by temperature and pH in their work.

5   Carbohydrases turn starch into simple sugars, lipases turn fats and oils into glycerol and fatty acids, and proteases turn protein into amino acids.

6   Teeth are specialized pieces of bone designed to break food up, so as to give a larger surface area for enzymes to act upon.

7   Digested food is absorbed via villi in the small intestine and most of it passes to the liver.

8   The liver processes food, directing it to where it is needed, via the blood.

9   The liver stores excess carbohydrate as glycogen, helps emulsify fats in the intestine by means of bile, and takes a hand in producing urea, bile pigments and cholesterol for excretion.

10 Foods that cannot be digested, such as cellulose (fibre), and excess bacteria are egested through the anus after reabsorption of much water in the colon.

Chapter 7

Water uptake and loss in plants and animals

7.1 Importance of water

Water makes up two-thirds or more of living active cells.
Water covers two-thirds of the globe – a very important habitat for organisms.

- **It is a solvent:**
    - (*a*) all *reactions* of metabolism occur in solution.
    - (*b*) foods, hormones, etc. are *transported* in solution (in blood, sap).
- **It is a reactant:**
    - (*a*) with CO_2 during *photosynthesis*.
    - (*b*) in *hydrolysis* reactions, e.g. digestion.
- **It is a coolant:**
    - (*a*) *absorbs a lot of heat* without much change in temperature, thus keeping habitats like the sea relatively stable in temperature.
    - (*b*) *removes a lot of heat* when evaporated, keeping bodies cool, e.g. in sweating, transpiration.
- **It provides support:**
    - (*a*) aquatic organisms need less strong skeletons than land organisms because water's '*buoyancy effect*' (*Archimedes force*) makes them 'lighter'.
    - (*b*) turgor pressure in plant cells supports leaves and herbaceous plant stems; without it they wilt.
- **It is a lubricant:**
    E.g. synovial fluid in joints (see Unit 13.8); mucus in guts.

7.2 Diffusion and active transport

Substances move into cells by:

1 **Diffusion** (gases and liquids)
2 **Active transport**

Diffusion is a random movement of molecules from a region of their high concentration (A) towards a region of their low concentration (B). The difference in concentration between A and B is called the **concentration gradient** (Fig. 7.1).

The rate of diffusion increases:
(*a*) with high concentration gradients
(*b*) with rise in temperature

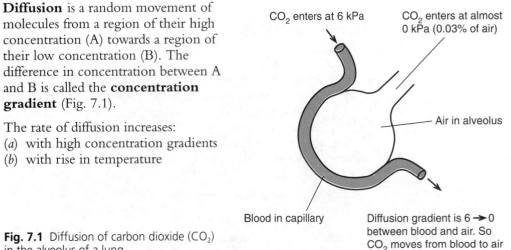

Fig. 7.1 Diffusion of carbon dioxide (CO_2) in the alveolus of a lung

Active transport is a selective movement of molecules across living cell membranes. This requires energy from respiration in the cell concerned. The molecules usually move *up* a concentration gradient. For example, mineral salts in *low* concentration in soil may still be absorbed into root cells where their concentration is *higher*.

Table 7.1 Comparison of diffusion and active transport

Diffusion	Active transport
Not selective	Selective (cell absorbs only what it needs)
Substances move only down a concentration gradient	Substances move in even *against* a concentration gradient
Living membrane not essential	Living membrane essential
Cell provides no energy	Respiration provides energy for absorption

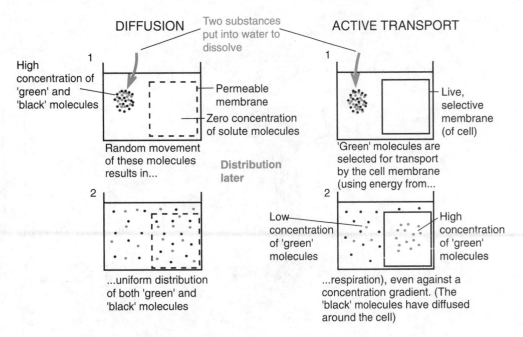

Fig. 7.2 Diffusion contrasted with active transport

When diffusion plays a large part in a biological process, the organs concerned, e.g. leaf, lung, have a large surface area (see Unit 22.6).

7.3 Osmosis

Osmosis is the diffusion of water *only*, through a selectively permeable membrane, from where *water is in high concentration* (a weak solution) to where *water is in low concentration* (a strong solution) (Fig. 7.3).

Requires *no* respiration (cf. active uptake of salts in roots).

Requires *live* cell membrane for osmosis to occur in cells, but will happen with suitable nonliving membranes (e.g. Visking dialysing membrane).

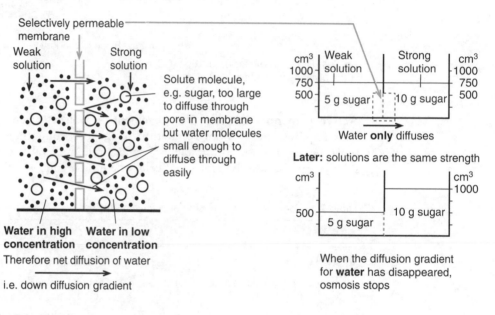

Fig. 7.3 Osmosis

Water entering a solution through a selectively permeable membrane exerts a pressure. This can be measured using a manometer (Fig. 7.4).

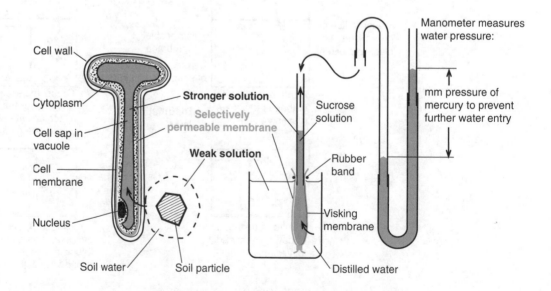

Fig. 7.4 Comparison of osmosis in a living cell (root hair) and a nonliving system

Cells prevent continued flow of water into them (which would burst them) by **osmoregulating** (see Unit 7.4 and Fig. 7.7).

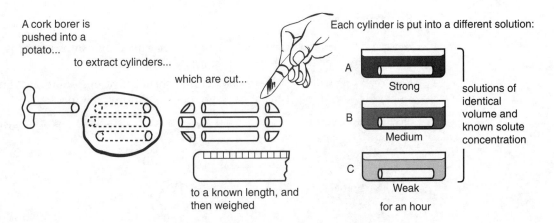

A cork borer is pushed into a potato...

to extract cylinders...

which are cut...

Each cylinder is put into a different solution:

A
Strong

B
Medium

C
Weak

solutions of identical volume and known solute concentration

to a known length, and then weighed

for an hour

The cylinders are removed, dried at their ends and rolled gently on blotting paper. They are then weighed again and measured for length. These measurements are then put on graphs

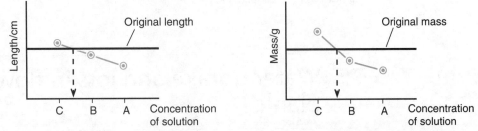

At the point where the graph cuts the line indicating the *original* length or mass the average osmotic potential of potato cells may be read off (see ▼). If this strength of solution were to be prepared, the potato cylinders should neither increase nor decrease in length or mass, i.e. no osmosis would occur

Fig. 7.5 Experiment to determine the concentration of the solution inside potato tissue

7.4 Osmosis in cells

Plant cells

Cells, in nature, fluctuate between being flaccid and fully turgid. However, plasmolysis is relatively rare (except in experiments) and will result in the cell's death if it is prolonged, e.g. when the cell suffers prolonged drying (Fig. 7.6). Such changes may be seen down a microscope when strips of rhubarb epidermis are mounted in strong, medium and weak solutions on three different slides.

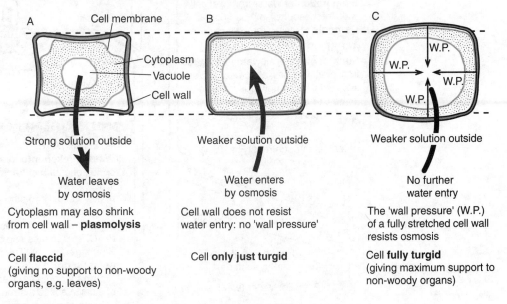

Fig. 7.6 Osmosis in plant cells

Animal cells

Amoeba takes an active part in ejecting water gained by osmosis from its weak solution (freshwater) habitat, to prevent bursting (see Fig. 7.12).

Red blood cells will burst in freshwater and shrink in strong solutions. They rely on the kidneys to keep the plasma at the right concentration (see Unit 10.2).

In strong solution:

In plasma:

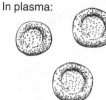

In weak solution:

A spiky outline – water left the cells

Normal – cells in balance with plasma solution

Cell membrane bursts – too much water entered the cells

Fig. 7.7 Osmosis in red blood cells

7.5 Water uptake and loss in flowering plants

① **Leaves and green stems** are waterproofed by a waxy *cuticle*, but most keep open *stomata* to get CO_2 for photosynthesis. Through stomata, **transpiration** (the loss of water vapour via the aerial parts of a plant) occurs. This creates a *suction upward* of water from below.

② **Old stems and roots** are waterproofed with cork (or bark). Their xylem allows passage of water. Some water loss occurs via *lenticels* (pores in bark).

③ **Young roots** – particularly *root hair* region – absorb water by osmosis. This continues owing to suction generated by transpiration.

If soil water supply dries up, leaf cells become flaccid and the leaf *wilts*. Only *after* this will guard cells become flaccid, closing stomata, thus conserving water but also stopping photosynthesis (see Unit 5.3 and Fig. 7.8).

TRANSPIRATION
1 **Diffusion of water vapour** to outside air via stomata
2 **Evaporation of water** from wet cell walls of mesophyll into air spaces
3 **Osmosis** of water from xylem cells

TRANSPORT
4 **Suction of water** upwards owing to transpiration. Salts, absorbed actively into roots, travel upwards passively in the **transpiration stream**

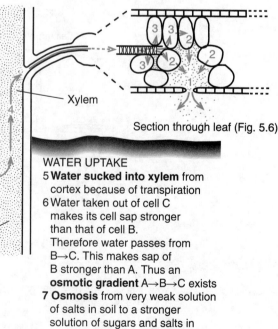

Section through leaf (Fig. 5.6)

Section through root (Fig. 16.1)

Xylem

Xylem

Root hair cell sap (strong solution)

Soil water (weak solution)

WATER UPTAKE
5 **Water sucked into xylem** from cortex because of transpiration
6 Water taken out of cell C makes its cell sap stronger than that of cell B. Therefore water passes from B→C. This makes sap of B stronger than A. Thus an **osmotic gradient** A→B→C exists
7 **Osmosis** from very weak solution of salts in soil to a stronger solution of sugars and salts in root hair cell sap within the vacuole

Fig. 7.8 Water uptake, transport and loss in a flowering plant

7.6 Guard cells and stomata

Guard cells are kidney-shaped green cells found in pairs in the epidermis ('skin') of leaves and green stems. The pore between them is a **stoma** (plural: **stomata**). This appears when guard cells are turgid; disappears when they are flaccid (Table 7.2).

The flaccid cells (green outline) take in water by osmosis from epidermis cells. This stretches the thin outer walls of guard cells, so bending the thickened inner walls (black outline) to open up a pore between them.

Table 7.2 Features of guard cells in the turgid and flaccid states

	Stoma open	Surface view of the same two guard cells in the turgid and flaccid states	Stoma closed
Solute concentration of cell sap	High	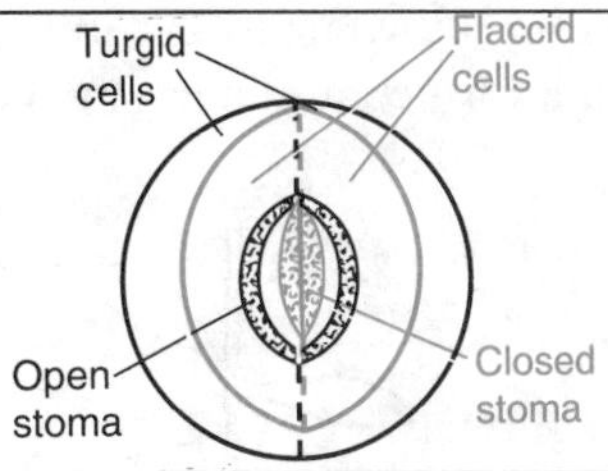	Low
Turgidity	Turgid		Flaccid
Gas exchange and transpiration	Possible		Impossible
Normal rhythm	Open in day		Closed at night

(Diagram labels: Turgid cells; Flaccid cells; Open stoma; Closed stoma)

Determining whether conditions around the leaf affect the opening and closing of stomata:

A film of nail varnish or stencil-correcting fluid painted onto a non-hairy leaf can be peeled off with forceps when dry (30 sec). Under the microscope the dried film bears impressions of stomata. The number open can be recorded, e.g. '5/20' for the 20 stomata observed.

Films from the *same* plant leaf after being in different conditions (e.g. of light, dark, CO_2, wind and temperature) can be compared. *One* condition should be changed at a time.

Different species of plant can behave differently.

7.7 Transpiration

Transpiration is the loss of water vapour through the aerial parts of a plant. It occurs
(i)   mainly through open stomata
(ii) through waxy cuticle (a small amount)
Functions:
(i)   provides a means of transporting salts upward in xylem
(ii) cools the leaf heated by the sun, by evaporation (cf. sweating).

Factors raising transpiration rate (opposite conditions lower the rate)

1. **High temperature** – provides more energy to evaporate water.

2. **Low humidity** – greater diffusion gradient between air inside leaf spaces and the drier air outside.

3. **Open stomata** – thousands of pores per leaf (usually open in *sunlight*).

4. **Wind** – removes water molecules as fast as they arrive outside stomata, thereby maintaining high diffusion rate. Water vapour is also 'pumped out' due to bending and unbending of leaf. (Severe buffeting by wind actually closes stomata, reducing transpiration.)

Measurement of transpiration rate

(Temperature, humidity and wind must be recorded.)

1. **Weighing** – a leaf, or cut shoot, in a test-tube of water covered by oil; or a whole pot plant, the pot and soil sealed off in a polythene bag.

2. **Cobalt chloride** – blue when anhydrous (dry), turns pink when hydrated (moist). Thus dry blue cobalt chloride paper, taped to upper and lower leaf surfaces, green stems and bark-covered stems turns pink with moisture of transpiration. Timing how long it takes compares rates.

3. **Potometer** – measures water uptake (not loss) of a cut shoot (a little of the water is used in photosynthesis). Change *one* condition at a time to determine which factor has greatest effect.

Note: light and dark affect opening and closing of stomata. Light may also have a heating effect.

Allow time for plant to adjust to new conditions before taking new measurement of rate.

Never allow air to get into cut end of shoot (air bubbles block the xylem) – cut shoot under water, and keep the cut wet (Fig. 7.9).

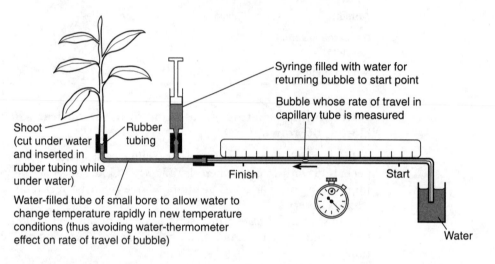

Fig. 7.9 A potometer in action

Evidence for pathway of water in a stem

If cross-sections of a stem are taken 30 minutes after putting a leafy shoot in red ink, only the xylem is stained red (Fig. 7.10). The xylem of a stem in water, used as a control, does not become red.

7.8 Transport of organic food

Flows through **phloem** sieve tube cells in bark (see Fig. 7.11). Flow rate is affected by temperature, available oxygen, poisons – this suggests a mechanism involving *living* cells. Mechanism not fully understood.

Flows both *upwards and downwards*. Photosynthesized sugars are transported as sucrose (see Unit 4.4) from leaves *up* to stem tips (for growth); to fruits and seeds (for storage as starch); *down* to root tips (for growth); and to or from storage organs, e.g. tubers (see Unit 14.2).

Evidence for pathway of organic food

- **Ring barking:** sugars accumulate where bark ends (due to cutting).
- **Tracers:** radioactive $^{14}CO_2$ supplied to a photosynthesizing leaf becomes part of sucrose (or other organic molecules). Cross-sections of stems below such leaves,

when placed next to photographic film (for a week in a refrigerator), will become exposed only where there is phloem (see Fig. 7.10). Control film remains unexposed. This shows that radioactive sucrose is transported in phloem.

- **Systemic insecticides** when sprayed onto leaves are absorbed by them and pass to the phloem. Insects, e.g. aphids, sucking out the sugary sap, are thus poisoned.

7.9 Tissues in the stem and root

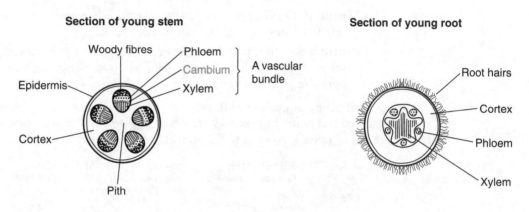

Fig. 7.10 Cross-sections of young stem and root of a flowering plant

Epidermis: waterproof outer 'skin' of waxed non-green cells – and some guard cells (see leaf: Fig. 5.6).

Root hairs: water-absorbing cells having a large surface area (see Fig. 7.4).

Cortex and pith: large cells capable of storing food, e.g. starch
Cambium: cells that can divide to cause growth in diameter
Woody fibres: give strength in the wind
Xylem vessels (also woody): (*a*) give strength
                              (*b*) transport water and mineral salts *upward*
Phloem sieve tubes: transport sugars and amino acids *up and down*
(These cells/tissues are common to both stem and root)

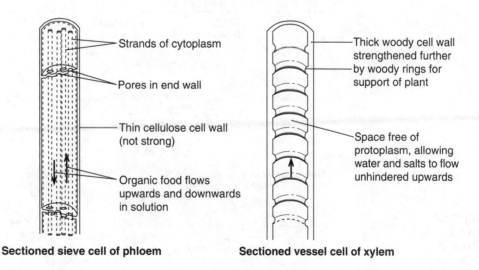

Fig. 7.11 The structure of cells conducting food in xylem and phloem

7.10 Water uptake and loss in animals

Animals have two problems that plants do not have:

1. **Lack of cell walls** to prevent excess water entering (see Unit 1.1). Thus cells are liable to burst (see Fig. 7.7) unless they osmoregulate by ejecting water, e.g. via contractile vacuoles or 'kidneys'.

2. **Excretion of nitrogenous wastes** which need water for their removal:

    (a) **ammonia** (NH_3) – very poisonous; needs large quantities of water to dilute and remove it. Freshwater animals, particularly, excrete this.

    (b) **urea** ($CO(NH_2)_2$) – less poisonous; needs some water to remove it. Many terrestrial animals, e.g. mammals, excrete this.

    (c) **uric acid** – not poisonous, since insoluble; can be removed as a paste. Essential for all animals laying eggs on land to avoid poisoning of embryo, e.g. insects, birds. Very little water wasted.

As with plants, animals have three problems: obtaining water, conserving what has been obtained and removing excess water that has entered. These problems and the ways they are solved differ according to the animal and the habitat in which it lives (Fig. 7.12).

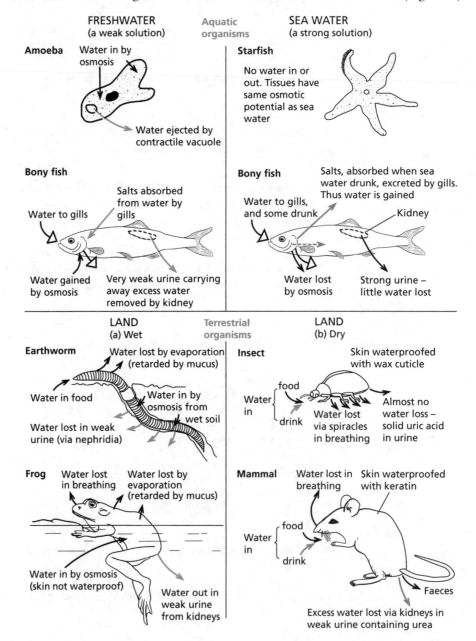

Fig. 7.12
Osmoregulation in animals:
→ problem created by animal's environment
→ corrective measures employed by animal

1 In **freshwater**, water *enters* by osmosis, tending to flood tissues since they have a higher osmotic potential than their external surroundings.

2 In **sea water**, the water inside tissues tends to *leave* by osmosis into the sea since its salty water has a higher osmotic potential than tissues in many cases.

3 In **wetland** habitats, water still *enters* tissues by osmosis through non-waterproof skin, but there is the hazard of desiccation in the air. Such animals do not drink but can gain some water from food.

4 In **dryland** habitats, animals must have waterproof skins to prevent desiccation in the air, replacing what they lose in breathing and excreta by *drinking*. Egg-layers excrete uric acid, so little water is lost in urine.

Summary

1 Life as we know it could not exist without water – as a solvent, reactant, coolant, support-giver and lubricant.

2 Substances move into and out of cells by diffusion or by active transport.

3 Diffusion is a slow, random process, occurring along a concentration gradient.

4 Diffusion of water across a selectively permeable membrane is called osmosis.

5 Organisms have to guard against osmosis by a variety of means to avoid bursting their cells, but also use it to their advantage, losing excess water by evaporation and urination.

6 Transpiration, the evaporation of water from the aerial parts of plants is useful because it cools the plant and is ultimately responsible for the uptake of water through the roots.

7 The transpiration stream provides an upward transport flow of mineral salts in the xylem.

8 The phloem transports manufactured food, e.g. sucrose, both up and down the plant, using methods that involve metabolism.

9 Active transport is the absorption or secretion of substances from cells using energy from respiration, often against a concentration gradient.

Chapter 8
The blood and lymphatic systems

8.1 Blood systems

The need for blood pumped to cells by a heart

Animals are more active than plants and diffusion would be too slow to supply cells with their needs and remove their wastes. A more *rapid transport system* is necessary to prevent them from dying.

Functions of blood systems

1. Supply **foods** – sugars, fats, amino acids, vitamins, salts, water.
2. Supply **oxygen** – (exception: insects – oxygen direct to cells at tracheoles).
3. Supply **hormones** – chemical 'messages' controlling metabolism and development (see Unit 12.10).
4. Supply **leucocytes** – white blood cells for defence against invading organisms.
5. Supply **clotting materials** – to stop loss of blood at wounds.
6. Remove **wastes** – CO_2 and nitrogenous wastes, e.g. urea.
7. Carry **heat** – either away from cells, e.g. muscle, to cool them, or to cells needing to be warmed up, e.g. during 'sunning' of lizards.

8.2 Mammal blood and other body fluids

Blood consists of:

(*a*) **plasma**, a straw-coloured liquid (90% water, 10% dissolved substances);
(*b*) **cells**, a variety of kinds (see Table 8.1).

Exact composition of blood depends on location in the body (see Unit 8.5) and on health. Human body has 5–6 litres of blood, about 10% of body weight, pumped through arteries, capillaries and veins (see Table 8.2). Blood does not bathe cells. At capillaries, **tissue fluid** – a colourless nutritive liquid containing O_2 – oozes out to bathe cells and carry away wastes. Tissue fluid returns mainly into the capillaries; but the excess passes into the lymph vessels to become part of **lymph**. Lymph is discharged into veins.

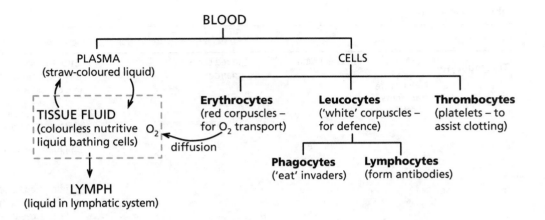

Fig. 8.1 Constituents of blood and their functions

Serum is plasma less fibrinogen (protein needed for clotting). Stored by hospitals for transfusions.

Plasma consists of:

1. **Water** – (90%) solvent for substances listed below; carrier of heat (for temperature regulation).

2. **Blood proteins** – (7%) e.g. fibrinogen (for blood clotting), antibodies (for defence against pathogens) and albumen (for osmosis, Fig. 8.7).

3. **Soluble foods** – (1%) e.g. glucose, oil droplets and amino acids (from digestion).

4. **Mineral salts** – as ions, e.g. Na^+, Cl^-, Ca^{2+}, HCO_3^- (hydrogencarbonate, the main method of transporting CO_2) .

5. **Wastes** – e.g. CO_2, urea.

6. **Hormones** – in minute traces, e.g. adrenaline and insulin.

7. **Gases** – small quantities, e.g. of O_2, N_2.

Table 8.1 Blood cells and their functions

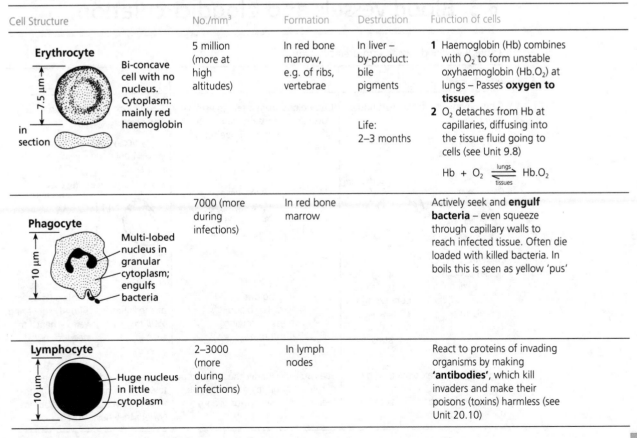

Cell Structure		No./mm³	Formation	Destruction	Function of cells
Erythrocyte	Bi-concave cell with no nucleus. Cytoplasm: mainly red haemoglobin	5 million (more at high altitudes)	In red bone marrow, e.g. of ribs, vertebrae	In liver – by-product: bile pigments Life: 2–3 months	1 Haemoglobin (Hb) combines with O_2 to form unstable oxyhaemoglobin (Hb.O_2) at lungs – Passes **oxygen to tissues** 2 O_2 detaches from Hb at capillaries, diffusing into the tissue fluid going to cells (see Unit 9.8) $Hb + O_2 \underset{\text{tissues}}{\overset{\text{lungs}}{\rightleftharpoons}} Hb.O_2$
Phagocyte	Multi-lobed nucleus in granular cytoplasm; engulfs bacteria	7000 (more during infections)	In red bone marrow		Actively seek and **engulf bacteria** – even squeeze through capillary walls to reach infected tissue. Often die loaded with killed bacteria. In boils this is seen as yellow 'pus'
Lymphocyte	Huge nucleus in little cytoplasm	2–3000 (more during infections)	In lymph nodes		React to proteins of invading organisms by making **'antibodies'**, which kill invaders and make their poisons (toxins) harmless (see Unit 20.10)

Table 8.1 *(continued)*

Cell Structure	No./mm³	Formation	Destruction	Function of cells
Thrombocyte 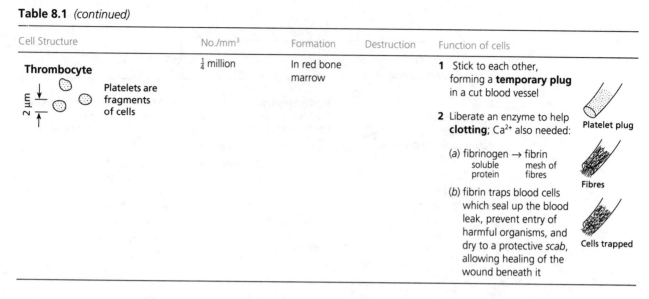 Platelets are fragments of cells (2 µm)	¼ million	In red bone marrow		**1** Stick to each other, forming a **temporary plug** in a cut blood vessel **2** Liberate an enzyme to help **clotting**; Ca²⁺ also needed: (*a*) fibrinogen → fibrin soluble protein → mesh of fibres (*b*) fibrin traps blood cells which seal up the blood leak, prevent entry of harmful organisms, and dry to a protective *scab*, allowing healing of the wound beneath it

Notes:

1 Haemoglobin combines 230 times more readily with carbon monoxide (CO) than O_2, forming a stable compound, **carboxyhaemoglobin** (Hb.CO), with it. Thus even at small concentrations in the air, CO (which is odourless) tends to be taken up into the blood, preventing O_2 from being carried. This can kill, e.g. someone tuning a car engine behind closed garage doors. See also *smoking* (Unit 9.11).

2 Haemophiliacs ('bleeders') continue to bleed for a long time, even from minor wounds. They bruise easily and joints may be painful from bleeds. Whereas death was premature in the past, today haemophiliacs may live less dangerously by receiving the 'clotting factor VIII' which they lack (see Unit 17.9).

3 Abnormal blood counts. Anaemia: red blood cell numbers down; exertion difficult (too little oxygen carried). Leukaemia: white blood cell numbers very markedly up; cancer of blood.

8.3 Blood vessels and blood circulation

Table 8.2 Blood vessels and their functions

Arteries	Capillaries	Veins
Carry blood *away* from heart under *high* pressure Carry *oxygenated* blood (except pulmonary artery)	Carry blood from artery to vein, very slowly, giving maximum time for diffusion, through a huge surface area.	Carry blood *towards* heart under *low* pressure Carry *deoxygenated* blood (except pulmonary vein)
T.S. — Elastic layer, Elastic and muscle layer, Endothelium (*a*) Heart refilling: elastic walls squeezing on blood to help it along (*b*) Heart pumping: 'pulse' felt as bore expands. *Thick walls* needed, but *no valves*	Endothelium only — Phagocyte emerging between cells of endothelium (10µm) Tissue fluid leaking out to cells – blood pressure forcing it through	T.S. L.S. (a) free flow (b) back pressure Valve open Valve closed No pulse: pressure is low at capillaries. *Wall thinner* than in arteries Blood returns partly by muscles of body squeezing veins – hence the need for *non-return valves*.
Bore of arteries can be altered by nerve messages to muscle, e.g. more blood to legs and less to gut during exercise.	See capillaries under the microscope in the tail of guppy fish or tadpole (head end in wet cotton wool)	Massage blood in an arm vein towards the fingers with the other thumb; valves show up as bumps (where they have closed)

Portal veins have capillaries at either end, i.e. they carry blood from one organ to another (e.g. hepatic portal vein between small intestine and liver – see Fig. 8.5).

The heart and double circulation

The heart consists of two pumps fused together, each having an **atrium** and a **ventricle**.

The two pumps contract simultaneously according to a heart cycle (see Fig. 8.4).

Right side pumps deoxygenated blood to the lungs for oxygenation.

Left side pumps oxygenated blood to the body, which deoxygenates it.

Thus blood passes twice through the heart before going to the body (Fig. 8.2).

The resulting high blood pressure ensures:

(*a*) speedy supplies to the tissues;

(*b*) squeezing out of tissue fluid at capillaries.

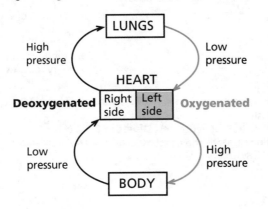

Fig. 8.2 Double circulation of blood through the heart of a mammal

8.4 The heart

The heart lies between the two lungs inside the chest cavity.

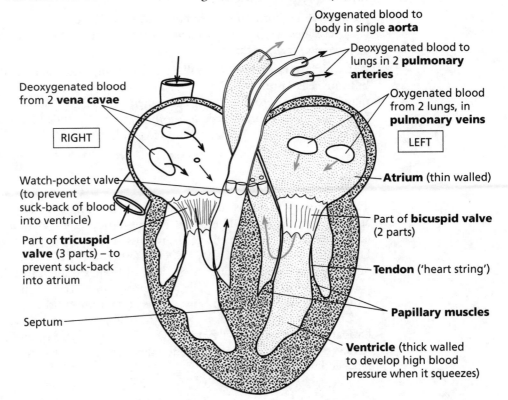

Fig. 8.3 The mammalian heart in section: structure and function

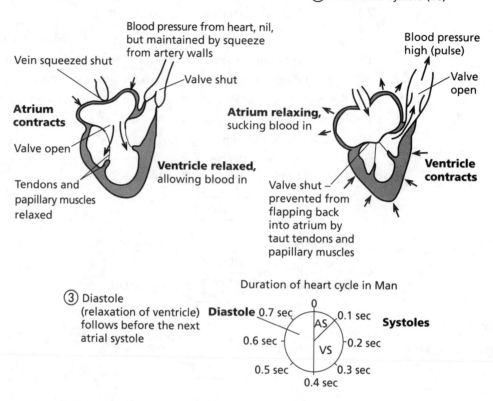

Fig. 8.4 The heart cycle of a mammal

Heart beat

Controlled automatically by a **pacemaker**: special tissue in the atrium wall. The rhythm speeds up when

(a) adrenaline (hormone) is secreted (see Unit 12.10);

(b) nerve messages to the pacemaker arrive from the brain. A rise in blood CO_2 (from exercise) triggers this off.

Artificial pacemaker: a small electronic unit, attached to the chest, powered by lithium cells lasting 6–12 years, which sends minute electrical shocks to the heart muscle, causing it to contract. Used when the heart rhythm has become irregular. The best ones adjust to the needs of the body, e.g. demands of exercise, by sensing bodily changes, e.g. blood temperature and oxygen levels.

Heart disease

Two **coronary arteries** supply heart muscle with blood. They exit just above the valve at the base of the aorta. This blood returns into the right atrium. Blockage of this mini-circulation may cause death of heart muscle by starving it of nutrients and oxygen. Heart disease results from fatty material (atheroma) deposited in the coronary arteries. Smoking, excessive drinking, stress, lack of exercise, and a diet rich in saturated fats all seem to promote blockage with atheroma. This carries a high risk of heart attack – which may cause death. Warnings of this come from heart pain (angina).

    Coronary artery bypass grafts (CABG) can now relieve angina and survival is 88% after 10 years. Usually the long vein at the back of the leg (saphenous vein) is removed and sections of it, without valves, are grafted to replace the sections of artery blocked by more than 50%.

8.5 Changes in blood around the circulatory system

Changes in the composition of blood

As blood passes through the capillaries of organs, it is modified. Blood leaving endocrine glands has gained hormones, while that leaving the kidneys has lost urea and water. Thus *overall* blood composition is kept constant, ensuring that the cells of the body have a constant environment (tissue fluid) to live in.

Table 8.3 Changes in blood composition in the human body

Region of body	Blood gains	Blood loses
All tissues	CO_2, nitrogenous wastes	O_2, food, hormones
Lungs	O_2	CO_2, water
Small intestine	Food: water, salts, vitamins, sugars, amino acids	
Liver	Urea, controlled quantities of glucose and fats	Glucose (for storage as glycogen), excess amino acids, worn out erythrocytes
Kidneys		Urea, water, salts
Bones	New erythrocytes and phagocytes	Iron (for haemoglobin), calcium and phosphate (for bone growth)
Skin	Vitamin D	Heat (by radiation and by evaporation of water in sweat), salts and urea (in sweat)
Thoracic duct	Fats, lymphocytes, lymph	
Thyroid gland	Thyroxine	Iodine (to make thyroxine)

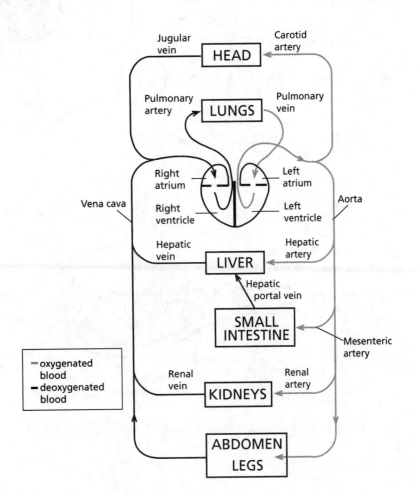

Fig. 8.5 The circulatory system of a mammal

8.6 Lymphatic system

A system of fine tubes ending blindly among the tissues, e.g. lacteals in villi of small intestine (see Unit 6.8), which join up into ever larger tubes with non-return valves. Along their length are swellings (lymph nodes). The largest tube (thoracic duct) discharges into the main vein of the left arm.

Functions:

1. **Returns excess tissue fluid** to blood as lymph.
2. **Adds lymphocytes** to blood (for defence).
3. **Absorbs fats** (into lacteals of villi) to discharge them to blood.
4. **Filters out bacteria** from lymph by means of phagocytes stationary within lymph nodes (Fig. 8.6).

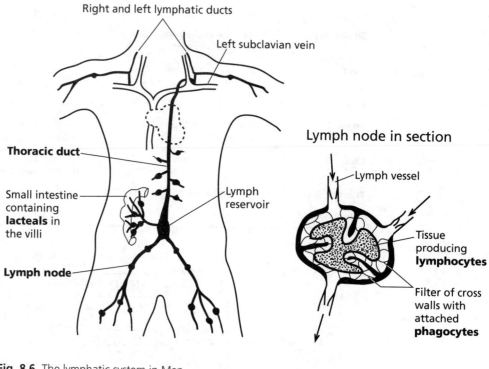

Fig. 8.6 The lymphatic system in Man

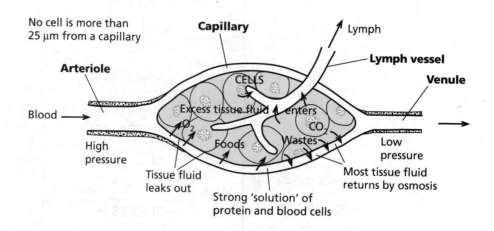

Fig. 8.7 The relationship between blood, tissue fluid, cells and lymph

Summary

1   Animals need to develop a blood system to supply their tissues rapidly enough with oxygen, food and hormones and remove from them wastes and heat from metabolism.

2   Most animals have a pumping heart and blood vessels to contain blood.

3   Mammalian blood contains red cells for carrying oxygen and white cells for defence, lying in a clear fluid called plasma.

4   Blood leaves the heart in arteries, reaches tissues in capillaries and is returned to the heart in veins.

5   Part of the plasma leaks out of the capillaries under pressure as tissue fluid, which bathes cells with nutrients and returns wastes via the capillaries and lymph vessels.

6   The heart is four chambered: the right atrium and ventricle supplying the lungs with blood, those on the left supplying the body – a double circulation pump.

7   Heart disease is a serious killer in the UK and may require bypass surgery to restore blood circulation to heart muscle, or the fitting of an artificial pacemaker when the pumping rhythm becomes faulty.

8   Blood clotting is a defence mechanism to prevent serious loss of blood. It involves blood platelets and a number of clotting factors in the plasma.

9   Haemophiliacs are males that lack factor VIII and so do not clot their blood when they should, putting their lives at risk unless they are given factor VIII by injection.

Chapter 9
Respiration

9.1 Breathing, gaseous exchange and cellular respiration

Respiration is the sum of processes in organisms that leads to the release of energy from organic molecules, for use in vital functions. *All* organisms respire, plants as well as animals, forming ATP (see Unit 9.14), the energy molecule that powers the chemical reactions of metabolism. Depending on the kind of organism, up to *three processes* may be involved:

1. **Breathing** (= ventilation): *movements*, in animals, that bring a source of O_2 to a surface for gaseous exchange, e.g. chest movements of mammals bring air into lungs; throat movements in fish bring water (containing dissolved O_2) to gills.

2. **Gaseous exchange:** diffusion of O_2 into the organism and of CO_2 outwards. All gaseous exchange surfaces are moist, thin and have a large surface area.

   (a) In *single-celled* organisms this exchange surface is the cell membrane (see Fig. 9.9).
   (b) In *multicellular animals* specialized body parts, e.g. lungs, tracheoles or gills, provide the surface for gaseous exchange. Usually gases are transported rapidly by blood between these surfaces and a second extensive surface area where gaseous exchange occurs between the blood and cells (see Fig. 9.12). Only insects pipe air directly to cells and do not use blood for this purpose (see Fig. 9.11).
   (c) In *multicellular plants* a network of air spaces *between* cells allows for direct gaseous exchange between cells and the air. There is no blood system.
   Thus gaseous *exchange* occurs only when organisms respire using oxygen.

3. **Cellular respiration** (= internal respiration): the chemical reactions occurring within cells that result in the release of energy to form ATP. These reactions can occur under two conditions:

   (a) anaerobically – no oxygen needed (thus **1** and **2** above unnecessary);
   (b) aerobically – oxygen needed (thus **2** above essential).

Note: since breathing and gaseous exchange are essentially *physical* processes occurring *outside* cells, they are often lumped together as **external respiration** to distinguish them from the *chemical* processes occurring *within* cells which are **internal respiration.**

Unfortunately the terms above are sometimes used loosely, e.g. since *Amoeba*, the earthworm and the flowering plant do not make *movements* to gain O_2, strictly speaking they do not *breathe* but they do respire.

9.2 Cellular respiration (aerobic and anaerobic)

Glucose is the main substance respired (other foods can be turned into glucose). The results of respiration are different under anaerobic and aerobic conditions:

1 Aerobic
In plants and animals:

$$\underset{C_6H_{12}O_6 \quad\quad 6O_2}{\text{glucose} + \text{oxygen}} \xrightarrow[\text{and in mitochondria}]{\text{enzymes in cytoplasm}} \underset{6CO_2 \quad\quad 6H_2O}{\text{carbon dioxide} + \text{water}} + \textbf{a lot of energy} \quad \text{(2890 kJ/mole)}$$

2 Anaerobic
(a) in plants:

$$\underset{C_6H_{12}O_6}{\text{glucose}} \xrightarrow[\text{matrix}]{\text{enzymes in cytoplasmic}} \underset{2C_2H_5OH \quad\quad 2CO_2}{\text{ethanol} + \text{carbon dioxide}} + \textbf{a little energy} \quad \text{(210 kJ/mole)}$$

(b) in animals:

$$\underset{C_6H_{12}O_6}{\text{glucose}} \xrightarrow[\text{matrix}]{\text{enzymes in cytoplasmic}} \underset{2C_3H_6O_3}{\text{lactic acid}} + \textbf{a little energy}$$

Table 9.1 Comparison of the two stages in respiration

	Anaerobic	Aerobic
Oxygen requirement	Nil	Essential
Useful energy from each glucose molecule respired	2 ATP	38 ATP
Chemical products	Organic, i.e. still energy-rich, e.g. lactic acid, ethanol	Inorganic: CO_2 and H_2O, i.e. no energy left
Takes place in	Cytoplasmic matrix (Unit 1.2)	Mitochondria (Unit 1.2)

Note: Aerobic and anaerobic respiration are *not* alternatives. Anaerobic reactions are the *first few stages* in a much longer set of reactions made possible under aerobic conditions (Fig. 9.1). Since aerobic respiration has the great advantage over anaerobic of providing about twenty times more energy, not surprisingly most organisms respire aerobically. Only certain bacteria cannot. However, some organisms are forced to respire anaerobically in their environment, e.g. tapeworms, or yeast in brewing operations. See Fig. 9.1 for a summary of respiration.

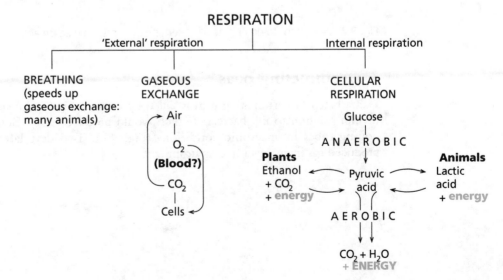

Fig. 9.1 Respiration: breathing, gaseous exchange and cellular respiration

Note: Pyruvic acid (a 3-carbon compound) is common to all three respiratory pathways

9.3 Anaerobic respiration

Examples of anaerobic respiration in aerobic organisms

1 Man

(a) At rest, most of the pyruvic acid the cells produce is oxidized to CO_2 and H_2O. The blood contains very little lactic acid.

(b) During exercise, blood samples show that the lactic acid level rises at least ten-fold, indicating that despite increased breathing and heart rates, oxygen supply to tissues is inadequate. In this relatively anaerobic state Man is in **'oxygen debt'**.

(c) After exercise this debt is 'paid off' by continued rapid aerobic respiration. One-fifth of the lactic acid is respired to CO_2 and H_2O. This provides energy to turn the other four-fifths of the lactic acid back into glycogen (stored in liver and muscles).

How soon a person stops panting after exercise ('recovery time') is a measure of their **fitness**. During training, miles of extra capillaries grow, so increasing the oxygen supply to muscles. This increases muscle power, and reduces recovery time.

2 Yeast

(a) If aerated, the colony grows very rapidly in nourishing sugared water until all the glucose disappears as CO_2 and H_2O (no use to brewers!).

(b) Without air, in similar conditions, the colony grows more slowly, eventually killing itself in the ethanol it produces. This is the basis for *making wine and beer*. The ethanol can be distilled off (as in making *spirits*, e.g. whisky). This will burn, showing it is energy rich.

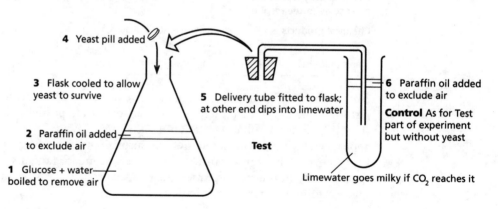

4 Yeast pill added

3 Flask cooled to allow yeast to survive

2 Paraffin oil added to exclude air

1 Glucose + water boiled to remove air

5 Delivery tube fitted to flask; at other end dips into limewater

Test

6 Paraffin oil added to exclude air

Control As for Test part of experiment but without yeast

Limewater goes milky if CO_2 reaches it

Fig. 9.2 Experiment to determine whether yeast will respire glucose anaerobically

3 Germinating peas

Half a batch of germinating peas is killed by boiling. Live and dead peas are washed in thymol solution to kill bacteria (which would produce CO_2). Both batches are put in boiling tubes in anaerobic conditions (Fig. 9.3). Two days later the live peas have produced gas in an anaerobic environment.

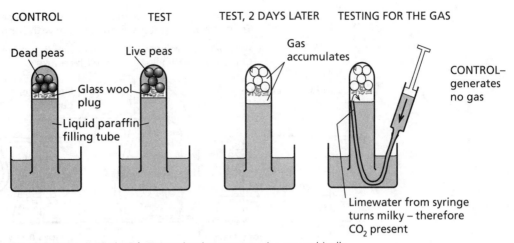

Fig. 9.3 Demonstration that germinating peas respire anaerobically

9.4 Aerobic respiration

Three lines of evidence that organisms are respiring aerobically

1 **CO_2 evolved** (see Fig. 9.6).

2 **O_2 absorbed** (see Fig. 9.4).

3 **Heat** evolved. The energy in glucose is not totally converted into useful energy (ATP) during respiration. Some energy (around 60%) is wasted as heat (see Fig. 9.5). In the experiment shown in Fig. 9.5 both the dead peas (killed by boiling and then cooled for half an hour) and the live ones had been washed in thymol solution to exclude the possibility that bacterial respiration could be causing a rise in temperature. (An animal, e.g. locust, could be substituted for peas with similar, quicker results.)

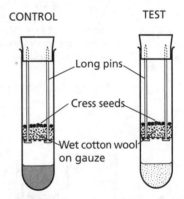

CONTROL   TEST

Long pins

Cress seeds

Wet cotton wool on gauze

Caustic soda (NaOH) – absorbs CO_2

Alkaline pyrogallol (NaOH + pyrogallic acid) – absorbs CO_2 **and O_2**

Result: seeds germinate fully

Result: seeds do not germinate fully

Fig. 9.4 Demonstration that seeds need oxygen to germinate

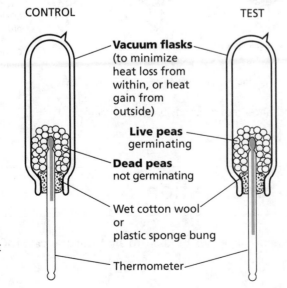

Fig. 9.5 Demonstration that germinating peas generate heat

CONTROL   TEST

Vacuum flasks (to minimize heat loss from within, or heat gain from outside)

Live peas germinating

Dead peas not germinating

Wet cotton wool or plastic sponge bung

Thermometer

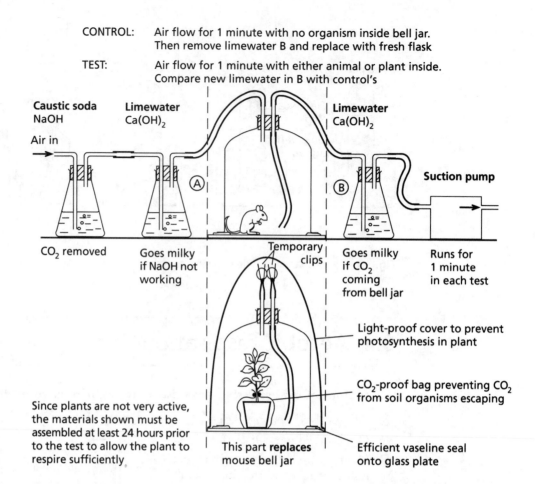

CONTROL: Air flow for 1 minute with no organism inside bell jar.
Then remove limewater B and replace with fresh flask

TEST: Air flow for 1 minute with either animal or plant inside.
Compare new limewater in B with control's

Caustic soda
NaOH

Air in

Limewater
Ca(OH)₂

Ⓐ

Ⓑ

Limewater
Ca(OH)₂

Suction pump

CO_2 removed

Goes milky
if NaOH not
working

Temporary
clips

Goes milky
if CO_2
coming
from bell jar

Runs for
1 minute
in each test

Light-proof cover to prevent
photosynthesis in plant

CO_2-proof bag preventing CO_2
from soil organisms escaping

Since plants are not very active,
the materials shown must be
assembled at least 24 hours prior
to the test to allow the plant to
respire sufficiently

This part **replaces**
mouse bell jar

Efficient vaseline seal
onto glass plate

Fig. 9.6 Experiments to determine whether a mammal and a flowering plant produce CO_2

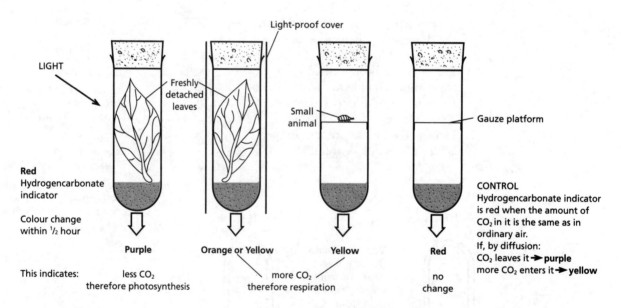

Light-proof cover

LIGHT

Freshly
detached
leaves

Small
animal

Gauze platform

Red
Hydrogencarbonate
indicator

Colour change
within ½ hour

This indicates:

Purple

less CO_2
therefore photosynthesis

Orange or Yellow

more CO_2
therefore respiration

Yellow

no
change

Red

CONTROL
Hydrogencarbonate indicator
is red when the amount of
CO_2 in it is the same as in
ordinary air.
If, by diffusion:
CO_2 leaves it ➡ **purple**
more CO_2 enters it ➡ **yellow**

Fig. 9.7 Demonstration that animals and leaves respire, using an indicator method

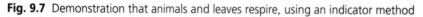

9.5 Rate of respiration

The rate of gaseous exchange can be used to find out the **rate of respiration** (Fig. 9.8).

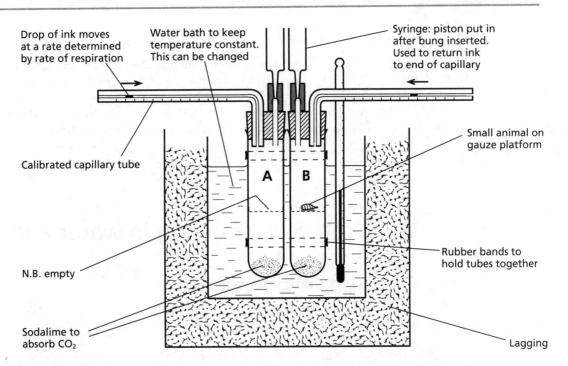

Fig. 9.8 Experiment to find out the rate of respiration, using a respirometer

Tube A will reach the temperature of the water in a few minutes. Insert its syringe plunger. Add an ink drop to the end of the capillary tube. No volume change (and therefore no movement of ink drop) is expected once the soda lime has absorbed the CO_2 in the air, since there is no organism respiring in it. Cooling or warming the surrounding water will, however, move the bubble. The distance the bubble moves in A must be subtracted from the distance moved in B.

Tube B is treated exactly as A is and at the same time. In B, however, the organisms take in O_2 and give out CO_2. Since the CO_2 is absorbed by soda lime, the volume of air in the tube becomes reduced. This causes more movement of the bubble, i.e. in addition to the movement, noted in B, owing to temperature change.

The respirometer can be used in water of different temperatures. The distance moved – in say 5 minutes – by the two ink drops is noted at each temperature.

9.6 Gaseous exchange

All cells receive O_2 and lose CO_2 through **thin, moist membranes of sufficient surface area.** Multicellular organisms follow the same rules at their respiratory surfaces. They maintain a large surface area to volume ratio (see Unit 22.6) to overcome the slow process of diffusion.

1 **Cells must remain small** if CO_2 and O_2 are to diffuse across the cytoplasm fast enough to maintain life. Cell division ensures this. Thus the volume of *Amoeba*, say $0.1 mm^3$, is adequately served by its cell membrane area, say $2.5 mm^2$.

2 **A high rate of diffusion** can be maintained by keeping a steep diffusion gradient (see Unit 7.2). This happens by

(a) *breathing* (continually changing the air supply);
(b) *blood flow* (e.g. continually removing the O_2 absorbed into capillaries).

3 **The rate of supply** of O_2 and removal of CO_2 can be increased during exercise, e.g. in Man the breathing rate goes up four-fold, the volume inhaled per breath seven-fold, the heart rate doubles and the volume of blood pumped doubles or trebles (athletes can do better).

④ **The surface area** for gaseous exchange must remain high:

(a) *with air*, e.g. in Man about 700 million alveoli in his two lungs provide a total of about 80 m² (area of a badminton court)★ to service his volume of about 80 dm³;

(b) *with tissues*, e.g. in Man about 95 000 km of capillaries provide an area of about 700 m² of which about 200 m² are in use at any one time.

★ Not tennis court size (261 m²) as often quoted.

9.7 Organisms respiring in water and air

Gaseous exchange in water

Water contains < 1% dissolved O_2.
1 Amoeba: gaseous exchange over whole *cell membrane* (Fig. 9.9).

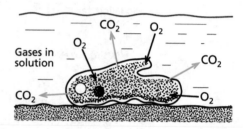

Fig. 9.9 Respiration in *Amoeba*

2 Bony fish: gaseous exchange at minutely branched *gill filaments* aided by blood containing red blood cells flowing in capillaries. Breathing requires use of mouth, pharynx and operculum (Fig. 9.10).

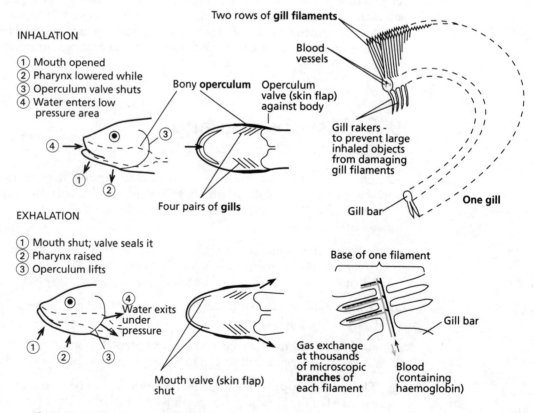

Fig. 9.10 Respiration in a bony fish

Gaseous exchange in air

Air contains almost 21% O_2.

Insect: gaseous exchange at *tracheoles*, thin tubes 1 μm in diameter supplying cells with air *direct* – blood not used for this. Much of the time O_2 and CO_2 just diffuse via *spiracles* and *tracheae* to tracheoles (Fig. 9.11). Active or strong-flying insects, e.g. bees and locusts, have air sacs. Abdominal *breathing movements* squash and unsquash these, assisting ventilation of tracheae. Locust group have a 'through system' for air (in through anterior spiracles, out through posterior).

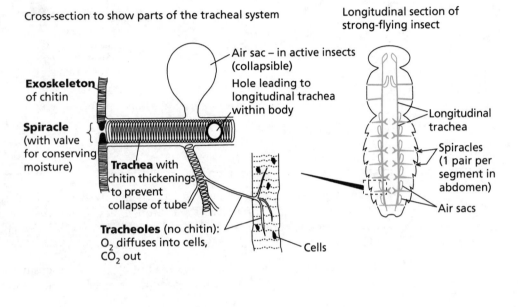

Fig. 9.11 Gaseous exchange in an insect

9.8 Mammal respiration

Gaseous exchange at millions of tiny air sacs (*alveoli*). By diffusion, O_2 from air enters erythrocytes and CO_2 enters air from plasma. Flow of blood, in a network of capillaries around each alveolus, speeds up the exchange. The barrier to diffusion is slight – both the alveolus and the capillary walls are each only one cell thick (Fig. 9.12).

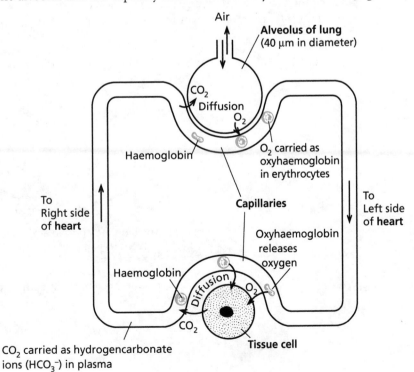

Fig. 9.12 Gaseous exchange at lungs and tissues of mammals

Table 9.2 Breathing movements

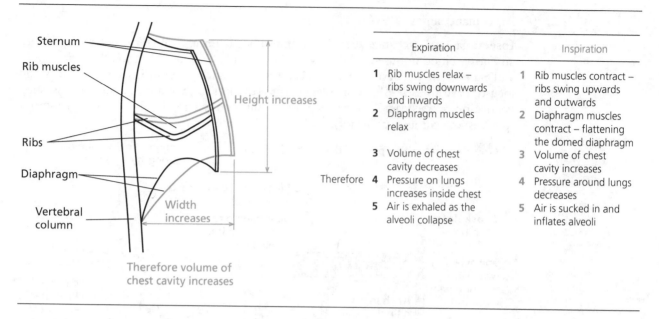

		Expiration	Inspiration
	1	Rib muscles relax – ribs swing downwards and inwards	1 Rib muscles contract – ribs swing upwards and outwards
	2	Diaphragm muscles relax	2 Diaphragm muscles contract – flattening the domed diaphragm
Therefore	3	Volume of chest cavity decreases	3 Volume of chest cavity increases
	4	Pressure on lungs increases inside chest	4 Pressure around lungs decreases
	5	Air is exhaled as the alveoli collapse	5 Air is sucked in and inflates alveoli

Note: When resting, breathing out occurs mainly because lung is elastic, collapsing if allowed to, thus deflating alveoli and bronchioles. Lungs may be made functionless by introducing air between pleural membranes, e.g. medically when treating tuberculosis (TB), or accidentally in a motor crash or a stabbing.

The breathing rate is determined mainly by the CO_2-sensitive part of the brain (see Unit 12.7). A rise in CO_2 from exercise raises breathing rate (and heart rate) and depth of breathing.

The kiss of life (mouth-to-mouth resuscitation)
A person suffering *asphyxia* (lack of oxygen, e.g. due to drowning or carbon monoxide poisoning) may need their breathing restored:

1. Force the victim's head back (to open the glottis) and pinch the nose shut.
2. Apply mouth to mouth and breathe forcibly into the victim's lungs.
3. Remove mouth for 4 seconds to allow the victim to breathe out.
4. Continue nos. 2 and 3 until breathing is restored.
5. Once the victim is breathing, place face down in the 'survival position'; this prevents inhalation of any vomit that may be produced.

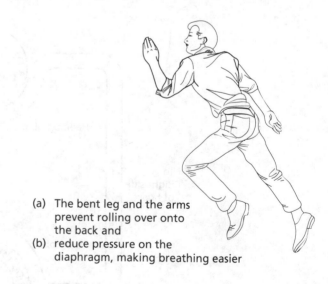

(a) The bent leg and the arms prevent rolling over onto the back and
(b) reduce pressure on the diaphragm, making breathing easier

Fig. 9.13 The survival position

9.9 Gas changes during breathing

Air breathed

Tidal air: about 0.5 dm³ (½ litre) – quiet breathing at rest.
Vital capacity: about 3.5 dm³ – volume inhaled or expelled in forced breathing.
Residual air: 1.5 dm³ – air that cannot be expelled at all (remains in lungs).

Table 9.3 Approximate composition of air inhaled and exhaled (after removal of water vapour)

	Inhaled	Exhaled	Approx. change
Oxygen	21%	17%	20% decrease
Carbon dioxide	0.04%	4%	100-fold increase
Nitrogen	79%	79%	Nil

Air exhaled is also always saturated with water vapour (6%) – a variable loss of water from the body occurs, depending on how moist the inhaled air was.

9.10 The respiratory pathway

Air passes to alveoli via nostrils, nasal cavity, trachea, two bronchi with many branches, and millions of bronchioles (Fig. 9.14). Dust, including bacteria, is 'filtered out' on sticky *mucus* in the nasal cavity as well as in the trachea. In both of them, *cilia* of lining cells pass the dirty mucus to the throat to be swallowed into the acid bath in the stomach.

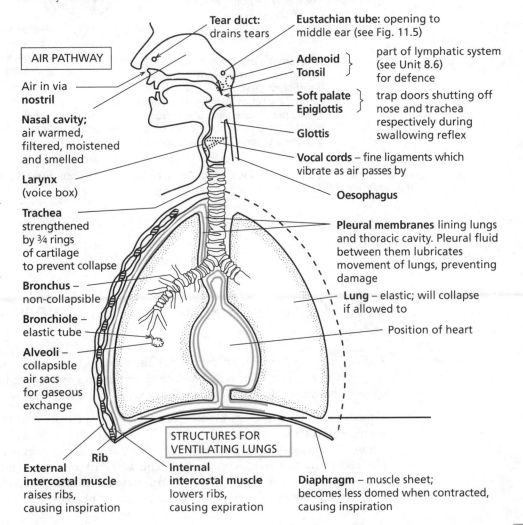

Tear duct: drains tears

Eustachian tube: opening to middle ear (see Fig. 11.5)

AIR PATHWAY

Adenoid
Tonsil } part of lymphatic system (see Unit 8.6) for defence

Air in via **nostril**

Soft palate
Epiglottis } trap doors shutting off nose and trachea respectively during swallowing reflex

Nasal cavity; air warmed, filtered, moistened and smelled

Glottis

Vocal cords – fine ligaments which vibrate as air passes by

Larynx (voice box)

Oesophagus

Trachea strengthened by ¾ rings of cartilage to prevent collapse

Pleural membranes lining lungs and thoracic cavity. Pleural fluid between them lubricates movement of lungs, preventing damage

Bronchus – non-collapsible

Lung – elastic; will collapse if allowed to

Bronchiole – elastic tube

Position of heart

Alveoli – collapsible air sacs for gaseous exchange

STRUCTURES FOR VENTILATING LUNGS

Rib

External intercostal muscle raises ribs, causing inspiration

Internal intercostal muscle lowers ribs, causing expiration

Diaphragm – muscle sheet; becomes less domed when contracted, causing inspiration

Fig. 9.14 Respiratory pathway in Man

9.11 Smoking or health

Tobacco smoking has both short-term and long-term harmful effects (Fig. 9.15).

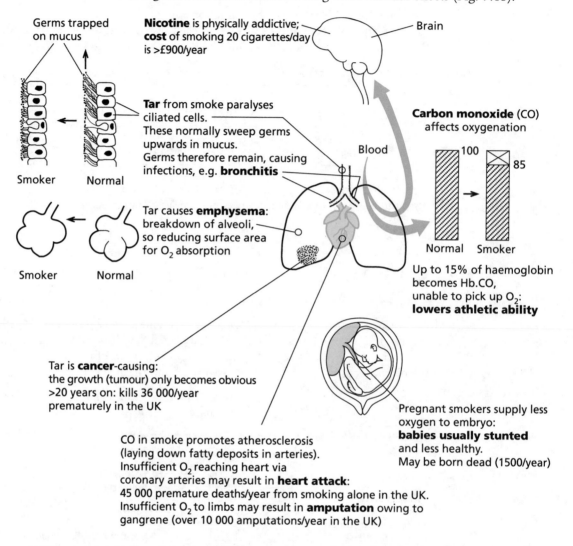

Germs trapped on mucus

Nicotine is physically addictive; **cost** of smoking 20 cigarettes/day is >£900/year

Brain

Tar from smoke paralyses ciliated cells. These normally sweep germs upwards in mucus. Germs therefore remain, causing infections, e.g. **bronchitis**

Smoker   Normal

Blood

Carbon monoxide (CO) affects oxygenation

100

85

Normal   Smoker

Tar causes **emphysema**: breakdown of alveoli, so reducing surface area for O_2 absorption

Smoker   Normal

Up to 15% of haemoglobin becomes Hb.CO, unable to pick up O_2: **lowers athletic ability**

Tar is **cancer**-causing: the growth (tumour) only becomes obvious >20 years on: kills 36 000/year prematurely in the UK

Pregnant smokers supply less oxygen to embryo: **babies usually stunted** and less healthy. May be born dead (1500/year)

CO in smoke promotes atherosclerosis (laying down fatty deposits in arteries). Insufficient O_2 reaching heart via coronary arteries may result in **heart attack**: 45 000 premature deaths/year from smoking alone in the UK. Insufficient O_2 to limbs may result in **amputation** owing to gangrene (over 10 000 amputations/year in the UK)

Will-power and the use of nicotine chewing-gum or body patches are successful methods of breaking this addictive habit

Fig. 9.15 Effects of cigarette smoking

9.12 Gaseous exchange in flowering plants

Angiosperms are flowering plants. Air diffuses through *stomata* (mostly on leaves; some on green stems) (see Unit 5.5) and *lenticels* (pores on cork-covered roots and stems) to *air spaces* between cells, particularly of cortex and mesophyll.

Gaseous exchange: O_2 is absorbed and CO_2 released direct from cells to air spaces during **respiration** both day and night. However, *green cells* in sunlight absorb CO_2 and release O_2 during **photosynthesis** (see Unit 5.5) at a rate far greater than the reverse process (owing to respiration). In dim light, e.g. dusk or dawn, rates of respiration and photosynthesis can be equal – the **compensation point**. The dead cells, e.g. xylem vessels (the majority in a big tree), do not respire or photosynthesize.

9.13 Uses for energy from respiration

1. **Mechanical** work, e.g. in contraction of muscles.
2. **Electrochemical** work, e.g. in passing nerve impulses.
3. **Chemical** work, e.g. synthesizing large molecules, such as protein, from amino acids during growth.
4. **Heating,** e.g. maintaining mammal body temperature.
5. **Transporting,** e.g. 'active transport' of materials across cell membranes (see Unit 7.2).

Mnemonic: Make tea (MECH T)

9.14 ATP (adenosine triphosphate)

ATP is the 'energy molecule' of cells.

When the end phosphate group is removed, leaving ADP (adenosine diphosphate), energy is released for use in any vital function, e.g. movement or growth. The phosphate may be added to ADP again, making ATP, during respiration in mitochondria. The energy for this comes from the energy in the sugar that is respired:

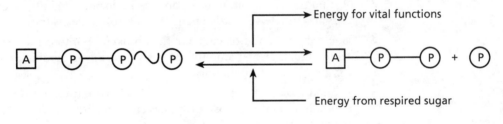

9.15 Measuring energy values of foods

To measure energy in foods they must be dried and burned. During respiration, food is neither dry nor are there any flames. But the methods below are the best we can use (Fig. 9.16).

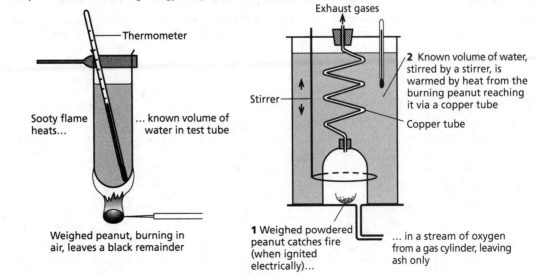

(a) A simple means of measuring energy in a peanut

Thermometer

Sooty flame heats...

... known volume of water in test tube

Weighed peanut, burning in air, leaves a black remainder

(b) A calorimeter for measuring energy values of foods

Exhaust gases

Stirrer

2 Known volume of water, stirred by a stirrer, is warmed by heat from the burning peanut reaching it via a copper tube

Copper tube

1 Weighed powdered peanut catches fire (when ignited electrically)...

... in a stream of oxygen from a gas cylinder, leaving ash only

Fig. 9.16 Measuring energy values of foods

In Fig. 9.16(b) there is complete burning of the peanut, and better transfer of heat to water.

$$\text{The heat energy released (in kJ)} = \frac{\text{volume of water (cm}^3) \times \text{rise in temp (°C)} \times 4.2}{1000}$$

The efficiency of transforming chemical energy of fuels and foods into mechanical energy (movement) can be judged from Table 9.4:

Table 9.4

	Efficiency of engines (%)			Efficiency (%)
	Steam	Petrol 4 stroke	Diesel	Respiration
Theoretical	30	58	65	40
Actual (approx.)	10	28	36	22

The wasted energy is lost as heat, in friction, etc.

Summary

1 Respiration supplies energy for vital functions of organisms of every kind.

2 Within the cytoplasm of cells, organic molecules are initially crudely broken up by enzymes to release a little energy by anaerobic means (not requiring oxygen).

3 The crude bits of molecules are then broken up into carbon dioxide and water to release much greater amounts of energy during an aerobic process (requiring oxygen) in the mitochondria.

4 Around 60% of the energy released in cellular respiration is wasted as heat and by controlling their heat loss, mammals and birds have a constant, warm body temperature.

5 The majority of organisms use aerobic respiration for their energy needs, obtaining oxygen and releasing carbon dioxide at wet gaseous exchange structures of large surface area, e.g. leaves and lungs.

6 To change the air at the gaseous exchange surface, many animals make breathing movements.

7 To make the pick-up of oxygen by flowing blood more efficient, mammals use red blood cells containing highly absorptive haemoglobin.

8 Smoking in particular makes gaseous exchange less efficient by causing lung diseases and diminishing the ability of haemoglobin to take up oxygen.

9 Energy values of foods may be calculated by burning small amounts in oxygen inside a 'bomb calorimeter' and measuring the temperature rise of water surrounding the burning food.

Chapter 10
Excretion, temperature regulation and homeostasis

10.1 Wastes and means of excretion

Excretion is the removal of waste products of metabolism. Wastes are often toxic, particularly if they accumulate. Examples of excretion:

- In **animals:**
  (i) CO_2 and water (from respiration);
  (ii) ammonia, urea or uric acid (from protein metabolism – see Unit 7.10).

- In **green plants:**
  (i) O_2 (from photosynthesis);
  (ii) shedding leaves or bark (contain various wastes).

- In **all organisms:**
    Heat energy (from metabolism, especially respiration, see Unit 10.6). An important waste only in animals, when they move around. Loss of water unfortunately accompanies most forms of excretion.

Mammalian excretory organs

1. **Lungs:** excrete CO_2; lose water vapour.
2. **Kidneys:** excrete urea; eliminate excess water and salts.
3. **Liver:** excretes bile pigments (see Fig. 6.12).
4. **Skin:** excretes some urea; loses water and salts (in sweat).

10.2 Mammal urinary system

Two **kidneys** (see Fig. 10.1) at back of abdominal cavity:

- **excrete** waste **nitrogen** (from excess protein in diet) as urea;
- **eliminate** excess **salts** (e.g. NaCl in very salty food);
- **osmoregulate** to maintain **water** content of blood.

Blood pathway (see Fig. 10.1 (B))
Blood containing urea (made in the liver) passes into kidney from aorta via renal artery to about one million **glomeruli** (knots of capillaries); thence via further capillary network to renal vein and posterior vena cava. Blood is filtered at the glomeruli.

The filtrate produced is modified into urine as it passes through **nephrons** (filtration units) (see Fig. 10.2).

Urine pathway (see Fig. 10.1 (A))
Urine formed by kidneys is passed by peristalsis along two **ureters** to the bladder (storage); thence via **urethra** to outside (urination).

Urine in Man is a 2–4% solution of urea, some salts, yellow colouring (bile pigments accidentally absorbed in intestine), poisons, drugs and hormones (variously modified). Exact composition varies according to diet, activity and health. It is dilute if excess water is drunk; is concentrated after exercise. Normally about 1.5 dm^3 of urine is lost daily.

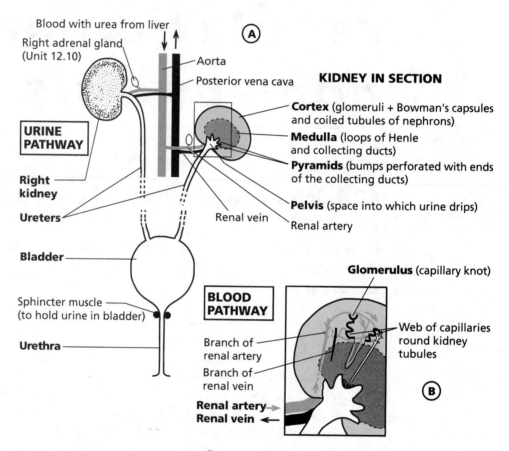

Fig. 10.1 The mammal urinary system: (A) urine pathway from kidney; (B) blood pathway in the kidney

10.3 The nephron

A nephron (see Fig. 10.2) is a kidney unit receiving tissue fluid and modifying it into urine. Tissue fluid (a filtrate of blood lacking cells and proteins) is forced out from the glomerulus (because of blood pressure) into the cavity of a **Bowman's capsule**. As filtrate passes along the tubules, all food and most other useful substances are reabsorbed from the tissue fluid, leaving urine (see Fig. 10.3).

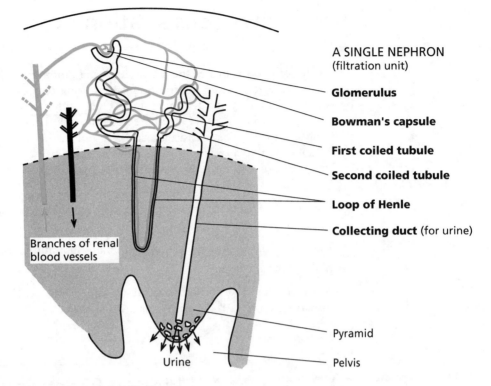

Fig. 10.2 A single nephron of a kidney

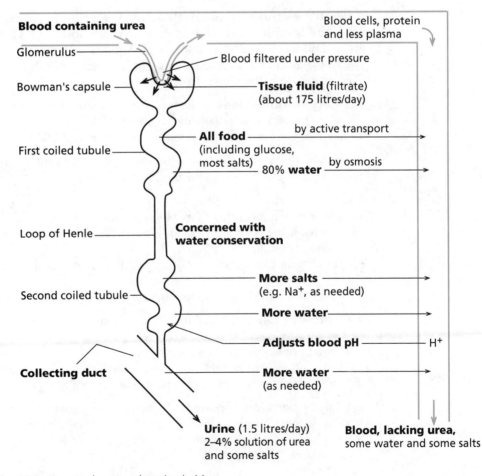

Fig. 10.3 How nephrons make urine in Man

10.4 Water conservation

The **loop of Henle** makes the tissue fluid surrounding it salty (by secreting salt from the fluid it receives). This salty solution causes water to pass out of the **collecting duct** by osmosis (but *only* if the hormone ADH, which makes the duct's walls water-permeable, is secreted). ADH is only secreted if water needs to be conserved, e.g. owing to sweating. If *excess* water is drunk, it passes out in the urine since it is not reabsorbed by the collecting duct owing to lack of ADH secretion (see Unit 12.10).

The jerboa (desert rat) conserves its water by all possible means (compare rat in Fig. 7.12):

1 Makes *very concentrated urine* owing to long loops of Henle and high levels of ADH.

2 *Does not sweat* – no sweat glands.

3 *Evaporates little water* from its lungs – remains in a humid burrow by day.

4 Makes very *dry faeces*.

The small volume of water lost is much the same as the volume it gains from respiration (see equation, Unit 9.2). Jerboas never need to drink.

10.5 Abnormal kidney function

1 Faulty excretion: sugar diabetes – glucose is passed out in urine. Lack of hormone **insulin** allows high glucose level in blood (see Unit 12.10). Consequently tissue fluid is too glucose-rich for the first coiled tubule to reabsorb it all into the blood. Therefore glucose is drained, little by little, from the body; can cause coma and death. Remedied by regular insulin injections.

2 Faulty osmoregulation: water diabetes – large quantities of dilute urine, e.g. 20 litres per day. Caused by lack of hormone ADH. Leads to dehydration of body unless large volumes of water drunk. Remedied by regular ADH ('vasopressin') nasal spraying.

3 Kidney disease: nephritis – protein appears in urine. Glomeruli are letting plasma proteins through with the tissue fluid (filtrate).

Kidneys may fail
(a) suddenly, e.g. because of low blood pressure or severe infection (so killing the cells);
(b) gradually, e.g. because of high blood pressure or an obstruction preventing urine leaving the kidney.
If only one kidney fails, the other healthy one is capable of doing the job of two.

There are three kinds of treatment for kidney failure:

1 Controlled Diet: reduced intake of protein (less urea produced); less salt and water (less urine volume); and in particular less potassium-rich foods, e.g. oranges, chocolate, mushrooms (high K^+ can stop the heart).

If this fails to help and the blood urea level rises (to five times the normal 0.3 g/dm^3) the kidneys must be either assisted by dialysis or 'replaced' by healthy ones.

2 Dialysis by 'kidney machine': blood from an artery in the arm is passed through 10 m of dialysis ('Visking') tubing bathed in a special solution. This solution is similar to blood plasma but lacks protein and urea (see Unit 8.2). The patient's urea and other wastes diffuse from the blood in the tubing into the bathing solution. The 'cleaned' blood returns to a vein in the arm. Fresh solution is used on every occasion.

It costs about £3000 per patient per year to give the necessary 12–18 hours of dialysis per week. The machines cost about £10,000.

A much simpler method of dialysis is 'CAPD' (body cavity dialysis). It allows the patient to remain active whilst dialysing (i.e. not attached to a machine.) A litre bag of glucose solution is drained into the body cavity. Wastes diffuse into the solution through the blood vessels of the gut. After some hours the solution is drained back into the bag and discarded.

3 Kidney transplant: a healthy kidney (from a person only just dead or a living relative) is surgically inserted near the bladder. Certain precautions must be taken to avoid death of the transplanted kidney:

  (i) the *blood group* of the donor (giver) and recipient (receiver) of the kidney must be the same (see Unit 17.3);
 (ii) if the *tissue type* of donor and recipient are also the same, the success rate can be over 80%;
(iii) the recipient's *antibody system* (see Unit 20.10) must be suppressed by drugs for the rest of his or her life. This avoids rejection of the kidney but also risks serious illness from other, ordinary, infections. So antibiotics are often also given.

10.6 Body temperature in organisms

Skin and temperature control

The *body generates heat* by its metabolism (60% of the energy from respiration is wasted as heat), e.g. blood leaving contracting muscles or the liver is warmer than when it entered them.

At the *skin*, blood either *loses* this heat to cooler surroundings or *gains* even more if the surroundings are warmer.

Gain or loss of heat can happen in four main ways (Fig. 10.4);

- radiation (important in air) – Man, at rest in shade, loses most this way.
- conduction (important in water) – e.g. elephants bathing.
- convection – air circulation; speeds up radiation and conduction.
- evaporation (heat *loss* only): heat transfers to water which gains enough energy to vaporize. This happens during breathing, panting and sweating in animals; and during transpiration in plants.

Some heat is also lost in *urine* and *faeces*.

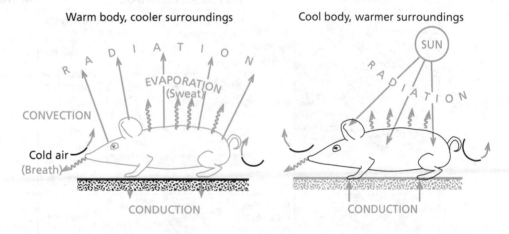

Fig. 10.4 Heat gain and loss by a mammal

Thus *most animals* (and all plants) have **body temperatures that fluctuate** with that of their environment. These animals are called poikilotherms or **ectotherms** or 'cold-blooded'.

Birds and mammals have **body temperatures that remain constant** despite the fluctuating environmental temperature. They are called homoiotherms or **endotherms** or 'warm-blooded'.

Table 10.1 Comparison of ectotherms and endotherms

	Ectotherms	Endotherms
In cold conditions	Become sluggish as they cool because their enzymes work more slowly. To avoid death by freezing may need to **hibernate**	Can remain **active** even in polar regions because their enzymes are kept working at their best (optimum) temperature. Only small mammals, e.g. dormice, marmots, need to hibernate
In hot conditions	Active, but may need to **aestivate** to avoid overheating, e.g. earthworm curls up into an inactive ball deep in soil	**Active** – cooling measures work; none aestivate. Some avoid heat by being active at night (cooler)
Main disadvantage	**Fall easy prey to endotherms** when not fully active – particularly when hibernating or aestivating	**Require a lot more food** to keep up their temperature

Temperature control in ectotherms and flowering plants

1 Ectotherms: rely on behaviour to keep a constant temperature – move to warm or cold places as the situation demands. Do not use skin or metabolic means as mammals do. However, wood-ant nests (28 °C) and honey-bee hives (35 °C) *are* maintained at the temperatures indicated.

2 Flowering plants: cannot move; they perennate if temperature becomes impossible (see Unit 14.3). If hot they *transpire* more (water evaporation) or *wilt* (reducing area of leaves gaining heat from sun) (see also Unit 10.8).

10.7 Mammal temperature control

Mammals have a *thermostat* in the forebrain (see Unit 12.7) which monitors blood temperature. Its information causes changes in:

1. **Behaviour:** e.g. seeking shade or getting wet if it is hot; seeking shelter and huddling into a ball if it is cold (see Fig. 10.5).

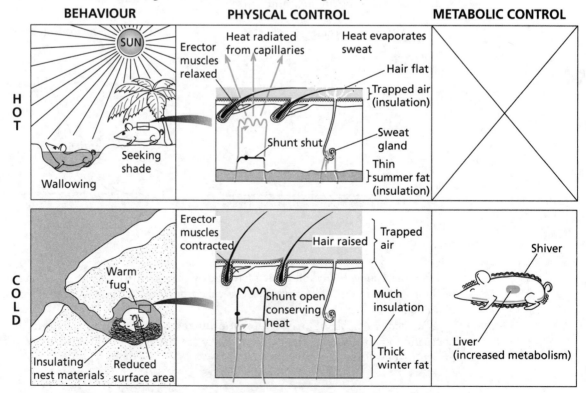

Fig. 10.5 Three ways of maintaining constant body temperature

2 Skin (physical control):

- **hair:** traps air – a good insulator. Amount of insulation can be varied by raising or lowering hair using erector muscles. Thicker 'coats' in winter – moulted in summer.
- **fat:** also a good insulator. Whales (in very cold water) have thick 'blubber' but camels have no fat except in hump. Mammals prepare for winter cold by laying down more fat.
- **capillaries and shunts:** skin 'flushes' with blood flowing through surface capillaries (*vasodilation*) which radiate heat when mammal is hot. Skin goes pale if cold since blood is diverted from surface capillaries (*vasoconstriction*) often by going through a 'shunt' deeper down.
- **sweat glands:** secrete sweat (salty water containing some urea). Water evaporates, removing excess heat.

3 Metabolic control:

- **shivering:** involuntary contractions of muscles generate heat.
- **liver:** metabolizes faster owing to increased thyroxine secretion.

4 Shape: a large surface area to volume ratio (see Unit 22.6) assists heat exchange, e.g. body stretched out to lose heat. The opposite, e.g. body curled up, conserves heat. For the same reasons, large ears of desert foxes and hares radiate heat well; small ears of arctic foxes and hares radiate less.

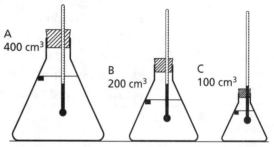

Fig. 10.6 Experiment to discover the importance of surface area to volume ratio in the cooling of water

Flasks A, B and C are filled with water at, say, 60 °C. Their temperature is read every 2 minutes and recorded. The surface area is measured by shaping and cutting graph paper to fit the outside and counting squares.

Results show that C cools fastest and A slowest.

This may help explain why small mammals, e.g. shrews, need to eat so much for their size (respire a large part of their food to maintain temperature).

10.8 Adaptations to extreme conditions: polar bear, camel and cactus

All three live where water and food are scarce and temperatures extreme.

Polar bear (carnivore)

1 Small surface area to its large volume: has small ears, curls up if cold – to retain heat (see Unit 22.6).

2 Insulation: 8 cm blubber layer below skin, thick greasy fur which sheds water easily after swimming – to prevent hypothermia. Females build snow dens in winter to shelter their new born until summer.

3 Locomotion: rough horny pads on feet give traction on slippery ice, fur between pads and large feet help in snow and spread weight, streamlined body to swim powerfully for miles, run down prey easily (25 mph).

Camel (herbivore)

1. **Temperature tolerant** allowing its body to cool below normal at night and rise slowly by day to as much as 9 °C above normal.

2. **Dehydration tolerant** allowing up to 25% water loss over a week. Can drink over 20 gallons (90 litres) of water all at once to rehydrate without harm (c.f. Man, Unit 6.5).

3. **Loses little water:** urine scanty and concentrated, little sweating.

4. **Sand tolerant:** large feet to spread load, eyelids and nostrils close tight against sandstorms.

5. **Fat** only in hump, provides energy for 10 days (and some water) when respired.

Cactus (xerophytic plant)

1. **Reduced surface area:** leaves are spines (to deter herbivores), stem photosynthesizes – reduces heat gain and water loss.

2. **Stores water** in 'succulent' stem unattractive to herbivores by taste or poisons.

3. **Reduced transpiration** (see point 1): stem stomata are few and open only in the cool of the night to allow CO_2 in, retaining water by day.

4. **Temperature tolerant** tissues – in desert it is very cool by night, very hot by day.

5. **Extensive shallow roots** – to pick up all available moisture.

10.9 Homeostasis

Homeostasis is the maintenance of a constant environment immediately around cells. For unicellular organisms this is the water they inhabit and their only means of homeostasis is to move (if they can) to a suitable area. The immediate environment of cells in a multicellular animal is the tissue fluid. In mammals the composition of this is kept very constant by a variety of organs, each of which controls particular factors in the blood (the source of tissue fluid).

Table 10.2 Organs concerned with homeostasis in Man

Organs concerned	Factors controlled in blood	Healthy blood levels in Man
Liver and islet tissue of pancreas (Unit 6.10)	Glucose	1 g/dm³
Skin, liver (Fig. 10.7)	Temperature	36.8 °C (under tongue)
Kidneys (Units 10.2–10.4)	Osmoregulation (water)	90%
	pH (acidity/alkalinity)	pH 7.4
	Urea (nitrogen waste)	0.3 g/dm³
Lungs (Unit 9.8)	Carbon dioxide (carbon waste)	550 cm³/dm³ (at rest, deoxygenated)
	Oxygen	193 cm³/dm³ (at rest, oxygenated)

Note: blood does of course vary in composition according to where it is in the body (see Unit 8.5), but *overall* the levels of factors affecting the vital functions of cells are kept within narrow limits.

10.10 Skin functions

1. **Sensory:** sensitive nerve endings give warning of harm – pain, touch, heat or cold.

Protection: skin acts as barrier between the internal environment of cells (tissue fluid) and the external environment (anything from climate, air or water to bacteria or predators).

Skin *resists:*
(*a*) **puncture** – (from slashes, blows or friction) by being tough and hair-padded;
(*b*) **desiccation** – (drying of body) by the waterproof protein keratin, aided by oils;
(*c*) **entry of pathogens** – (viruses, bacteria, etc.);
(*d*) **damage from ultraviolet light** – ('sunburn'; skin cancer) by suntanning, i.e. producing more pigment when in sunshine.

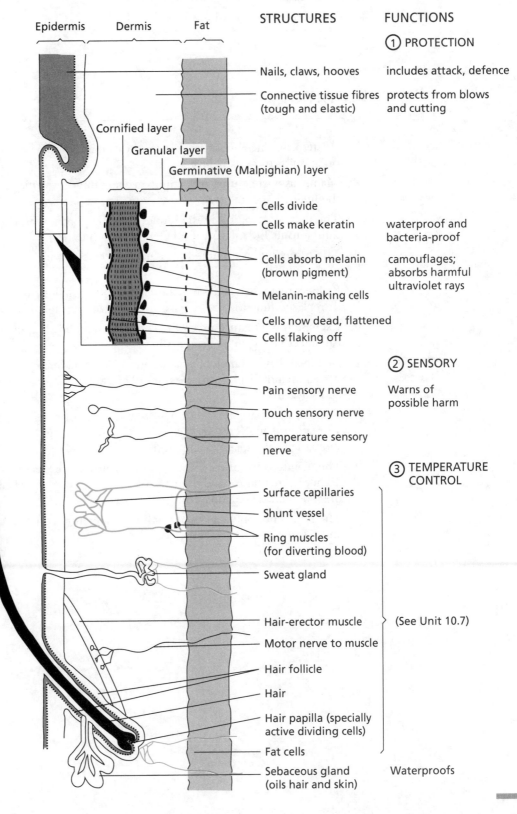

Fig. 10.7 The structure and functions of mammal skin

Skin *assists* predators and prey by providing:

(e) **weapons** from modified skin – (claws, hooves) for attacking or defending;

(f) **camouflage** – by special distribution of pigment in three ways:

    (i) *blending:* similar colour to background, e.g. khaki colour of lion.

    (ii) *countershading:* pale belly is darkened by shadow; dark back is made paler by sun. Therefore from the side the animal looks 'flat'; difficult to see, e.g. deer.

    (iii) *disruptive:* regular outline broken up by stripes or blotches to blend with light and shade among vegetation, e.g. leopard.

③ **Synthesis:** certain oils in the skin are changed to *vitamin D* (see Unit 4.5) when subjected to ultraviolet light.

④ **Excretion:** some *urea* is lost in sweat.

⑤ **Temperature control** (dealt with in Unit 10.7).

Summary

1 Wastes from metabolism and excess heat must be got rid of by excretion if an organism is to remain alive.

2 Mammals excrete urea and water via the kidneys as urine, and carbon dioxide via the lungs.

3 The unit of excretion in the kidney is the nephron, whose glomerulus sends tissue fluid into its Bowman's capsule by pressure filtration.

4 The tissue fluid is modified into urine by reabsorption of all food and much water in the tubules.

5 Kidneys that work badly may be replaced surgically by those from suitable people, or replaced functionally by passing the blood through a 'kidney machine'.

6 Exercise is the main source of excess heat in a body, but environmental conditions can affect heat gain or heat loss markedly.

7 Mammals have a range of adaptations to maintain a constant body temperature, which include behaviour, the use of hair, fat, blood capillaries and sweat glands, and shivering.

8 Certain mammals live in hot deserts and cold polar regions. They show extra adaptations and even tolerance to temperature change and dehydration. Cacti show their own, plant, adaptations.

9 The maintenance of constant conditions around cells is called homeostasis. Temperature control and the control of water, glucose and carbon dioxide levels in the blood are all examples of homeostasis.

10 The skin is not only an organ used in temperature control, it is also a sense organ and is protective to the body.

Chapter 11
Sensitivity

11.1 Sensitivity in plants and animals

Organisms must be aware of their surroundings and respond to them, where necessary, to keep alive. Plants must seek light; animals, food. Organisms respond to various **stimuli** (detectable changes in the environment). Plants respond to light, gravity, touch (see Unit 12.14); and animals also respond to these and to temperature, chemicals in air (smells) or water (tastes) and sound. Plants use much simpler means than animals to detect and respond to stimuli (see Unit 12.1).

Table 11.1 Comparison of sensitivity and response in animals and plants

Multicellular animals	Multicellular plants
1 **Special sense cells** or organs (which usually do nothing else – e.g. eyes which only see)	No *special* sense organs, e.g. shoot tips sense light
2 **Nerves** relay messages from sensory areas	No nerves
3 **Brain** (present in most) 'computes a decision', sent to muscles	No brain
4 **Muscles** which can move the whole body towards or away from the stimulus	No muscles: cannot move the whole body

11.2 Mammal sense organs

Sense organs pick up stimuli – they *sense*. But sensations are interpreted (*perceived*) by the brain, e.g. eyes may work perfectly but if the optic nerve or the visual centre of the brain is damaged, the person is blind.

Sense organs sense stimuli in both the external and internal environments:

External

- *Skin* – touch, heat, cold, pressure (extremes of which can cause pain) (see Unit 10.10).
- *Nose* – air-borne chemicals (smells – including the 'taste' of food).
- *Tongue* – chemicals causing perception of bitter, sweet, salt and sour tastes.
- *Ear* – sound (high frequency pressure changes); changes of body position; gravity sense.
- *Eye* – light (as light or dark, colour, and the form of objects).

Internal (often concerned with homeostasis, see Unit 10.9). Examples:

- *Thermostat* in hypothalamus of brain (see Unit 12.7).
- *Breathing centre* (CO_2-sensitive) in medulla oblongata of brain (see Unit 12.7).

- *Spindle organs* sense tension in muscles. These assist muscle coordination and supporting of loads (see Fig. 11.1a and b).
- *Tendon organs* sense tension in tendons. These prevent overloading of muscles and tendons (see Fig. 11.1a and b).

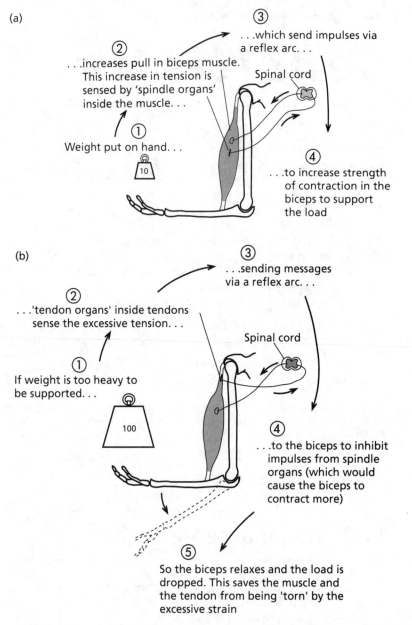

(a)

③ ...which send impulses via a reflex arc...

② ...increases pull in biceps muscle. This increase in tension is sensed by 'spindle organs' inside the muscle...

Spinal cord

① Weight put on hand...

10

④ ...to increase strength of contraction in the biceps to support the load

(b)

③ ...sending messages via a reflex arc...

② ...'tendon organs' inside tendons sense the excessive tension...

Spinal cord

① If weight is too heavy to be supported...

100

④ ...to the biceps to inhibit impulses from spindle organs (which would cause the biceps to contract more)

⑤ So the biceps relaxes and the load is dropped. This saves the muscle and the tendon from being 'torn' by the excessive strain

Fig. 11.1 The role of stretch receptors in the arm: 'feedback' to muscles. (a) Supporting a load, (b) dropping a load

11.3 The eye

❶ The outer covering of the eyeball is the tough, white **sclera**. It joins with the transparent **cornea** in front. Both are kept in shape by pressure from tissue fluid secreted from **ciliary body** capillaries (Fig. 11.2).

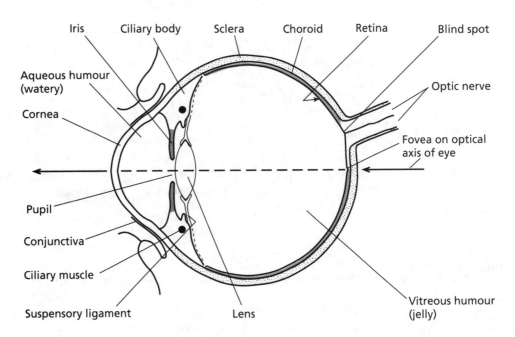

Fig. 11.2 Horizontal section through a human eye

2. It is **protected** within a bony socket (*orbit*) and by **three reflexes:**

   (a) *weep reflex: dust and irritants* sensed by the **conjunctiva** cause an increase in tears and blinking to wash them away;

   (b) *iris reflex: strong light* on the *retina* causes a narrowing of the pupil to prevent damage to the light-sensitive cells;

   (c) *blinking reflex:* seen *objects* which may hit the head cause the eyelids to close.

3. The **iris** is a muscular sheet bordering a hole, the **pupil**. Its size is controlled by two sets of muscle (Fig. 11.3).

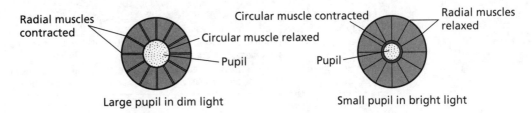

Fig. 11.3 View of the iris from within the eye

4. The **retina** contains nerve cells linked with two kinds of **light-sensitive** cell:

   (a) *rods:* sense in black-and-white, in dim light; most are outside fovea.

   (b) *cones:* sense in colour, in brighter light; very high numbers at fovea.

   The *fovea* (called the 'yellow spot' in Man) enables objects to be seen in colour and in great detail. Image is in complete focus at this spot only. Is virtually blind in very dim light. The *blind spot* has only nerve cells (gathering into the *optic nerve*): no vision.

5. The **choroid:**

   (a) Black pigment cells prevent internal reflection of light.

   (b) Capillaries supply the retina with tissue fluid.

6. **Focusing** (Fig. 11.4)

   Cornea: responsible for most (at least 70%) of the converging of light rays.

   Lens: makes the final adjustment, i.e. *accommodates*.

   Far focusing: lens pulled thin by strain on suspensory ligaments exerted by sclera under pressure from tissue fluid.

   Near focusing: lens collapses fat owing to its elasticity, when strain on suspensory ligaments is reduced by contraction of ciliary muscle.

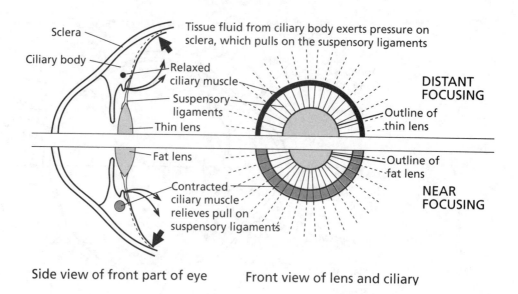

Fig. 11.4 Focusing by the eye

Side view of front part of eye   Front view of lens and ciliary

⑦ **Binocular vision:** the two different views obtained by human eyes overlap. The brain 'computes' how far away objects are.

Six muscles, attached to the sclera of each eye, swivel the eyes in their orbits to look at the same object.

11.4 The ear

Table 11.2 Functions and parts of the ear

Functions	Parts
Hearing	Outer: ear *pinna* and *canal* for sound-gathering Middle: *eardrum* vibrates; *3 ossicles* transmit vibrations; together they amplify the sound at *oval window* Inner: *(a) cochlea* (a 3-part spiral tube filled with liquid) receives the amplified sound waves which stimulate *hair cells* in the middle tube
Detecting change in position	Inner: *(b) 3 semicircular canals* (set at right angles to each other) whose liquid moves inside *ampullae* (swellings), so stimulating *hair cells* there

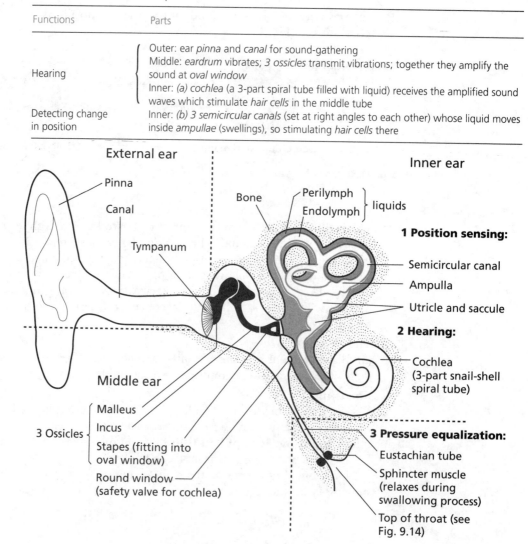

Fig. 11.5 Structure and function of the three parts of the ear and Eustachian tube

Messages from both sets of hair cells go via the *auditory nerve* to the brain: the *cerebrum* interprets sounds received and the cerebellum contributes to sense of balance (see Fig. 12.6).

1 Hearing

Man can hear sound *frequencies* of 20–20 000 Hertz.

Volume can be amplified up to 22 times: pressure of sound waves reaching the tympanum is transmitted by the three ossicles to an area 22 times smaller – the base of stapes. Muscles attached to the ossicles can also diminish their movements during loud noise, preventing ear damage.

The stapes vibrates because the tympanum does; thus air-borne sound waves are changed into liquid-borne sound waves in perilymph. These waves cause movement of a membrane on which hair cells sit. These hairs, embedded in a jelly shelf, are pulled or squashed as the cells rise or fall on the membrane, sending impulses along the auditory nerve. The sound-sensing part of the cochlea is called the organ of Corti (Fig. 11.6).

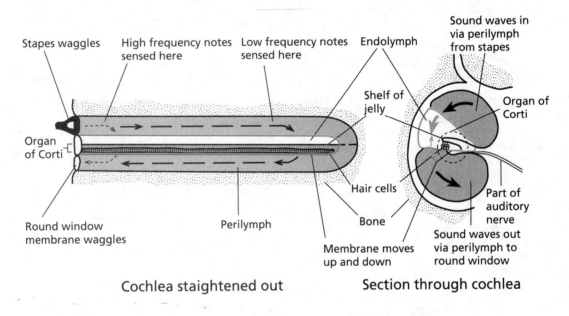

Fig. 11.6 How sounds are sensed in the cochlea

2 Detecting change in position

(*a*) Inside each **ampulla** are hair cells capped by a cone of jelly (cupula). The cupula can move like a swing-door. It swings only when its semicircular canal and the head are moving in the same plane. Although the canal moves, the fluid does not (owing to inertia). So the cupula swings, bending the hairs, which send impulses to the brain (Fig. 11.7). According to which of the 6 semicircular canals (in 2 ears) are stimulated, the brain 'compute' how to keep balance. Information from the eyes assists in this.

(*b*) The **utricle** and **saccule** also each contain hair cells with a cupula. The cupulae are weighted with chalk grains. As the head tilts forwards or backwards the weight of the cupula pulls more on the hair cells of the utricle. These send impulses to the brain via nerves. The saccule deals with sideways tilts of the head. This way we know whether we are upright or at a tilt (Fig. 11.8).

3 Detecting where a sound is coming from

Sound from the right or left of an animal reaches the two ears at slightly different times. The brain 'compute' this difference to decide where it came from.

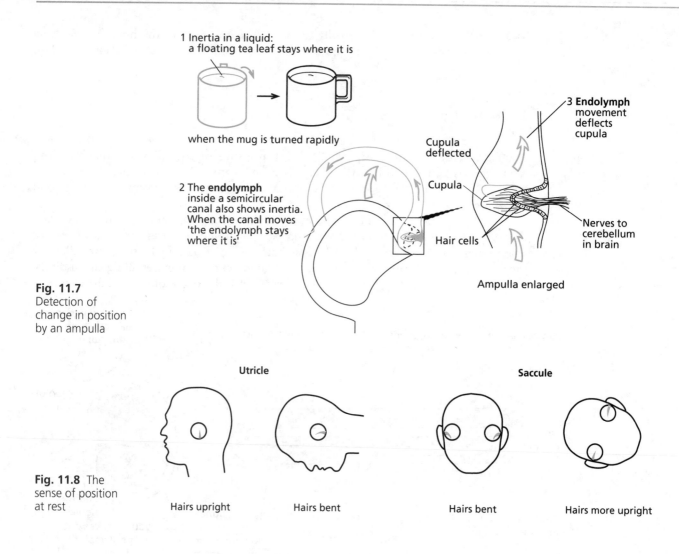

1 Inertia in a liquid:
  a floating tea leaf stays where it is

when the mug is turned rapidly

2 The **endolymph** inside a semicircular canal also shows inertia. When the canal moves 'the endolymph stays where it is'

3 **Endolymph** movement deflects cupula

Cupula deflected

Cupula

Hair cells

Nerves to cerebellum in brain

Ampulla enlarged

Fig. 11.7
Detection of change in position by an ampulla

Utricle

Saccule

Hairs upright

Hairs bent

Hairs bent

Hairs more upright

Fig. 11.8 The sense of position at rest

Summary

1   Organisms must be sensitive to stimuli around them and from within their bodies.

2   If they do not respond to these changes they are unlikely to survive.

3   Mammals have a range of sense organs and sensors, of which the eye and the ear are particularly important.

4   Eyes focus images via the cornea and an adjustable lens onto the retina where rod cells sense in greys and cone cells sense in colour.

5   Ears sense sounds in the cochlea and sense changes of position in the semicircular canals.

6   Ears and eyes, in pairs, both contribute to the sense of balance and the ability to judge distance.

7   Plants do not have sense organs but are nonetheless sensitive to light, gravity, chemicals and pressure.

8   Animals are sensitive to a wider range of stimuli, particularly within their bodies, to achieve control of body processes.

Chapter 12
Coordination and response

12.1 Information, messages and action

1 Information from both an organism's external and its internal environments is received by sensory cells (see Unit 11.1). Often this has to be acted upon if the organism is to remain alive.

2 Messages of two types result from the information:
(*a*) *chemical* – hormones, transported in solution, relatively slowly (animals and plants);
(*b*) *electrical* – impulses along nerves, relatively quickly (animals only).
    This accounts for the different rates at which plants and animals react.

3 Action resulting from the message:
(*a*) in *plants* (which have no muscles or obvious glands like the liver, as animals have) is usually by:
    (i) *special growth,* e.g. tropisms, flowering, or
    (ii) *inhibiting growth,* e.g. dormancy of seed, leaf shedding;
(*b*) in *animals* action is by:
    (i) *movement* (muscles), or
    (ii) *secretion* (glands).
  Growth, although also controlled by hormones, as in plants, is a response only to the rate at which food can be built up into protoplasm.

Coordination of actions
Each response to a stimulus, unless coordinated with others, would lead to chaos. Thus feeding on bread includes muscle coordination to get the bread into the mouth (and not the ear) and to cause chewing, swallowing and peristalsis, as well as coordination of secretion of saliva, mucus and pancreatic juice (at the right times).

12.2 Mammal nervous system

Composed of *neurones* (nerve cells). Neurones are bundled up into *nerves* in the *peripheral nervous system (PNS)*. Nerves link sensory cells and action cells (effectors) with the *central nervous system (CNS)* – the brain and spinal cord (see Figs. 12.1, 12.2).

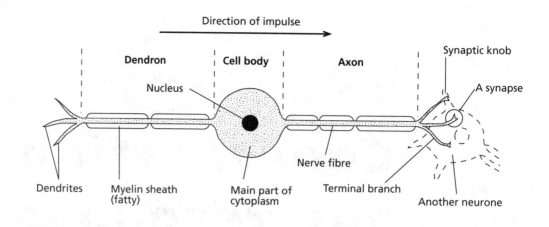

Fig. 12.1 A
generalized
neurone

As far as function is concerned there are *four types of neurone:*

① **Sensory:** may connect with sensory cells, e.g. in retina of eye, or have sensory ends themselves, e.g. touch receptors in skin. Have long dendrons, short axons; carry 'messages' about the environment *to* the CNS.

② **Relay:** always act as links between neurones, e.g. sensory neurones and either motor neurones or pyramidal neurones. This allows a large number of cross-connections, as in a switchboard.

③ **Motor:** usually link with relay neurones and with muscle or gland cells, to which they carry 'messages' *from* the CNS, calling for action; have short dendrons, long axons.

④ **Pyramidal:** connect with relay neurones and other pyramidal neurones which have a vast network of cell branches (up to 50 000), each a possible interconnection. This allows the 'computer' function of the brain (see Fig. 12.4).

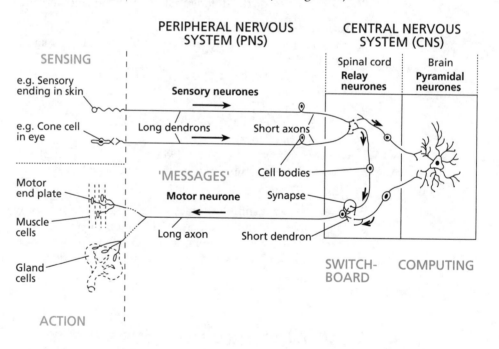

Fig. 12.2 Four
different kinds of
neurone and their
functions in the
body

12.3 Nervous impulses

An impulse ('message') is produced by the flow of Na^+ ions into a neurone and K^+ ions out. It passes along the neurone at up to 120 m/s.

Impulses *cause secretion* of a chemical substance at a *synaptic knob* which, for less than one millisecond, 'connects' two neurones electrically, allowing the impulse to pass on.

The chemical is destroyed and re-created after each impulse (Fig. 12.3). Thus neurones are not physically connected to each other (as in an electrical circuit) and each neurone generates its own electricity (there is no central battery). Each synapse is effectively a connecting switch.

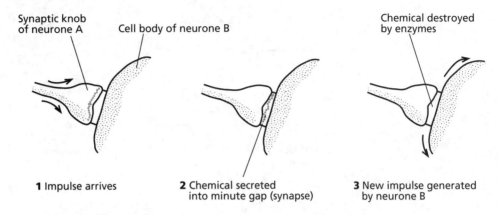

Fig. 12.3 Passing a 'message' at a synapse

1 Impulse arrives

2 Chemical secreted into minute gap (synapse)

3 New impulse generated by neurone B

12.4 Reflex action

Reflex action: an automatic rapid, *unlearned* response to a stimulus which helps the animal survive. It is a reaction to sensory information of an *urgent* nature (e.g. withdrawing hand from flame; righting oneself when overbalancing; swallowing) which could mean the difference between survival and death (see also Unit 11.3 – eye).

A maximum of *five* kinds of cell (*reflex arc*) take part in a reflex action (see Fig. 12.4, numbers ① – ⑤).

A knee-jerk reflex arc has no relay neurone.

12.5 Learned behaviour

❶ **Conditioned reflex action:** a *learned* reflex, i.e. the brain is involved. During the training period an inappropriate stimulus is substituted for the appropriate one, as Pavlov discovered with dogs (see Table 12.1).

Conditioned reflexes can be 'unlearned' too, if the reaction is not rewarded. Many skills, e.g. feeding oneself, writing, riding a bicycle, are conditioned reflexes learned by hard practice (training).

Table 12.1 Pavlov's experiment – conditioned reflex in dogs

	Stimulus	Reaction
Reflex action	Smell of food	Saliva flows
Training period	Bell rung when food given	Saliva flows
Conditioned reflex	Bell rung (inappropriate)	Saliva still flows

❷ **Conscious action:** sensory information goes to the brain before action is taken (see Fig. 12.4). All the little delays in transmission of impulses at thousands of synapses in the brain add up to make reaction time slower than in reflex actions.

Animals with small brains rely mostly on automatic reactions (instinct). Those with larger brains have more scope for working out solutions (intelligence).

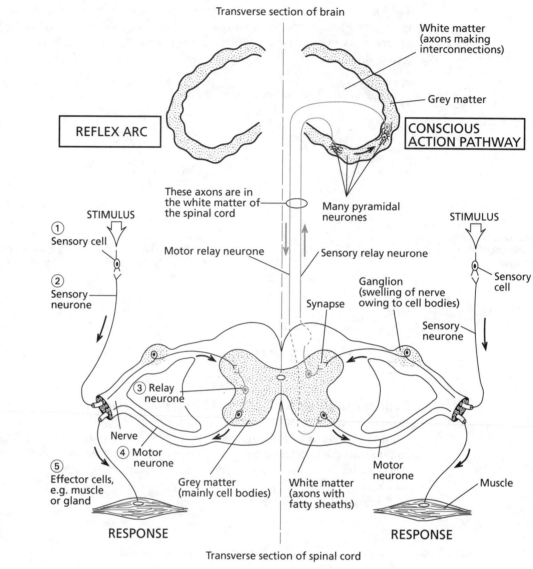

Fig. 12.4
Comparison of reflex and conscious action pathways

12.6 Instinctive behaviour

Instinctive behaviour: a series of unlearned actions, the completion of one being the signal for starting the next. Often a highly complex 'behaviour pattern', any disruption of which leads to total failure and a recommencement of the sequence of actions, e.g. provision of food for a hunting wasp's larvae (Fig. 12.5). See also Units 21.16 and 21.18.

12.7 The brain

Expanded front part of nerve cord; but grey matter is outside the white. In primitive vertebrates, the brain has three main parts; forebrain, midbrain and hindbrain.

In most mammals the same three parts are easily seen.

In Man, the front part (cerebrum) is so vast that it covers the midbrain and part of the hindbrain too (Fig. 12.6).

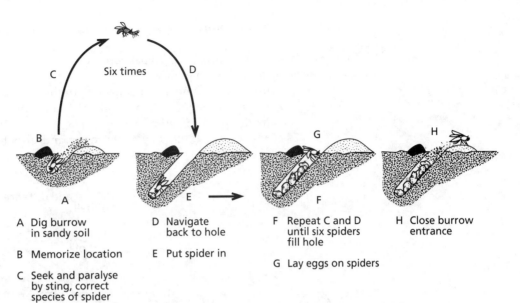

Fig. 12.5
Instinctive behaviour of a hunting wasp in providing food for its larvae

A Dig burrow in sandy soil

B Memorize location

C Seek and paralyse by sting, correct species of spider

D Navigate back to hole

E Put spider in

F Repeat C and D until six spiders fill hole

G Lay eggs on spiders

H Close burrow entrance

If at stage E spiders are removed by forceps, wasp continues to bring more spiders, eventually giving up and starting at A again, elsewhere

1 Forebrain

- **Olfactory lobes** (in front) – sense of smell.
- **Cerebrum** (upper part) – centre for memory, aesthetic and moral sense, hearing, vision, speech and muscular action other than in the gut and blood vessels.
- **Hypothalamus** (lower part) – receptors for control of internal environment (homeostasis), e.g. temperature, water content of blood. An outgrowth of it is the **pituitary** (the 'master' endocrine gland, see Unit 12.10).

2 Midbrain

Optic lobes (upper part) – simple auditory and visual (pupil) reflexes.

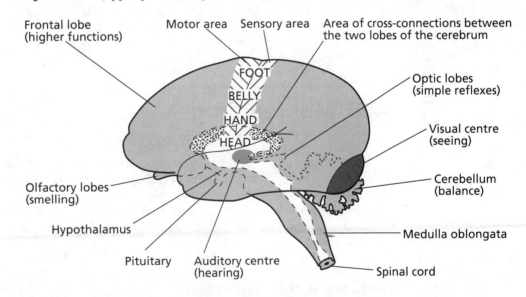

Fig. 12.6
Functional areas of the human brain. (Forebrain shown overlying midbrain and hindbrain in section)

3 Hindbrain

- **Cerebellum** (large upper outgrowth) – balance, coordination of muscle action.
- **Medulla oblongata** (brainstem, merging with spinal cord behind) – control of many vital 'automatic' actions, e.g. breathing, heart rate, constriction of arteries to direct blood to specific regions of the body, etc.

Summary of brain functions: receives all sensory information and 'processes' it (Fig. 12.7) either:

(*a*) immediately – reflex action (as in spinal cord), or

(*b*) more slowly – *storing* it as 'memory'
- using past memory to compare with the new, and *calculating*
- *coordinating* memories from other brain centres
- reaching a *'decision'*
- passing out *'orders'* via neurones and also hormones (from the pituitary).

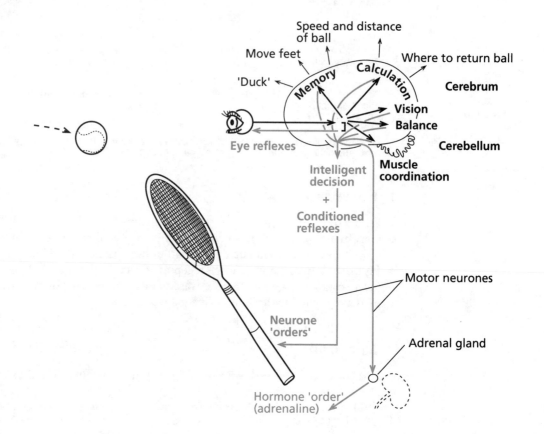

Fig. 12.7
Coordinating role of the brain in returning a tennis ball

12.8 Misused drugs

Certain substances used by Man affect the nervous system and particularly the brain. These include alcohol, tobacco, misused medicines, e.g. heroin, and a wide range of plant products of no medicinal value, e.g. LSD, marijuana. Their use is frequently commonplace in one country and forbidden or illegal in another. For example, Britain uses alcohol extensively but forbids marijuana smoking; the exact opposite applies in some Middle Eastern Muslim countries.

Features of the 'drug scene'

- All 'drugs' *affect the mind*, distorting judgement or sensations – which is their attraction. They probably affect the way neurones transmit impulses at synapses (see Fig. 12.3).
- They may cause *dependence*, i.e. addiction, if used regularly:
  (*a*) *psychological* dependence – addict *thinks* he needs the drug but the habit can be broken with no ill effects.
  (*b*) *physical* dependence – addict *needs* the drug. Breaking the habit results in illness (withdrawal symptoms), often severe.

- Regular drug use results in *tolerance*: the body needs ever greater amounts to achieve the same effect. This becomes very expensive and addicts may resort to crime to obtain money.
- *Addiction* imprisons the mind. Taking the drug becomes an obsession in the worst cases, excluding any possibility of a useful life.
- *Embryos* of pregnant drug users are forced to share the drugs of their mothers through the placenta.
- Injecting drugs directly into veins carries the risk of AIDS and hepatitis when syringes are shared.

Motives for drug taking

- *Social pressure*, particularly at parties: 'I don't want to be called chicken'. 'Friends', not drug pushers, are your worst enemy.
- *Being daring:* 'I'm not afraid of these so-called dangerous things', and 'I will not get hooked'. With all the evidence around you, why test your courage in *this* way?
- *Escape:* 'I want to forget my problems'. The problems are still there when you recover – drugs do not solve them. Talk about problems with friends; then take positive action to solve them, if necessary with help.
- *Creativity:* 'Some poets and writers were addicts and did their best work under the influence'. For every famous drug-taker there are many thousands who are failures.

12.9 Alcohol – ethanol

Alcohol is a **sedative** (sleep-making) drug, *not* a stimulant.
Benefit: taken in moderation it reduces shyness, improving social contact; relieves stress.
Harm: excessive intake can lead to abusiveness, violence, illness and even death. Regular excessive intake (alcoholism) is an addiction, causing long-term health and social problems.

Table 12.2 Units of alcohol

Drink	Single whisky, gin	Glass of sherry, port	Glass of wine	Half pint beer	Gives approx. 15 mg alcohol per 100 cm³ blood if drunk all at once
Alcohol content	40%	20% (approximate values)	8–12%	5%	

Maximum healthy drinking at one session (*not* regularly): men, 8 units; women, 6 units. For people of small body size these figures should be reduced. Recommended limits per week: men 21 units; women 14 units.

❶ Effects on behaviour

Table 12.3 Alcohol and its short-term effects

Units drunk	Blood level mg/100 cm³	General effect	Effect on driving
2	30	Less cautious	Greater chance of accident
3	45	Judgement worse	Reaction time slower, e.g. braking
5	75–80	Not in full control	UK legal limit is 80 mg per 100 cm³ blood If exceeded (breathalyser test) loss of licence for 1 year, minimum
10	150	Slurred speech Loss of self-control	Very dangerous driver
13	200	Double vision Loss of muscle coordination	Incapable
26	400	Unconsciousness Vomit may be inhaled causing death	–

The effects of a drinking session may last more than a day: headache (hangover), lack of alertness, greater chance of accident at work. A healthy liver breaks down alcohol, reducing the level in the blood by about 10 mg/100 cm^3 per hour.

② Effects on health of an alcoholic (long-term)

(a) *Liver cirrhosis:* liver shrinking due to death of cells poisoned by alcohol. Liver functions become less efficient (see Unit 6.10).
(b) *Brain damage:* fewer neurones live; cavities in brain enlarge. This is irreversible.
(c) *Heart disease:* pumping action weaker owing to lack of vitamin B$_1$, through a neglected diet.
(d) *Babies* born to alcoholic mothers are smaller, less intelligent and disfigured (Foetal Alcoholic Syndrome, FAS) in most cases. Miscarriage is also more likely.

③ Social effects

Excessive *spending* on alcohol means little to spend on food and clothes for the family.
Effects of *violence* may have consequences beyond losing friends, e.g. hospitalization, prison, divorce.
Poor work performance may lead to loss of job.

Alcohol is said to be 'the most expensive drug on the market'.
In the UK (1992), 9% of men (1.8 million) and 4% of women (0.8 million) are 'problem drinkers' (shaking hands, early morning drinking and psychological problems).
More than half the drivers involved in drunken driving accidents are under 20 years old; about 70% of all road deaths at night involve alcohol.
One in five pedestrians fatally injured on the road had excess alcohol in their blood.

12.10 Endocrine system

A variety of endocrine (ductless) glands discharge their products, hormones, in minute quantities directly into the blood. The pituitary is the 'master gland' controlling the rest (Fig. 12.8).

Hormones are organic compounds (secreted by endocrine glands in minute quantities into the blood) which affect certain specific body parts or processes. These 'messages':
(a) arrive at the speed blood travels;
(b) have long-lasting effects (hours, days);
(c) control factors in the internal environment needing constant adjustment, e.g. blood sugar level; or processes needing integrated control over a long period, e.g. growth or sexual development.

Glands and their hormones

① Pituitary

(a) **Tropic hormones:** stimulate other endocrine glands, e.g. TSH (thyroid-stimulating hormone).
(b) **Growth hormone:** promotes growth of muscle, bone (protein synthesis). Deficiency results in a dwarf; excess – a giant.
(c) **Antidiuretic hormone** (ADH or vasopressin): water conservation in kidney. Deficiency causes *water diabetes* (see Unit 10.5).
(d) Secretes many other hormones, including *oxytocin* (ensures contraction of uterus during birth and milk ejection during suckling) and *prolactin* (milk synthesis).

② Thyroid

Thyroxine: affects energy release at mitochondria (see Unit 1.2) in all cells, raising metabolic rate. Deficiency causes sluggishness, puffy skin; excess produces over-active person with 'pop-eyes'. Deficiency, in baby, causes *cretinism* – mental and physical retardation (see also Down's syndrome, Unit 20.9) – and in adults, *goitre* (swelling of the thyroid gland).

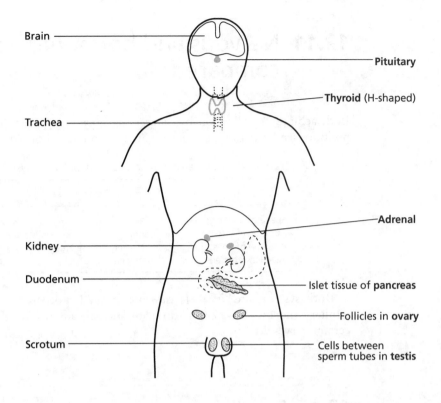

Fig. 12.8 The endocrine system in humans

Labels: Brain, Trachea, Kidney, Duodenum, Scrotum, Pituitary, Thyroid (H-shaped), Adrenal, Islet tissue of **pancreas**, Follicles in **ovary**, Cells between sperm tubes in **testis**

③ **Islet tissue of the pancreas**

Insulin: causes absorption of glucose from blood into cells, e.g. by liver and muscles to store it as *glycogen*. Deficiency causes sugar diabetes (diabetes mellitus – see Unit 10.5).

Glucagon: causes release of glucose into the blood by breakdown of glycogen (opposite to effect of insulin).

④ **Adrenals**

Adrenaline (the 'fight or flight hormone'): raises blood glucose level (from glycogen breakdown in liver), increases heart and breathing rates, diverts blood from guts to limb muscles. Nerves (not hormones) stimulate the adrenal, so adrenaline secretion is rapid.
　For control of blood glucose level see Unit 6.10.

⑤ **Ovaries and testes**

Produce **sex hormones,** e.g. oestrogen and testosterone respectively, which promote changes in body proportions, development of gametes and hair, and changes in behaviour and voice, at *puberty* (Fig. 12.9). (For oestrous cycle, see Unit 15.3.)

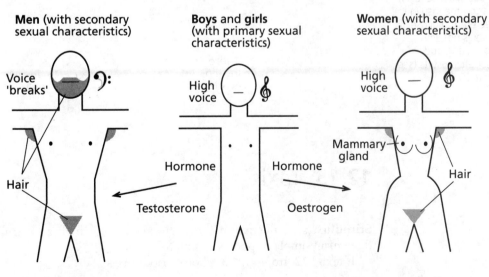

Men (with secondary sexual characteristics) — Voice 'breaks', Hair, Sperm production

Boys and **girls** (with primary sexual characteristics) — High voice, Hormone, Testosterone

Women (with secondary sexual characteristics) — High voice, Mammary gland, Hair, Ova production, Hormone, Oestrogen

Fig. 12.9 Changes at puberty in humans

12.11 Nervous and hormonal systems compared

Both achieve coordination by *antagonistic action,* e.g. biceps/triceps control of forearm position (see Unit 13.9), and insulin/glucagon control of blood sugar (see Unit 6.10).

Table 12.4 Comparison of nervous and endocrine systems

	Nervous system	Endocrine system
Speed of 'message'	Fast	Slow
Duration of effect	Short	Long
Precision of 'message'	To a very precise area	A more general effect
Reaction required	Immediate	Long-term

Both systems are *linked to each other,* e.g. hypothalamus (nervous) stimulates the pituitary (hormonal); nerves stimulate adrenal; adrenaline stimulates the heart, just as certain nerves do.

12.12 Feedback

Feedback is the means by which a hormone adjusts its own output by affecting the endocrine glands that cause its secretion. Very important in menstrual cycle (see Unit 15.3). If faulty, can cause metabolic disease, e.g. diabetes (Fig. 12.10).

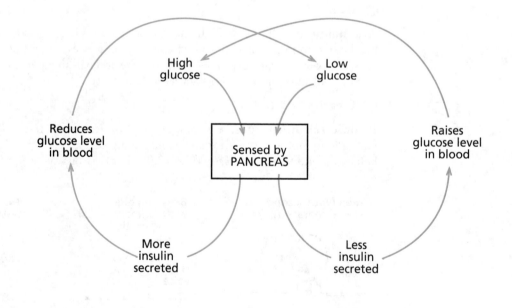

Fig. 12.10 How feedback controls blood glucose level; if too little insulin is secreted, glucose level is not self-correcting and diabetes results (see Unit 10.5)

12.13 Taxis

Stimulus: an influence in the environment to which an organism reacts. There are three main simple responses to simple stimuli:
1 taxis, 2 tropism, 3 photoperiodism.

Taxis: movement of an organism bodily towards or away from a stimulus. Applies to many invertebrate animals, unicells and even sperm. For examples see Table 12.5.

Table 12.5 Examples of taxis

Stimulus (and response prefix)	Responses	
	Positive (+ = towards stimulus)	*Negative* (– = away from stimulus)
Light (photo-)	Fly, having escaped swatting, flies towards window	Woodlouse seeks darkness
Water (hydro-)	Woodlouse seeks humid area	
Gravity (geo-)	Fly maggots burrow to pupate	
Chemicals (chemo-)	Blowflies are attracted to meat; so are pond flatworms (*Planaria*)	Earthworms rise from soil dosed with formalin
Contact (thigmo-)	Woodlice huddle together	

Thus woodlice can be described as negatively phototaxic and positively hydrotaxic.

12.14 Tropisms

Tropism: the growth-movement of a plant towards or away from a stimulus. Usually controlled by hormones. For examples see Table 12.6.

Table 12.6 Examples of tropisms

Stimulus	Main shoot response	Main root response	Notes
Light	+ Phototropic	Neutral usually	(Lateral roots and shoots do not behave in this way)
Gravity	– Geotropic	+ Geotropic	

Key: + = positively   – = negatively

Phototropism: the growth of plant organs towards or away from light. By growing towards light (positive phototropism), plant shoots get the sunlight they need for photosynthesis.

Mechanism: auxin (hormone) is made at shoot tips (which are sensitive). It diffuses back to region of cell elongation (Fig. 12.11) and here it affects the rate at which cells swell by osmosis (vacuolate). Under normal conditions, equal distribution of auxin gives even growth. With a one-sided stimulus, distribution becomes unequal giving unequal growth.

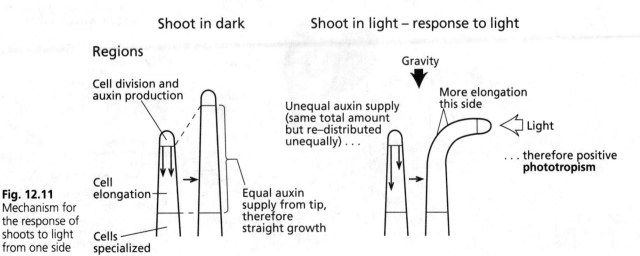

Fig. 12.11 Mechanism for the response of shoots to light from one side

Experiment to discover the region of sensitivity to light from one side in oat coleoptiles, and their response

Using *many* coleoptiles, grown in the dark, shields of three kinds are applied (Fig. 12.12). The seedlings are now given light from one side (only one seedling of each type shown):

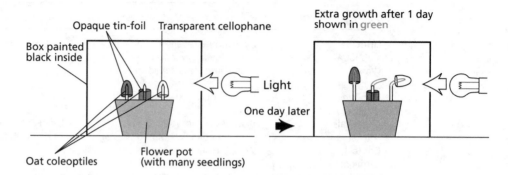

Fig. 12.12 The response of oat coleoptiles to light from one side

It may be concluded that (*a*) the coleoptile tip is sensitive to light;
(*b*) the response is positively phototropic.

12.15 Geotropism

Geotropism: the growth of plant organs towards or away from gravity. By growing downwards (positive geotropism) plant roots usually find the water they need. Plant shoots grow upwards (negative geotropism), so finding light.

Mechanism: auxin diffuses back from the tip unequally. In the root the greater concentration on the lower side *inhibits* growth there and the root grows faster on the upper side. In the shoot the greater concentration of auxin *stimulates* growth (as it does in phototropism) (Fig. 12.13).

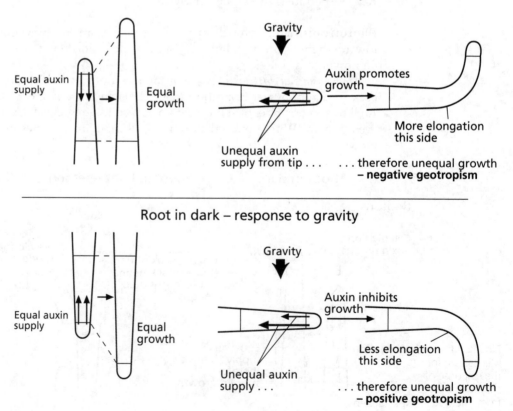

Fig. 12.13 Geotropism in roots and shoots

Experiment to test the response to gravity of bean roots
Five beans are pinned to each of two klinostats (one only shown).

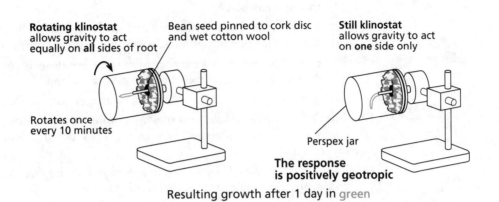

Rotating klinostat allows gravity to act equally on **all** sides of root

Bean seed pinned to cork disc and wet cotton wool

Still klinostat allows gravity to act on **one** side only

Rotates once every 10 minutes

Perspex jar

The response is positively geotropic

Resulting growth after 1 day in green

Fig. 12.14 The response of bean roots to gravity from one side

12.16 Photoperiodism

Photoperiodism: an organism's response to *length of day* (or night) by initiating an important event in the life cycle. This event (e.g. migration of birds, emergence of some insects from pupae, or flowering in most flowering plants) is usually linked with reproduction, ensuring that this occurs in the right season.

Flowering plants

Length of night is 'measured' by the leaves, within which is a blue pigment, *phytochrome*, which reacts differently to day and night. This acts as the 'clock' to start synthesis of a flowering hormone (florigen). Florigen starts flower formation.

Mammals

Many *mammals* have a breeding season, e.g. deer, lions (but not Man). Day length probably influences the pituitary gland via the eyes and brain. The pituitary secretes hormones influencing the testes and ovaries to grow and produce gametes. After breeding, the testes and ovaries become small again.

Daily rhythm probably sets Man's biological clock – which can require re-setting, e.g. after long journeys by jet, to new rhythms of day and night (jet-lag).

Summary

1 Information from sensors is carried to where an organism can respond to it either by chemicals (hormones) or by nerve cells (neurones).

2 Neurones pass electrical messages to other neurones across gaps called synapses, by means of chemicals which 'connect' them for milliseconds.

3 Sensory nerves carry messages from sensors to the central nervous system (which consists of spinal cord and brain).

4 Motor nerves carry messages from the central nervous system to where action can be taken – either at a muscle or a gland.

5 A simple automatic reaction to a stimulus is called a reflex action and uses a maximum of five cells called a reflex arc.

6 Any conscious action involves use of the brain where learning and coordination of information takes place.

7 'Drugs', including heroin, nicotine and alcohol, all affect brain function and can have serious effects, both immediately and in the long-term (through addiction).

8 The endocrine system is a number of ductless glands secreting hormone messages into the blood and is controlled by the pituitary gland.

9 The nervous system is designed to send messages very quickly to precise locations.

10 The endocrine system delivers messages more slowly to more general areas and controls long-term processes like growth, sexual development and control of blood sugar levels.

11 Hormones adjust their own level of secretion by their effects on the gland producing them – a process called feedback.

12 Invertebrates respond to simple stimuli by *moving* towards or away from them. This response is called a taxis.

13 Plants respond to simple stimuli by *growing* towards or away from them. This response is called a tropism.

14 Both plants and animals may respond to light intensity or light period (changes in day or season). Such responses are called photoperiodic.

Chapter 13
Support and locomotion

13.1 Principles of support

The mass of an organism is supported by its environment (water, land or air).

Plants transmit their weight to it via *cell walls* and animals via their *skeletons* (they have no cell walls). Since most animals move, their skeletons are used both for *support and locomotion*.

The environment provides support by a '*buoyancy*' effect too (Table 13.1).

Table 13.1

Water	Land and air
Great support: organism is made lighter by the mass of water it displaces	Very *little support* from air since volume of air displaced has small mass
Therefore plants and animals only need relatively *weak 'skeletons'*	Therefore *strong 'skeletons'* needed, particularly if organisms are large

13.2 Support in plants

Flowering plants use cell walls to support their weight. Cellulose walls are weak, woody ones strong.

1. **Small plants** (herbaceous), e.g. grasses, use osmosis to inflate vacuoles with water (see Unit 7.4). The vacuoles press outwards on the cytoplasm, causing the cells to inflate (become turgid). This stiffens cell walls. The combined effect of many such turgid cells causes stems to stiffen (the experiment in Fig. 7.5 demonstrates this).

    Woody cells play a small part in support.

2. **Larger plants** (shrubs, trees) use woody cells to provide most of their support. These cells are fibres and xylem vessels (see Unit 7.9). Both kinds of cell are dead, so osmosis plays no part in their support.

3. **Water plants,** e.g. Canadian pondweed, are largely supported by the water outside them. There is little xylem so stems are weak.

13.3 Support and locomotion in animals

The skeleton is used (a) for support, (b) for locomotion – where *shape* of the body and limbs is important (Fig. 13.1).

Water	Land	Air
(a) *Weak skeleton* (sharks manage on cartilage) and massive animals (e.g. whales and giant squids) are possible	*Strong skeleton* essential because full weight of body acts through the small areas where limbs are attached to body. Also prevents internal organs crushing each other as they sag downwards	
(b) *Streamlining* and *buoyancy* important in saving energy when moving through water (dense medium) (See Unit 21.16)	*Foot design* important for efficient movement on, e.g. sand (camel), rock (mountain goat), trees (leopard)	*Streamlining* and *wing design* important for sufficient lift and speed (see Unit 21.18)

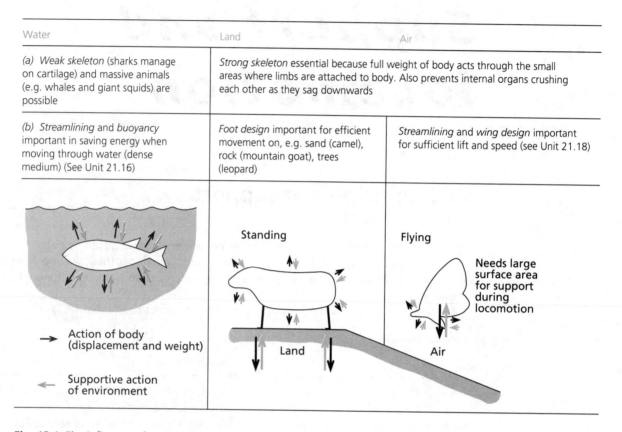

Fig. 13.1 The influence of environment on skeleton design

13.4 Principles of movement

- **Muscle** can only *contract* (pull) – cannot push. To be lengthened again it must *(a)* relax, *(b)* be pulled back into shape by another muscle, its antagonist, e.g. biceps and triceps (see Fig. 13.8). Thus muscles work in *antagonistic pairs*.
- **Nerve impulses** are essential to make muscles *contract* (except heart). The antagonistic muscles are kept *relaxed* by impulses too (reflex inhibition).
- **Skeleton** transmits the contraction force of muscle to the environment, e.g. water, land or air, during swimming, walking and flying.
- **Load-bearing surface** in contact with the environment must get purchase on it if locomotion is to result, e.g. fish tail on water, bird wing on air, hooves on ground or claws on trees.

13.5 Mammal tissues for support and locomotion

The skeleton is mainly bone. Bone is covered at joints by cartilage. Ligaments connect bones to bones. Tendons connect muscles to bones. Each tissue has its own special properties:

1. **Bone** is both hard and flexible to some extent. *Bone cells,* arranged in cylindrical layers, secrete the mineral calcium phosphate to give hardness. Cylinders are strong. Bone cells are attached to a network of fibres which give flexibility (Fig. 13.2).

   Soak a small long-bone in 3% hydrochloric acid for three days. It comes out rubbery – the minerals have been dissolved.

   Heat a bone in a Bunsen burner flame. It becomes brittle and breaks easily – the fibres have burnt away.

2. **Cartilage** is a rubbery protein secreted by cells. It cushions the ends of bones at joints (shock absorber and smooth surface) (Fig. 13.2).

3. **Connective tissue** is of two kinds:

   (a) **Ligaments** are elastic fibres allowing 'give' at joints and between vertebrae.
   (b) **Tendons** are inelastic fibres. They ensure that muscles pull bones immediately, without having to take up 'slack'.

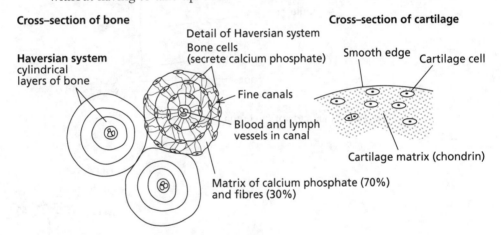

Fig. 13.2
Structure of bone and cartilage

4. **Muscle:** cells containing protein that contracts.

   (a) **Involuntary muscle,** e.g. in gut, causing peristalsis (Fig. 6.9); in iris, affecting pupil size; and arteries, affecting blood flow (Table 8.2). None are controlled by will-power.
   (b) **Voluntary muscle,** e.g. in arm. Controlled by decision.

13.6 Mammal skeleton

Skull: cranium protects brain; houses all major sense organs; jaws for chewing.
Vertebral column: protects nerve cord; acts as anchorage for four limbs via limb girdles and for ribs. Also a flexible, segmented rod from which internal organs are slung.

Typical vertebra (see Fig. 13.4) has:
(a) **neural spine** and *lateral processes* for ligament and muscle attachment;
(b) **centrum** which supports weight (aided by 'discs') and makes red blood cells (in its red bone marrow);
(c) **neural canal** which houses and protects nerve cord (nerves exit via two adjacent notches).

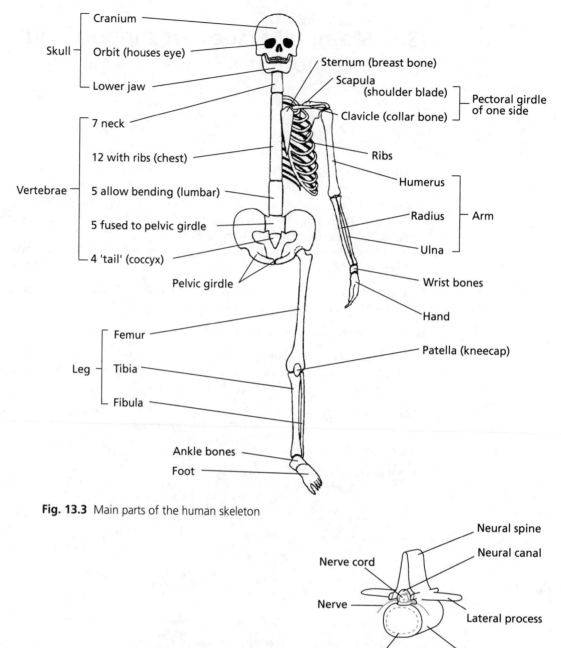

Fig. 13.3 Main parts of the human skeleton

Fig. 13.4 A generalized vertebra (with nearby structures shown in green)

Discs are shock absorbers between vertebrae. Their tough fibrous coat of connective tissue encloses a pulpy centre. A 'slipped disc' occurs when excessive pressure causes the disc to *bulge*, pressing on a nerve and causing pain. Most often lifting heavy objects with a bent back causes disc damage – particularly in the lumbar region (small of the back) – see Fig. 13.3

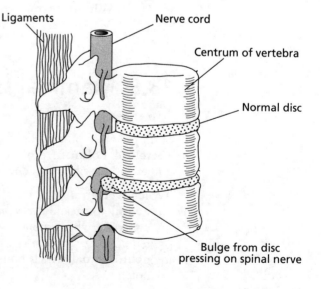

Fig. 13.5 Normal and 'slipped' intervertebral discs

13.7 Limbs and limb girdles of Man

- Arm is attached loosely to the vertebral column by the **pectoral girdle**: *scapula* has muscles to attach it to chest vertebrae; *clavicle* is linked to vertebrae via sternum and ribs (see Fig. 13.3).
- Leg is attached to the **pelvic girdle**. This strong hoop of bone is fused firmly to 5 vertebrae.
- **Limbs:** built on exactly the same plan (Fig. 13.6) – one upper bone, two lower, and same number of bones in wrist and hand as in ankle and foot.

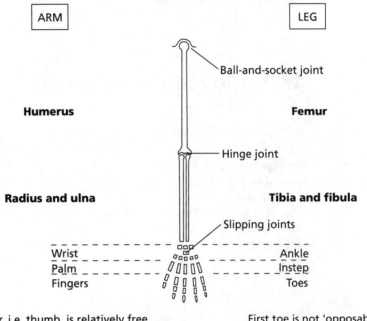

Fig. 13.6 Comparison of bones and joints of human arm and leg

13.8 Joints

Joints are where bones are linked (Fig. 13.7).
Immovable joints (sutures): wavy interlocking edges of bone, held together by connective tissue, e.g. bones of cranium.

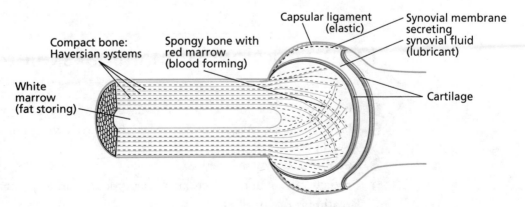

Fig. 13.7 Section through mammal synovial joint and bone

Movable joints (synovial joints): bones have cartilage ends; these move on each other, lubricated by synovial fluid secreted by a synovial membrane within a joint capsule.

Types:
- *Ball-and-socket*, e.g. at shoulder, hip – rotation in *two* planes of space (see Fig. 13.6).
- *Hinge*, e.g. at elbow (see Fig. 13.8) and knee – movement in *one* plane only (like a door).
- *Slipping*, e.g. at wrist and ankle – limited rocking movement.

Arthritis: damaged and painful joints which swell.
(a) *Rheumatoid arthritis* is usually a hereditary disease. Connective tissue grows across the joint making it immovable.
(b) *Osteoarthritis* results from breakdown of cartilage through excessive wear and tear, damage and old age. Joints no longer move smoothly.

Artificial joints of titanium alloys (metal) and nylon may be inserted surgically to replace arthritic joints.

13.9 Movement of an arm

Bending: nerve impulses make the biceps contract, so raising the forearm. Other nerve impulses travelling to the triceps *inhibit* its contraction, so it is extended by the biceps through leverage.
Extending: nerve impulses cause contraction of the triceps. This extends the biceps, and the arm moves down.
The biceps and triceps muscles are *antagonists*. Nerve impulses stimulate one muscle while other impulses inhibit the other muscle when movement occurs.

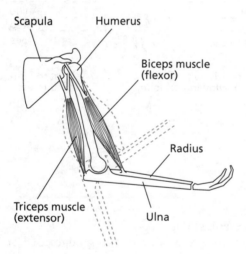

Fig. 13.8 Movement of the forearm in Man (hinge joint)

13.10 Functions of mammal skeletons

1. **Support:** of body off ground; of internal organs, preventing crushing.
2. **Shape:** important adaptations, e.g. Man's hand, bat's wing, porpoise's streamline and flippers.
3. **Locomotion:** system of levers.
4. **Protection:** cranium protects brain; ribs protect heart and lungs.
5. **Breathing:** role of ribs (see Unit 9.8).
6. **Making blood cells:** in red bone marrow, e.g. of ribs, vertebrae (and see Fig. 13.7).
7. **Sound conduction:** three ossicles in middle ear (see Unit 11.4).

13.11 Sports injuries

These may result from
1 lack of training – body not prepared for strains, e.g. pulled muscles;
2 sudden excessive stress, e.g. fractured bones, knee joint damage;
3 over-use – injuries never given time to heal properly;
4 self-inflicted causes.

① Lack of training

(a) *Stamina lacking:* The body is most vulnerable when tired. Most rugby injuries occur early in the season and in the last quarter hour of matches.

(b) *Strength lacking: both* antagonistic muscles must be built up and on both sides of the body to avoid self-injury.

(c) *Flexibility lacking:* 'warming up' must include stretching, to prepare tendons and ligaments for stress. Vital in sprinters.

(d) *Skill lacking:* poor positioning and timing can result in collision or other sudden stress.

② Sudden stress

(a) *Fractures:* bones may be cracked or broken across. The bone must be immobilized, e.g. by splints, in the right position by experts. This allows:
  (i) broken ends to be joined by connective tissue fibres;
  (ii) bone cells to attach to fibres and secrete bone minerals;
  (iii) reabsorption of any extra bone over some months.

(b) *Dislocation:* a bone displaced from its joint, straining or tearing ligaments. Best treated immediately by an expert, pulling the bone into its rightful place.

(c) *Knee joint injury,* e.g. in football or squash (Fig. 13.9). A damaged joint may swell with the extra fluid secreted into the synovial space (see also Section 13.8, arthritis). This may have to be drained by syringe, but natural reabsorption and repair takes a few days.

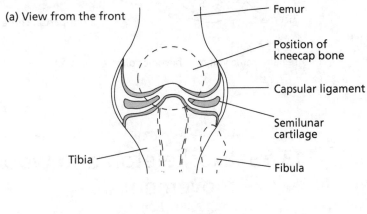

Fig. 13.9 Diagram of a knee joint (severe twisting of this hinge joint may lead to splitting of the semilunar cartilages – which then have to be removed surgically)

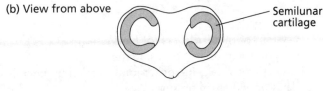

③ Over use

Damage due to severe competition must be given time to heal *fully.* Rest is needed to avoid 'staleness' and a drop in performance that may lead to obvious injury.

④ Self-inflicted causes

(a) Contact sports, e.g. rugby, need organization on a weight basis (and not age basis) at junior level.

(b) Anabolic steroids, while improving performance by building up muscles, have serious consequences. These include increases in atherosclerosis (see Unit 9.11) and blood pressure, damage to the liver and male sterility – when used long-term.

13.12 Hydraulic skeleton and earthworm movement

The earthworm is adapted to moving in *tunnels* and spaces in the soil (mucus lubricates) (see Fig. 13.10). Solid skeleton is a disadvantage for this. Watery 'skeleton' within a segmented body cavity (coelom) is incompressible, but can be forced hydraulically into different shapes by muscle action:

(a) when **circular muscles** contract, coelomic fluid is forced into long thin shape which *extends* the segments, and relaxes the longitudinal muscles.

(b) when **longitudinal muscles** contract, fluid is forced into short fat shape which *shortens* segments, and relaxes the circular muscles. Purchase on soil is obtained by pushing out pegs (**chaetae** – eight per segment) where segments are short and fat.

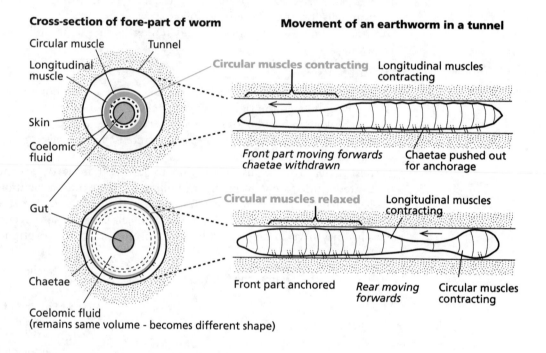

Fig. 13.10
Movement of an earthworm in a tunnel

13.13 Exoskeleton and woodlouse movement

Walking (Fig. 13.11)
A system of tubular levers (of hard chitin).
Antagonistic muscles are inside these tubes.
Levers pivot at peg-in-socket joints, sealed by flexible chitin.
Claws provide grip on surfaces.

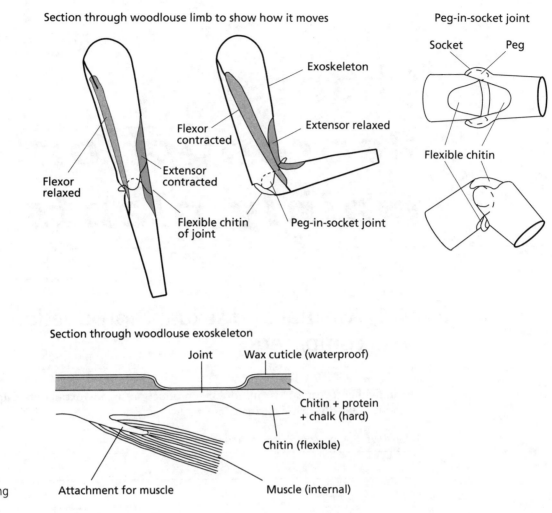

Section through woodlouse limb to show how it moves

Peg-in-socket joint

Socket   Peg

Exoskeleton

Flexor contracted

Extensor relaxed

Flexor relaxed

Extensor contracted

Flexible chitin

Flexible chitin of joint

Peg-in-socket joint

Section through woodlouse exoskeleton

Joint   Wax cuticle (waterproof)

Chitin + protein + chalk (hard)

Chitin (flexible)

Fig. 13.11
Woodlouse exoskeleton showing parts used for walking

Attachment for muscle

Muscle (internal)

Summary

1 Aquatic organisms are supported well by water and only need weak 'skeletons'.

2 Air and land provide little support, so strong 'skeletons' are needed to prevent the organism collapsing into a heap of cells.

3 The 'skeleton' of a plant is provided by cell walls, turgor pressure and lignin (wood) in the xylem.

4 The skeleton of mammals is made of bone and cartilage connected together by ligaments.

5 Muscles are connected to bones by tendons.

6 Muscles are only able to contract (shorten) and so are always found in antagonistic pairs. One muscle bends the limb and the other extends it.

7 Bones move upon one another at lubricated and cushioned ends called synovial joints.

8 The functions of mammalian skeletons include support of organs, protection and movement.

9 Sports injuries occur when undue stress is applied to bone, cartilage, ligaments and tendons. Many can be prevented by proper training, precautions and sensible rules for each sport.

10 As an alternative to the endoskeleton of mammals, arthropods use an exoskeleton of chitin and earthworms a fluid skeleton (more appropriate to burrowing).

Chapter 14
Reproduction: mainly plants

14.1 Asexual and sexual reproduction compared

No individual organism is immortal; reproduction avoids extinction. Most organisms reproduce sexually, many asexually as well.

Table 14.1 Comparison of asexual and sexual reproduction

	Asexual	Sexual
Parents	One	Two (unless parent is hermaphrodite, i.e. both sexes in same individual, e.g. flower)
Method	Mitosis forms either: (a) reproductive bodies, e.g. spores, tubers, or (b) replicas of adult by outgrowth, e.g. runners	Meiosis forms gametes (sperm and ova) which fuse to form zygotes (at fertilization) Zygote grows by mitosis into new organism
Offspring	Genetically identical to parent	Not identical – half its genes are maternal (mother's), half paternal (father's)
Advantage	Maintains a good strain exactly	Produces new varieties which, if 'better', favour survival and in the long-term their evolution (see Unit 18.3)
Disadvantage	Species liable to be wiped out, e.g. by disease, if not resistant to it	Excellent individuals, e.g. prize milk cow, cannot give identical offspring
Other points	Only one arrival needed to colonize a new area Often more rapid than sexual methods Always increases population	Both sexes needed Not rapid Need not increase population (two parents may produce only one offspring, then die)
Occurrence	Very common among plants and protists, e.g. *Amoeba*	Almost all plants and animals

14.2 Asexual methods of reproduction

All the offspring from one asexually reproducing parent are known as a **clone** (a genetically identical population). This is because mitosis alone has produced them (see Units 1.4 and 17.12).

Examples:

① **Binary fission,** e.g. bacteria (see Unit 3.2), *Amoeba* (see Unit 3.11).

② **Spores,** e.g. fungi (see Unit 3.7), mosses (see Unit 21.2).

③ **Budding,** e.g. flukes reproducing inside snails (see Unit 21.15).

④ **Identical twinning,** e.g. in humans, a single zygote may develop into two babies.

⑤ **Vegetative propagation** by outgrowths of new plantlets usually from *stems* (Fig. 14.1) but sometimes from *leaves*, e.g. *Bryophyllum*. Many of these methods of asexual reproduction also achieve **perennation** (survival over winter in a dormant state).

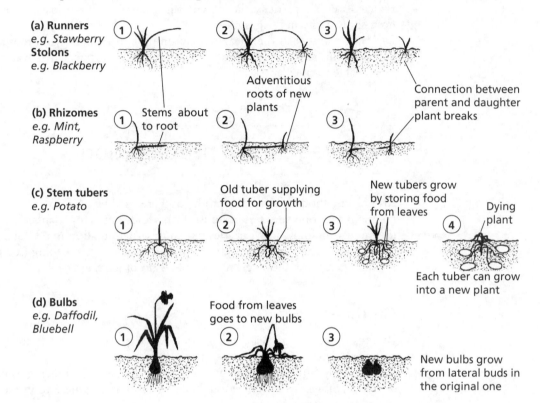

Fig. 14.1 Methods of asexual reproduction (and perennation) in flowering plants

Note: all the plants named also reproduce sexually (by flowers) at the end of the growing season.

Potato tuber: an underground *stem*-tip swollen with food (especially starch) received from the parent plant (which dies down in autumn). Each tuber is a potential new plant (thus *asexual reproduction*) and allows *perennation*. New shoots and adventitious roots arise from 'eyes' (Fig. 14.2) in spring.

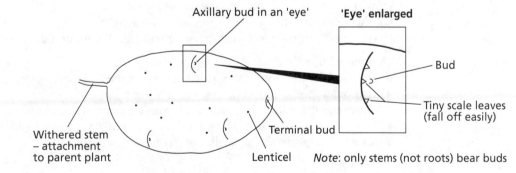

Fig. 14.2 A potato tuber

14.3 Surviving winter – perennation

Simple plants may survive as spores, e.g. fungi, mosses. Some survive below ground after the foliage dies down, e.g. ferns.

Flowering plants

(*a*) **Annuals,** e.g. poppies, complete their life cycle in one year, surviving as dormant seeds. Cold is often needed to break dormancy, i.e. to make germination possible next spring.

(*b*) **Biennials** Most root crops, e.g. carrots, live for two years. They survive underground at end of year 1, and use their stored food to flower and make seeds in year 2.

(*c*) **Perennials** live for a number of years, surviving both as seed and as vegetative structures (see Fig. 14.1).

Evergreens either partially die down, e.g. grasses, or have leaves that resist damage by frost, snow and wind, e.g. holly.

Deciduous plants shed their leaves in autumn. This reduces wind resistance and so avoids uprooting in gales. It also reduces transpiration at a time when water (frozen) may not be available to the plant.

14.4 Vegetative propagation

Artificial methods of asexual reproduction are used by Man to

(*a*) maintain good varieties of house-plants and some crop plants;

(*b*) rapidly multiply new varieties which arise by mutation (see Unit 17.15);

(*c*) rapidly multiply new varieties produced by selective breeding (see Unit 18.5);

(*d*) maintain seedless oranges and grapes – no other way possible.

Cuttings

Lengths of stem, e.g. *Pelargonium,* or a leaf, e.g. African violet, are made to grow into complete plants. This method requires:

(*a*) *sufficiently large piece:* enough food reserves to form the missing roots;

(*b*) *sand/peat mix for rooting:* enough air for respiration where roots are forming, enough water to supply needs;

(*c*) *removal of most leaves:* to reduce transpiration (plant would dry out);

(*d*) *rooting hormone:* applied to cut end, starts cells dividing to form roots.

Grafting

This is the insertion of a shoot or bud onto a related plant (Fig. 14.3a and b). The two grow into one plant which has the advantages of:

(*a*) the *vigour* of a specially chosen root – the **stock**;

(*b*) the *quality* of the product (flowers or fruit) on the grafted shoot – the **scion**.

Grafting requires:

- that cambia (see Unit 7.9) of stock and scion must meet (to grow together);
- firm binding at junction (to prevent joining tissue tearing);
- autumn grafting (to minimize death from excessive transpiration);
- waterproofing the cuts with tape or wax (minimizes infection and desiccation);
- compatible species (lemon will not graft onto an apple).

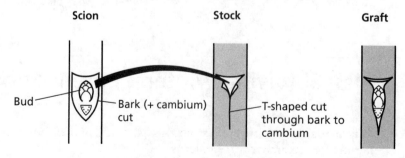

Fig. 14.3(a) Bud grafting

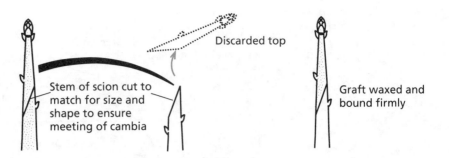

Fig. 14.3(b)
Stem grafting

Note: Neither stock nor scion are altered *genetically* by grafting. Thus in a garden rose 'Masquerade', large beautiful roses form on the scion, but only small wild briar roses can form on 'suckers' (stems) sprouting from the stock. The 'Masquerade' genes do not affect briar genes – or vice versa.

Grafting is used extensively in producing grapes, apples, pears, citrus fruit and roses. 'Family' apple trees have a number of different varieties of apple growing on the same trunk, from separate grafts.

Tissue culture

This is the growth of whole plants from small groups of cells using growth media and hormones.

Advantages: *very large numbers* of plants can be grown commercially from a single one in a short time – much faster than by cuttings.

Method:

1. Tissue, e.g. pith, is scraped out of the parent plant. It is spread on sterile agar containing nutrients (sucrose, mineral salts, vitamins) and auxin in a petri dish.

2. After some weeks each group of cells has divided into a formless mass of many thousands of similar cells – a **callus**.

3. The callus is now made to grow roots, stem and leaves by a special mix of hormones in agar containing nutrients.

4. The resulting small plants can be planted out (Fig. 14.4).

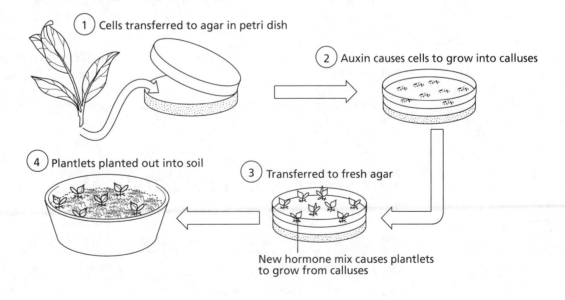

Fig. 14.4 Plant tissue culture to form a clone of new plants

14.5 Flowers

A flower is the organ of sexual reproduction in flowering plants (Fig. 14.5). It is usually bisexual (hermaphrodite) but sometimes unisexual, e.g. holly.

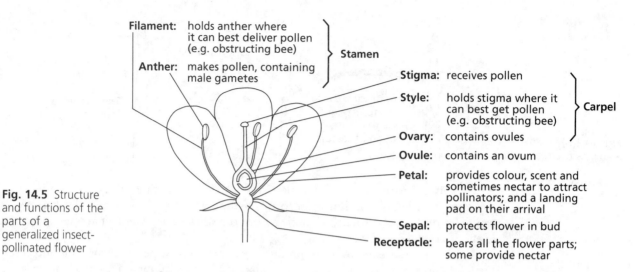

Filament: holds anther where it can best deliver pollen (e.g. obstructing bee)

Anther: makes pollen, containing male gametes

} **Stamen**

Stigma: receives pollen

Style: holds stigma where it can best get pollen (e.g. obstructing bee)

Ovary: contains ovules

} **Carpel**

Ovule: contains an ovum

Petal: provides colour, scent and sometimes nectar to attract pollinators; and a landing pad on their arrival

Sepal: protects flower in bud

Receptacle: bears all the flower parts; some provide nectar

Fig. 14.5 Structure and functions of the parts of a generalized insect-pollinated flower

A flower consists of an expanded stem-tip, the **receptacle,** on which is borne four rings of modified leaves:

(i)   *sepals* – almost leaf-like but protective
(ii) *petals* – often coloured and attractive
(iii) *stamens* – male parts
(iv) *carpels* – female parts

There are **two main stages in sexual reproduction:**

1 Pollination: transfer of pollen from stamens to stigmas.

2 Fertilization: fusion of male gamete with female gamete inside the ovule. This results from the growth of pollen tubes from the pollen on the stigmas to the ovules.

14.6 Self- and cross-pollination

Self-pollination: transfer of pollen from any stamen to any stigma on the *same plant* (not necessarily the same flower). Results in fewer varieties of offspring than cross-pollination. Frequent in cereal crops, grasses.

Cross-pollination: transfer of pollen of one plant to the stigmas of *another plant of the same species.* Thus rose pollen landing on an apple stigma will *not* germinate there. Results in a great variety of offspring. Since variety assists survival, many plants have means of improving the chances of cross-pollination (Fig. 14.6).

14.7 Wind and insect pollination

Table 14.2 Comparison of flowers adapted for wind or insect pollination

	Wind pollination	Insect pollination
1 Petals	**Not attractive:** usually green, unscented; no nectar **Small:** leaving stamens and carpels exposed	**Attractive:** coloured, scented, often with nectaries **Large:** protect stamens and carpels inside
2 Stamens	Long filaments and large mobile anthers **exposed to wind**	Stiff filaments and anthers **obstruct visiting insects**

Table 14.2 (continued)

	Wind pollination	Insect pollination
3 Pollen	**Large quantities** (enormous chances against it all reaching stigmas). Small, dry, light (easily wind-borne)	**Small quantities** (more certain 'delivery service'). Rougher, sometimes sticky (to catch on insect 'hairs')
4 Stigmas	**Large, exposed** to wind (to catch passing pollen)	**Small, unexposed,** sticky with stiff style (to obstruct insects)
Examples	Plantain, grasses, hazel, oak	Buttercup, deadnettle, horse-chestnut, cherry

Note: certain flowers, which appear to be suited for insect pollination, in fact use other methods. For example:

(*a*) *peas and French beans* **self-pollinate** when still in the bud stage;

(*b*) *dandelions* develop seed from ovules without fertilization, i.e. **asexually**.

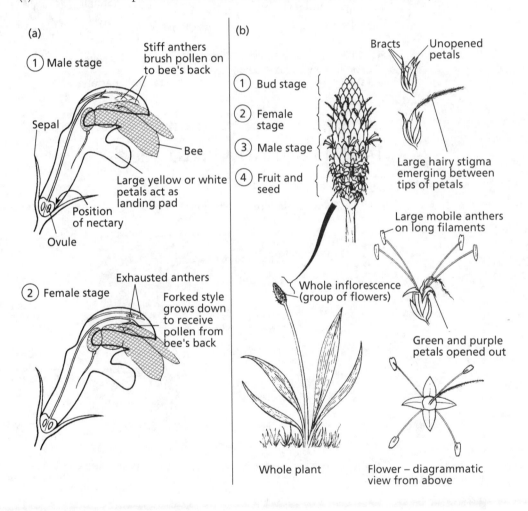

Fig. 14.6 (a) Features of an insect-pollinated flower illustrated by the deadnettle (seen in section) (b) Features of a wind-pollinated flower illustrated by the narrow-leaved plantain

14.8 Fertilization and its consequences

1. A pollen grain of the right kind on the stigma germinates to form a pollen tube (see Fig. 14.8).

2. The pollen tube grows down the style and ovary wall to the micropyle of the ovule.

③ A male nucleus passes from the pollen tube into the ovule to fuse with the ovum (fertilization):

male nucleus + ovum → zygote cell

④ The zygote divides by mitosis (see Unit 17.10) to form the **embryo**:

zygote → plumule (shoot), radicle (root) and cotyledons (seed leaves)

⑤ The integuments (thin wrappings around the ovule) grow and harden into the **testa** (seed coat), still with its micropyle.

Thus embryo + testa = **seed** (see Unit 16.4).

⑥ The ovary wall grows into the **fruit** – which contains seed(s).

⑦ Most of the other flower parts drop off, i.e. petals, stamens, stigma and style, and often sepals too.

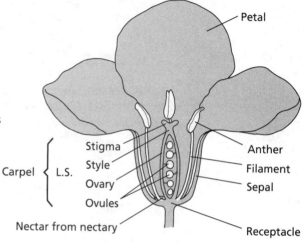

Fig. 14.7 Wallflower flower with a sectioned ovary and one petal, sepal and stamen removed

14.9 From flower to seed

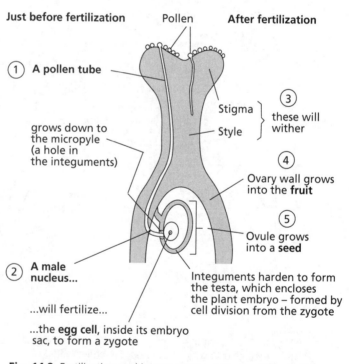

Fig. 14.8 Fertilization and its consequences in a wallflower flower

14.10 Fruits and seed dispersal

Fruits serve two main functions:

1 Protection of seed: particularly important when fruit is eaten by animals, e.g. in stone-fruits – peaches, cherries: inner part of fruit is hard.

2 Dispersal of seed (see Fig. 14.9).

(a) *Avoids overcrowding* (more likely with some methods of asexual reproduction, e.g. runners). Seedlings do not have to compete with parent for light, water and mineral salts.

(b) *Helps colonization* of new areas.

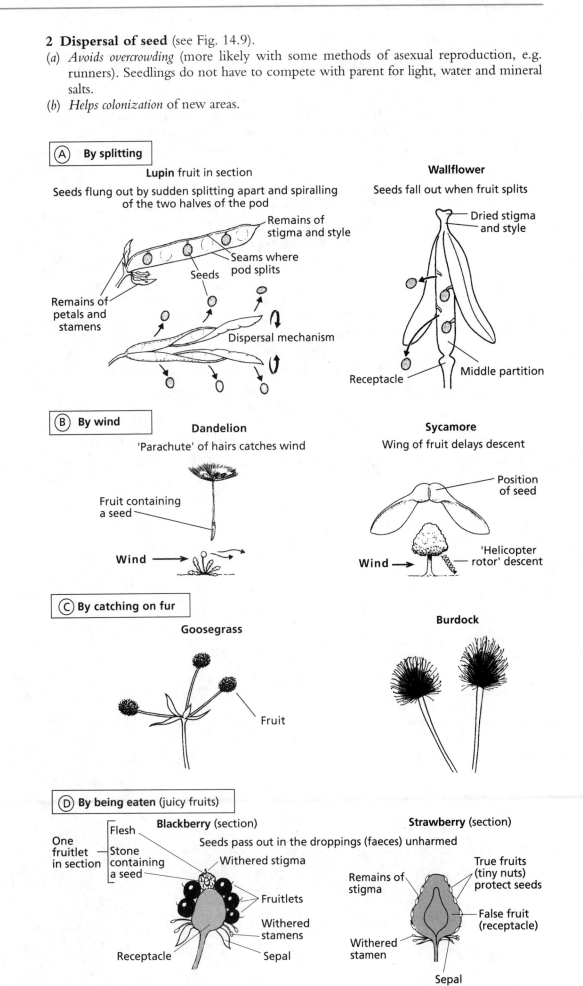

(A) By splitting

Lupin fruit in section

Seeds flung out by sudden splitting apart and spiralling of the two halves of the pod

- Remains of stigma and style
- Seams where pod splits
- Seeds
- Remains of petals and stamens
- Dispersal mechanism

Wallflower

Seeds fall out when fruit splits

- Dried stigma and style
- Receptacle
- Middle partition

(B) By wind

Dandelion

'Parachute' of hairs catches wind

- Fruit containing a seed
- Wind

Sycamore

Wing of fruit delays descent

- Position of seed
- Wind
- 'Helicopter rotor' descent

(C) By catching on fur

Goosegrass

- Fruit

Burdock

(D) By being eaten (juicy fruits)

Blackberry (section)

Seeds pass out in the droppings (faeces) unharmed

- One fruitlet in section
  - Flesh
  - Stone containing a seed
- Withered stigma
- Fruitlets
- Withered stamens
- Receptacle
- Sepal

Strawberry (section)

- Remains of stigma
- True fruits (tiny nuts) protect seeds
- False fruit (receptacle)
- Withered stamen
- Sepal

Fig. 14.9 Dispersal of seed by fruits

Summary

1   Asexual reproduction results from mitosis of a single organism's cells and produces identical offspring – a clone.

2   Sexual reproduction results from the meeting of a male and a female gamete at fertilization to form a zygote, which then grows into an offspring.

3   Offspring from sexual reproduction are always different.

4   Many plants reproduce naturally by asexual reproduction, e.g. from strawberry runners and potato tubers.

5   Man artificially reproduces plants by cutting, grafting and tissue culture.

6   Flowers are organs of sexual reproduction and usually produce both male pollen and female ovaries.

7   Pollination (pollen reaching the stigma) precedes fertilization (a male gamete inside the pollen tube fusing with an ovum).

8   Wind pollination is chancy owing to variable wind direction, but copious pollen and feathery stigmas make up for this.

9   Insect pollination is more certain and scented flowers with coloured petals and a nectar reward attract insects to the task.

10   Fertilization results in the formation of fruit (from the ovary) and seed (from the ovule).

11   Seeds are dispersed away from the parent plant by the fruit.

12   Fruits catapult seeds out or catch the wind or use animals to carry the seeds away.

Chapter 15
Reproduction: humans

15.1 Sexual reproduction in humans

The sexual organs of man and woman are shown in Fig. 15.1.

Sequence of events in human sexual reproduction

1. Development of secondary sexual characteristics at **puberty** (12–14 years old) making reproduction possible (see Fig. 12.9).

2. **Gamete production** (Table 15.1).

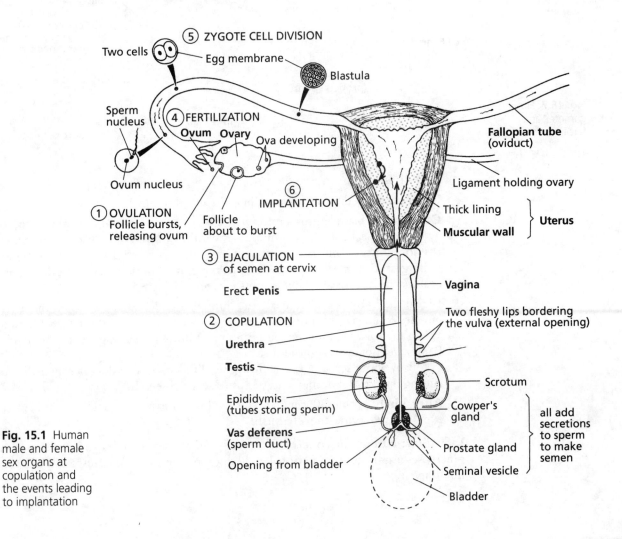

Fig. 15.1 Human male and female sex organs at copulation and the events leading to implantation

Table 15.1 Comparison of gamete production in humans

	Male	Female
Gonads	Two **testes**, kept outside the body in a sac (scrotum), produce sperm	Two **ovaries**, kept within the body cavity attached to a ligament, produce ova
Gametes	Many millions of **sperm** formed continuously throughout life after puberty (see Fig. 15.2)	Many thousands of potential **ova** formed before birth, but only about 400 will be shed between *puberty* and *menopause* (about 45 years old: end of reproductive life)
Gamete release	About **200 million** sperm are ejaculated into female by *reflex action* of the penis during copulation. They pass along sperm duct and urethra, picking up nutritive secretions from glands to form *semen*	Usually only **one** ovum is shed *automatically* per month (Unit 15.3) from an ovary. It passes into the oviduct (Fallopian tube), the only place where it can be fertilized. Once in the uterus, the ovum is lost

③ **Copulation:** the erect penis transfers sperm during ejaculation from the testes of the male to the end of the vagina (cervix) of the female.

④ **Fertilization:** any sperm that manages to swim into an oviduct containing an ovum has a chance of fertilizing it. Only one sperm enters the ovum and the two nuclei fuse, forming the zygote cell.

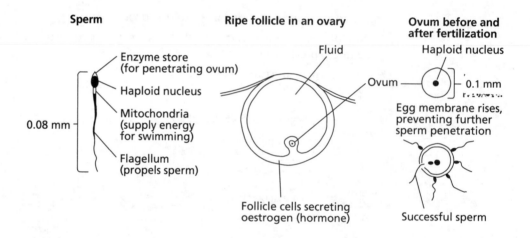

Fig. 15.2 Human gametes and fertilization

⑤ **Cell division:** the zygote divides into a ball of cells (blastula); passes down oviduct.

⑥ **Implantation:** the blastula sinks into the uterus lining.

⑦ **Growth:** the blastula grows into two parts – the **embryo** and its **placenta,** joined by the umbilical cord. The embryo lies within an **amnion,** a water-bag, which cushions it from damaging blows and supports it. Growth lasts 40 weeks (9 months) – the **gestation** period. Premature birth, before 7 months, results in the embryo's death (spontaneous abortion or miscarriage).

⑧ **Birth:** the **baby** is pushed head first through a widened cervix when the uterus muscles contract. This bursts the amnion. The umbilical cord is cut by the midwife. When the baby's end of the cord dries up, it drops off leaving a scar (the navel). Babies are usually born head first.

A baby about to be born *feet* first poses difficulties. The doctor may get it out by cutting open the abdomen and uterus (Caesarian section).

⑨ **After birth:** within 30 minutes after the birth, further contractions of the uterus expel the **placenta** (the afterbirth).

Infertility: a cause for concern for a rising number of couples (now 1 in 6) who are otherwise healthy. It raises personal and ethical problems. Some causes and treatments of infertility are:

Cause

1 Ovary not ovulating
2 Blockage of oviduct (see Unit 15.5)
3 Low sperm count

Treatment

1 Hormones given to promote ovulation. Permits pregnancy in the normal way. Can lead to multiple births.
2 (*a*) Doctors can sometimes clear tubes by blowing air up them.
  (*b*) Wife is given hormones to promote ovulation, ova are collected direct from the ovary by a small operation. Husband's sperm is collected and used to fertilize eggs in a laboratory (in vitro fertilization, IVF). Zygote is returned to wife's uterus once it is dividing. Other zygotes can be kept alive 'deep frozen' as a back-up.
3 (*a*) Wife is given an anonymous donor's semen by syringe (artificial insemination, AI).
  (*b*) Wife's own ova are collected (see 2(b) above). From a sample of the husband's semen, a single healthy sperm is selected and injected by microsyringe direct into the wife's ovum (intracellular sperm injection, ICSI). The zygote is returned to the wife's uterus once it is dividing.

15.2 Placenta

The placenta: a temporary organ grown in the uterus during gestation to supply the needs of the embryo. These needs are:

Supply of:
(*a*) *food* – soluble nutrients, e.g. amino acids, glucose.
(*b*) *oxygen* – for respiration.

Removal of:
(*a*) *urea* and other wastes.
(*b*) *carbon dioxide.*

This exchange of substances occurs at capillaries, inside villi, at the end of the umbilical cord (Fig. 15.3). The villi lie in spaces filled with mother's blood. Mother's blood does *not* mix with the embryo's blood. If it did

(*a*) her blood pressure might burst the embryo's blood vessels;
(*b*) blood clumping might occur if the two blood groups were different (see Unit 17.3).

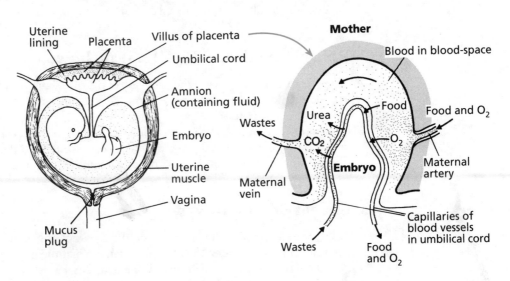

Fig. 15.3 Placenta: relationship between mother and embryo

15.3 Menstrual cycle

Menstrual cycles: periods of approximately 28 days during which a reproductive woman alternately ovulates and menstruates.

Ovulation: shedding of an ovum when a follicle in the ovary bursts (Fig. 15.4). Copulation within 3 days of ovulation could lead to fertilization, so the uterus lining (endometrium) is prepared for implantation.

Menstruation: shedding of most of the uterus lining 14 days after ovulation, when fertilization or implantation are unsuccessful. This occurs over 4 days as a loss of up to 500 cm^3 of blood and tissue through the vagina.

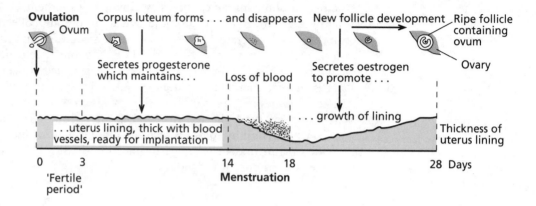

Fig 15.4
The menstrual cycle

15.4 Contraception

Contraception: the prevention of fertilization and implantation.

1 Unreliable methods

(a) *Withdrawal:* removing penis just before ejaculation;
(b) *Rhythm:* not copulating during the 'fertile period' of the menstrual cycle, i.e. when an ovum is passing down the oviduct (see Fig. 15.4). Ovulation is sometimes irregular; and sperm may survive for 48 hours inside the woman. Very healthy sperm may survive inside the woman for up to 7 days. The ovum can only be successfully fertilized in the first 12 hours after ovulation.

2 Reliable methods (Fig. 15.5) include:

(a) *temporary* methods allowing sensible spacing of a family. This places less physical strain on the mother; and more time and finance can be given to the care and attention of each child.
(b) *permanent* methods, when desired family size has been reached. Removal of testes (castration) or ovaries achieves the same result but is undesirable since a person's 'nature' is changed owing to lack of sex hormones from these organs.

3 Recent developments

1 Hormone implant (Norplant) of synthetic progestogen in six flexible matchstick size capsules inserted under the skin in a fan formation gives protection for up to 5 years. Remembering to take 'the pill' each day is banished, and fertility is restored within 12 hours of removal of the capsules.

2 The 'morning after pill': two pills of oestrogen of high dosage must be given by a doctor within 72 hours of intercourse, and a further two within 12 hours. If it is too late for this, a coil (IUD) inserted within 5 days usually prevents implantation. These methods must only be used in an emergency and should not be used as a regular contraceptive standby.

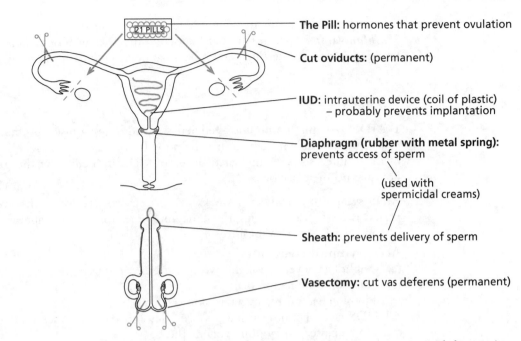

Fig. 15.5 Reliable methods of contraception

The Pill: hormones that prevent ovulation

Cut oviducts: (permanent)

IUD: intrauterine device (coil of plastic) – probably prevents implantation

Diaphragm (rubber with metal spring): prevents access of sperm

(used with spermicidal creams)

Sheath: prevents delivery of sperm

Vasectomy: cut vas deferens (permanent)

Practice of contraception worldwide is essential if humans are to avoid destruction of their environment by pollution (see Unit 20.6), erosion and social problems. A stable or falling birth rate has been achieved in a number of industrialized nations already; developing nations lag behind in effective contraception. A notable exception is the People's Republic of China where there are severe social penalties for couples who have more than one child. The birth rate has fallen (see Unit 16.9).

15.5 Sexually transmitted diseases (STD)

Sexually transmitted diseases are those passed on through copulation.

Copulation can occur in two ways:

1 *Heterosexually* (between man and woman) – the normal way, used in reproduction (see Unit 15.1). Both penis and vagina are adapted for this biologically important act.

2 *Homosexually* (between man and man). A penis is inserted into his partner's rectum. The rectum is not adapted for the sex act and tears easily, causing bleeding. This act has no biological function, so some people regard it as abnormal.

Bisexuals copulate both heterosexually and homosexually.

There are two main types of pathogen in STD:

1 **Bacteria** – which can be killed by antibiotics;

2 **Viruses** – incurable.

Bacteria

1 **Syphilis:** this disease occurs in three stages; by the third it is incurable.

(a) A painless *sore* appears at the point of contact, e.g. the penis tip or the cervix (thus the woman is often unaware of her infection) within 90 days of sexual contact. This disappears.

(b) Four to eight weeks later skin *rashes* may appear or patches of hair may fall out.

(c) After some weeks, infection reaches the *nervous system*, leading to paralysis, idiocy, blindness, etc.

Unborn babies can be infected via the placenta; they may suffer abnormalities or be born dead.

2 **Gonorrhoea:** within 2 to 8 days of sexual contact a yellowish discharge of mucus may appear from penis or vagina. In both sexes there may be permanent *problems with urination;* and both may become sexually *sterile* (through blocking of the sperm ducts or

the oviducts with scar tissue where there has been infection).

3 *Chlamydia:* causes inflammation of oviducts (may block them with scar tissue resulting in female infertility) and inflammation of epididymis in male.

Viruses

1 AIDS (**A**cquired **I**mmune **D**eficiency **S**yndrome): caused by the HIV virus. This attacks the immune system so that the body becomes defenceless against infection. Few of those infected with the virus develop AIDS immediately; the great majority are homosexual men (see below★).

AIDS symptoms can take 6 weeks to 15 years to develop – the average incubation period is 8–10 years. During this time antibodies to the virus appear in the blood: the person is well, but 'HIV-positive'.

AIDS symptoms include:
(*a*) weight loss, fever and night sweats, extreme tiredness;
(*b*) a rare kind of pneumonia;
(*c*) skin blotched purple by a rare skin cancer.
All AIDS cases die: no vaccine has been developed yet (but see Unit 17.16). The virus can also be passed on by nonsexual methods:
(*a*) the placenta and by breast feeding;
(*b*) any shared puncturing device (ear-piercing, needles for drug abuse);
(*c*) toothbrushes, razors (any chance of bleeding).
Saliva, tears, crockery and towels cannot pass the virus on.

2 Genital Herpes: caused by a virus related to chicken pox. Causes extremely uncomfortable sores around the genitals.

3 Genital warts: caused by the papilloma virus (a factor in cancer of the cervix). Takes 3 months to years to develop.

The simplest way to avoid all STD is not to have casual sex; and have a partner who is dependably clear of STD.

★*Note:* In the UK up to December 1993, there were 21 101 HIV-positive reports. There were 8529 AIDS cases. Of the HIV-positive cases, 12 741 resulted from homosexual intercourse, 2296 from heterosexual intercourse where the other partner had been to countries where the majority of cases arise heterosexually, 1364 from blood transfusion or haemophilia factor VIII use, and 1516 from drug abuse involving injection. The number of heterosexual transmissions has risen sharply (to about 600 in each of the three years 1991–1993).
Worldwide, the majority of cases have been transmitted heterosexually.

15.6 Abortion and amniocentesis

Abortion is the ending of pregnancy with the death and removal of an embryo. There are two types.
(*a*) *Spontaneous* (a 'miscarriage'): some abnormality of the embryo or the mother results in the embryo's death.
(*b*) *Induced:* the embryo is removed surgically by a suction device. Two of the legally accepted reasons for permitting an abortion are:
  (i) the mother's health is at risk in having the baby;
  (ii) the baby is likely to be born abnormal, e.g. with Down's syndrome (see Unit 17.15). **Amniocentesis** can warn of this: cells of the embryo present in a little amniotic fluid, withdrawn by syringe, can be grown in culture. Abnormal chromosome number in these cells may indicate Down's syndrome.
Abortion is *not* a means of contraception (see Unit 15.4). It carries some risk to the mother's health, it can cause severe depressions, and is regarded by some as murder of the unborn.

Summary

1.   Human sperm are produced in two testes; ova are produced in two ovaries.

2.   Copulation (insertion of penis into vagina) and ejaculation of sperm at the cervix precede fertilization within the oviduct.

3.   The zygote divides to form a ball of cells (blastula) which implants in the uterine wall.

4.   The blastula grows into an embryo surrounded by salty fluid within the amnion and is sustained by the placenta.

5.   The placenta provides the embryo with food and oxygen and removes its wastes.

6.   Eggs are shed (ovulation) monthly under the influence of hormones.

7.   These hormones also affect the thickness of the uterine lining, which is shed monthly through the vagina. This is the menstrual cycle.

8.   Contraception aims at preventing sperm meeting ova or preventing a blastula implanting.

9.   Sexually transmitted diseases are in many cases serious if not treated early.

10.   AIDS is a fatal sexually transmitted disease commonest in the UK amongst male homosexuals and injecting drug users.

11.   Abortion may occur spontaneously, but can be induced medically if the baby is likely to be born abnormal.

12.   Abnormality in embryos, e.g. Down's syndrome, can be detected by amniocentesis.

Chapter 16

Growth of cells and populations

16.1 Principles of growth

Growth: irreversible increase in size or mass of an organism.
Processes involved in growth

1. Formation of more protoplasm, especially proteins: cell size increases.
2. Cell division by mitosis (see Unit 17.10): maintains small size of cells.
3. Vacuolation – in plants only; absorption of much water, swelling the cell.
4. Differentiation – cells become different for special purposes (Fig. 16.1).

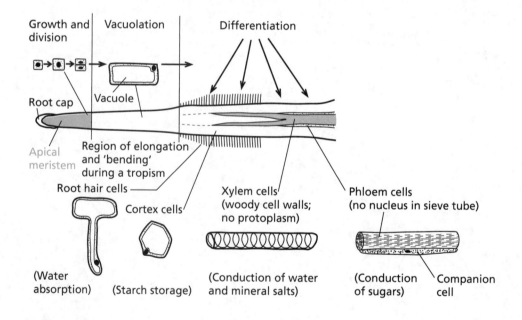

Fig. 16.1 Longitudinal section through a root showing regions of cell division (in green) and subsequent stages in growth

In a similar way, animal cells divide (but do not form vacuoles) and differentiate into cheek cells, muscle cells, neurones, blood cells, etc.

All four processes are controlled by hormones (see Unit 12.10, pituitary; Unit 12.14, auxin).

Growth involves changes of shape as well as size.

Shape

Plants and animals grow differently to suit their type of nutrition.

Green plants grow at their tips giving a branching shape with a large surface area for absorption of nutrients (necessary when anchored), and of sunlight energy.

Animals' bodies grow into a compact shape, except for their limbs (needed for food-seeking).

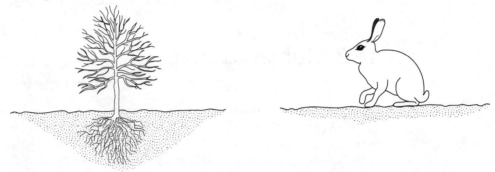

Size

Unicells have a large surface area for their tiny volume, so diffusion of materials meets most of their needs. The same applies to the individual cells of multicellular organisms.

Multicells specialize their cells, grouping them into tissues and organs. These meet the common needs of all cells more efficiently. Diffusion of food, oxygen and wastes through the body's large volume would be too slow to ensure survival (see Unit 9.6).

So special tissues are needed for

- *absorption and excretion*, e.g. in roots, guts, lungs, leaves, kidneys;
- *transport*, e.g. blood, xylem, phloem;
- *support*, e.g. bone, xylem;
- *coordination*, e.g. hormone-producing cells, neurones;
- *reproduction*, e.g. in genitals, flowers, and as gametes.

Large size gives advantages in nutrition. Tall plants can starve small ones by shading them. Large animals can use their greater power to gain more food than small ones; and to respond to predators' attacks.

Small size is useful where food is scarce, and for hiding from predators.

16.2 Factors affecting growth

Table 16.1 Some effects of genes and environment on growth

	Plants	Animals
Genes	Inherited factors: determine *size*, e.g. tall and dwarf varieties of pea plants – through growth hormones *shape*, e.g. beetroot, runner bean, gooseberry bush, poplar and oak trees *rate of growth*, e.g. pine trees grow faster than oak	Inherited factors: determine *size*, e.g. large and small dogs – through hormones (see Unit 12.10) *shape*, e.g. dachshunds and bulldogs *colouring*, e.g. tabby cats and Siamese *growth pattern* (see Units 16.3 and 21.7) *rate of growth*, e.g. sealions grow faster than humans
Climate	*Light* is essential for nutrition (photosynthesis) and therefore growth *Increased temperature* speeds up metabolism, e.g. respiration and photosynthesis, and thus rate of growth	*Light* is necessary for making vitamin D, needed for bone growth (see Unit 4.5) *Increased temperature* speeds up growth and development of ectotherms (Unit 10.6) but not endotherms, e.g. mammals
Nutrients	*Mineral salts* of the right kinds (see Unit 4.3) and quantity, e.g. from fertilizers, promote growth *Water* and carbon dioxide essential	*Food* of the right kinds and quantity (a balanced diet) promotes growth (see Unit 4.6) *Water* essential

Gene expression is affected by:

(*a*) *climate*: stoats change their brown summer coats for white ('ermine') ones in the winter; black markings of dark moths reared in cool conditions are paler (brown) if reared in warm conditions.

(*b*) *nutrients*: both size and intelligence of humans are less when they are continually under-nourished (see Unit 4.6); genes cannot express themselves fully.

16.3 Human growth

Growth from birth is *continuous* (compare insects, see Unit 21.7).
Rapid growth occurs at:

(*a*) suckling time;
(*b*) puberty (earlier in girls than boys) – see Figs. 16.2 and 16.3.

Given good nourishment, puberty is reached earliest in the Japanese and Chinese, followed by black African races and then Europeans. Under-nourishment delays growth and may reduce expected height and weight if it is continuous. Swedish 17-year-old boys of the 1880s were as much as 15 cm shorter than their 1970 equivalents.

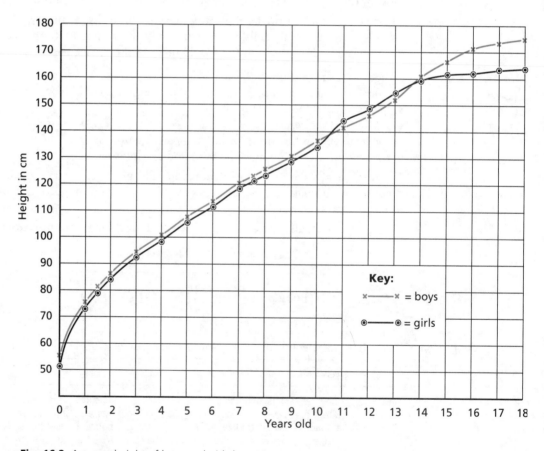

Fig. 16.2 Average height of boys and girls by age

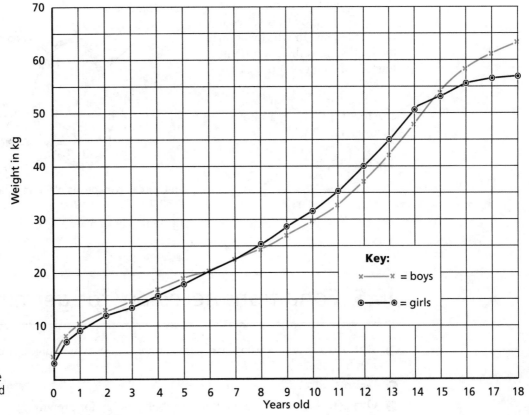

Fig. 16.3 Average weight of boys and girls by age

16.4 Seed structure and germination

Seeds are embryo plants enclosed by the testa (seed coat). They develop from the ovule after fertilization (see Unit 14.8). When shed they are dry (about 10% water).

The *embryo* consists of a radicle (root), a plumule (shoot) and one or more cotyledons (first seed leaves).

The *testa* bears a hilum (scar where the seed broke off the fruit) and a micropyle (pore for water entry during germination) (Fig. 16.4).

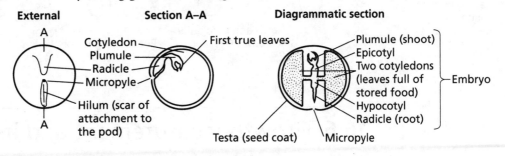

Fig. 16.4 Structure of a pea seed (beans are similar)

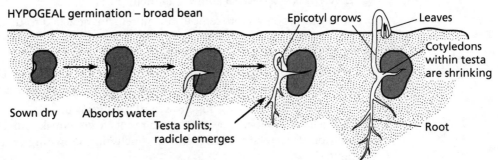

Fig. 16.5 Germination of a broad bean seed

In peas and beans the food for the seedling's growth is stored in the cotyledons. In wheat and maize the food store is the endosperm (outside the embryo) (Fig. 16.6).

When barley germinates, enzymes turn its starch into maltose. This 'malt' can be fermented by yeast to make beer (see Fig. 3.13).

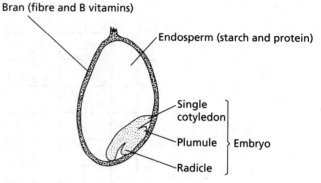

White bread is made mainly from endosperm. Wholemeal bread uses the whole grain

Fig. 16.6 A grain of wheat

16.5 Conditions necessary for germination

1 **Water:** to hydrate protoplasm, activating enzymes which digest stored food (e.g. starch to sugars).
2 **Warmth:** to enable enzymes to work.
3 **Oxygen:** for aerobic respiration to supply energy for growth.
 Some seeds require *light*, others dark, for germination; for most these do not matter.

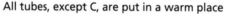

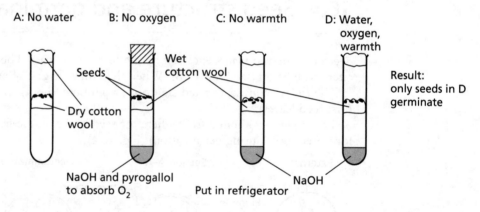

Fig. 16.7 Experiment to determine the conditions necessary for seed germination

16.6 Growth measurement and its difficulties

1 **Length or height** – all organisms. A crude method: volume would be better.
2 **Live mass** – terrestrial animals. Difficult for:
 (*a*) plants: roots are broken off, or soil remains attached to them;
 (*b*) aquatic organisms (how much should one dry them before weighing?).
3 **Dry mass** – all organisms, but they have to be killed (and dried in an oven at 110 °C). Avoids errors of hydration likely in no. 2 above, e.g. Did the animal drink or urinate before it was weighed? Were the plant cells fully turgid on weighing?
 It is essential when measuring growth of organisms to
(*a*) have a large number growing (avoids results from a freak individual);
(*b*) control *all* factors affecting growth (including crowding), e.g. food, temperature, light.

16.7 Growth of populations

The stages in growth of an individual organism are reflected by the changes in population of *cells* within it.

Table 16.2

	Stage	Cell population
A	Embryo	Rises very rapidly (exponentially)
B	Youth	Rises rapidly but more steadily (new cells formed greatly outnumber those dying)
C	Maturity	Reaches maximum (new cells cancelled out by the same number dying)
D	Senescence (growing old)	Falls slowly (more cells die than are formed to replace them)
E	Death	Falls very rapidly (failure of some part of the body on which all other cells depend)

There are similar stages in the growth of a population of *organisms*. An exponential increase is followed by a steadier increase in numbers until a maximum is reached (stationary phase). This maximum is decided by factors in the environment that affect birth rate, death rate (and immigration or emigration). If these effects are severe, the population may fall drastically, even causing extinction (Fig. 16.8). In this artificial (laboratory) example no other organisms, nor even the climate, contributed to the crash in numbers of bacteria.

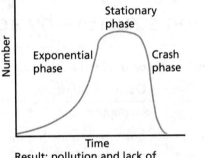

Result: pollution and lack of resources (food, O$_2$) cause death of the majority of bacteria

Fig. 16.8 Population of live bacteria growing on an agar plate

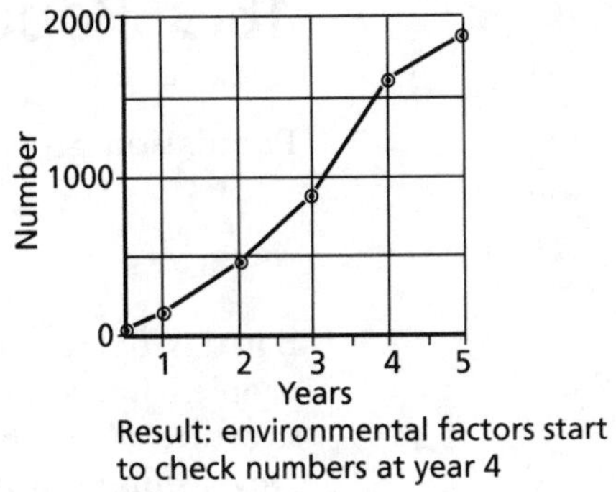

Result: environmental factors start to check numbers at year 4

Fig. 16.9 Offspring of six pheasants put onto Protection Island, USA in the 1930s

16.8 Human population

In a natural environment many factors control plant and animal numbers (see Fig. 16.9). Similar factors once controlled the population of Man's ancestors – until Man worked out ways of avoiding their controlling influence (Table 16.3).

Table 16.3 Man's avoidance of the factors controlling populations in nature

Factors controlling populations in nature	Man's methods of avoiding natural population control
1 Climate	Shelter (homes), clothes, fire
2 Predators	Tools – allowed Man's ancestors to overcome other animals with weapons
3 Food supply	Tools and science – adopting agriculture (which produces much more food than hunting and gathering it, as animals do)
4 Disease	Science and politics – understanding diseases so as to cure and prevent them (medically and by public health laws)
5 Water supply	Irrigation, reservoirs

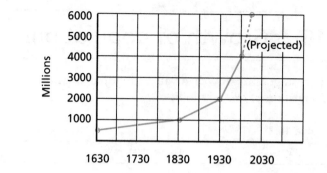

Fig. 16.10
Growth of the
human population
in the world

The human population, freed from the severe control imposed by disease (especially bacteria and viruses) and fed by abundant food, has increased rapidly (Fig. 16.10). This exponential population explosion continues. But 'developing' countries are the main ones contributing to it. Since 1975 the 'developed' countries (industrialized, wealthy ones, e.g. in Europe and N. America) have reduced their annual population increases. Some countries in Europe now show no increase at all.

If population growth in developing countries can rapidly be made to slow down (to a near stationary phase) the human race may avoid the fate of the bacteria represented in Fig. 16.8. Modern man must learn to live within the resources of the world without destroying and polluting it. Many 'primitive' races of Man, e.g. the Kung of Botswana, pygmies of African rain forest, bushmen of Australia, Inuit Eskimos and certain Amazonian tribes, have all learned to live in balance with their environments. We must relearn this lesson, to survive. Such issues are dealt with in Unit 20.12.

16.9 Population structure by age and sex

Population growth may be worked out by the following equation:

$$\frac{\text{Births} - \text{Deaths} \pm \text{Migration}}{\text{Total population}} \times 100$$

But this figure does not provide governments with enough information to plan for people's future needs, e.g. schools, work, hospitals and care of the aged. The age structure of the population may be shown by **population pyramids** (Fig. 16.11). **Developing countries** show a characteristic arrow-head shape. They have a high birth rate and high mortality. Emigration can affect the pyramid. **Developed countries** show a pillar-like shape. They have a low birth rate and low mortality. Immigration can affect the pyramid, but it is now usually restricted by laws.

16.10 Cancer

Tumours ('growths') appear when certain cells start to divide out of control. **Benign tumours** are harmless but may need to be cut out. **Malignant tumours** (cancers) are life threatening. They must be destroyed.

Treatment: cure is easiest when the cancer is detected early, i.e. when
(a) the tumour is small and easily destroyed;
(b) cells from the original tumour have not broken away into the blood to form new tumours in other organs, damaging their function.
The cancer can be destroyed by
(a) surgery;
(b) chemicals that stop cell division (chemotherapy);
(c) radiation, e.g. γ-rays focused on the tumour to kill it (radiotherapy).

Cause: 80 to 90 per cent of all cancers are *environmentally* caused, e.g. Japanese emigrants to the USA soon show a lower rate of stomach cancer (very high in Japan), but higher rates of bowel and breast cancer (matching those of Western people). Lung cancer rates rise greatly with smoking. See Table 16.4.

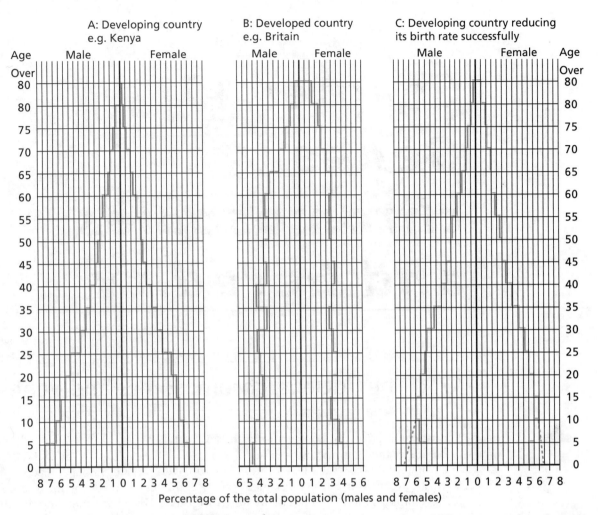

Fig. 16.11 The general shape of population pyramids for three countries, each at a different stage of development

Table 16.4 Some causes of cancer – radiation, chemicals and viruses

Cancer	Cause
Skin	Too much sunshine – ultraviolet radiation can cause cell mutations
Lung	Chemicals in tobacco smoke (90 per cent of cases are fatal)
Stomach	Diet and drink (the commonest form of cancer worldwide)
Cervical	Probably the papilloma virus, sexually transmitted (see Unit 15.5)

Prevention: health education (e.g. about diet and the risks of smoking); high safety standards in the nuclear and chemical industries; regular medical checks to increase early detection, e.g. the 'smear' test for cervical cancer and X-ray examination for breast cancer. About a third of all cancers are preventable, another third curable.

Summary

1 Growth is an irreversible increase in the size or mass of an organism.

2 Growth involves making more protoplasm, cell division by mitosis and differentiation into specialized cells.

3 Three main factors affect growth: the genes, the climate and the food available.

4 The factors necessary for germination of seeds are water, warmth and oxygen.

5 The growth curve for a population of organisms parallels that for the population of cells within an organism during its lifetime.

6 Human populations have sought to avoid the factors, such as climate, predators, disease, food supply and water supply, which control population growth in nature.

Chapter 17

Genes, chromosomes and heredity

17.1 The nucleus, chromosomes and genes

The **nucleus** normally contains long threads of DNA (see Unit 1.2) which are not visible under the light microscope.

Before cell division each DNA thread coils up, with protein, into a compact 'sausage' called a **chromosome**. When stained, this is visible under the light microscope (Fig. 17.1). Chromosomes are present in **homologous pairs**, both members having the same length (and number of genes). One chromosome of the pair came from the male parent, the other from the female parent, when their gametes fused together to form a zygote (see Fig. 17.6). Sections of the DNA threads are **genes**; each controls the making of an enzyme (see Unit 1.3).

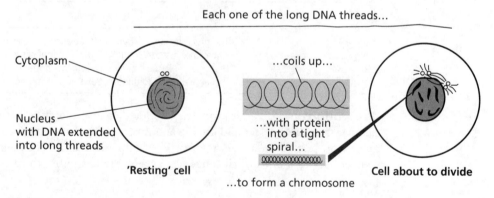

Fig. 17.1 Chromosome formation within the nucleus of a cell

17.2 Genes and characteristics

Two factors influence the characteristics of an organism: genes and environment.

Genes control the making of enzymes. Each enzyme controls a particular chemical change. This small change is a part of larger changes controlled by groups of enzymes. One or more chemical changes of this sort help to determine a characteristic.

For example:

one gene causes sickle cell anaemia (Unit 18.2);

many genes cooperate to give curly black hair – those for making hair protein, for black colour and for curly growth.

Environment influences the way genes act (see Unit 17.14). For example, a well-fed youngster is more likely to develop into a larger adult than his starved identical twin (even though both have identical genes). The genetic make-up of an organism is called its **genotype**. The interaction of its genotype with the environment is called its **phenotype**, i.e. its observable or measurable **characteristics**.

To simplify the above, consider an unfastened pearl necklace. The pearls are genes, the necklace a chromosome. A similar necklace would be its homologous partner (Fig. 17.2). Genes at an identical position on two homologous chromosomes determine a characteristic between them.

Diagram of chromosomes	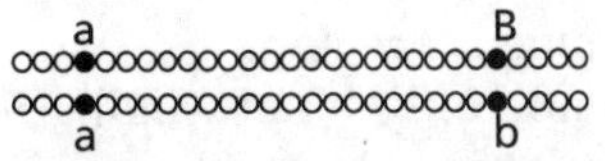 a ━━━━━━━━━━━ B **Pair 1** a ━━━━━━━━━━━ b		C^1 ━━━━━━ **Pair 2** ━━━━━━ C^2
Genotype	aa Homozygous	Bb Heterozygous	$C^1 C^2$ Heterozygous
Status of these genes	Recessive	B: dominant b: recessive	C^1 and C^2 are codominant
Phenotype	a	B	C^1/C^2 (both)

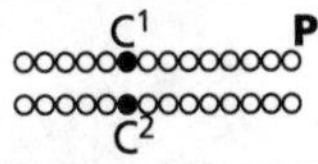

Fig. 17.2 Genetical terms illustrated with reference to two homologous pairs of chromosomes

Dominant genes (shown by capital letters) always express themselves as a characteristic. **Recessive genes** (shown by small letters) only express themselves when the partner is also recessive.

Thus genotype **AA** or **Aa** will be expressed as an **A** phenotype and genotype **aa** is the only way of producing the **a** phenotype (Fig. 17.3). Organisms with two identical genes at a locus (**AA** or **aa** genotypes) are said to be **homozygous**; those with alternative genes at the locus (**Aa**) are called **heterozygous**.

The alternative genes (**A** and **a**) are called **alleles**.

Gene	Phenotype	Genotype	Phenotype	Genotype
Dominant	Normal mucus secretion (in pancreas)	CC or Cc	 Free ear lobe	FF or Ff
Recessive	Fatal abnormal secretion (cystic fibrosis)	cc	 Attached ear lobe	ff

Fig. 17.3 Examples of dominant and recessive genes in humans

N.B. 'Tongue rolling' is a characteristic now known *not* to be inherited. You can learn, by practise, to roll your tongue into a gutter shape.

17.3 Human blood groups: codominance

Codominance

Certain alleles are **codominant**: both alleles express themselves, e.g. in the determination of human blood groups (Table 17.1).

Table 17.1 Genetics of blood groups A, B and O in humans

Gene status	Blood groups (i.e. phenotypes)	Genotypes
I^A (dominant)	A	$I^A I^A$ or $I^A I^O$
I^B (dominant)	B	$I^B I^B$ or $I^B I^O$
I^O (recessive)	O	$I^O I^O$
I^A and I^B are **codominant**	AB	$I^A I^B$

In **blood transfusion** the blood groups of both giver (donor) and the patient receiving blood should ideally be the *same*. This avoids clumping together of the donor's red blood cells inside the patient's veins. Clumping occurs if the patient's antibodies (in the plasma) react with the donor's red blood cells, making their cell membranes sticky. Note: clumping is *not* clotting.

Clumps not only block capillaries; but as the cells in them burst, the released products can cause kidney failure.

Incomplete dominance is not the same as codominance: the two alleles express themselves unequally. Examples are shown in Table 17.2.

Table 17.2

Characteristic	Genotypes and their phenotypic effect		
Blood clotting time (see Unit 17.9)	$B^H B^H$: normal	$B^H B^h$: very slightly longer	$B^h B^h$ or B^h – (in male): very long (haemophilia)
Anaemia (see Unit 18.2)	$H^N H^N$: none	$H^N H^S$: very slight	$H^S H^S$: severe (sickle cell anaemia)

17.4 Mendel's experiments

Genetics (the study of heredity) was only put on a firm basis in 1865 thanks to **Gregor Mendel**, an Austrian abbot, who published his research on inheritance in peas.

His materials: *Pisum sativum*, the garden pea. This:
(a) normally *self-pollinates* (and self-fertilizes) when the flower is still unopened. To *cross-pollinate* plants, Mendel had to remove the unripe anthers of strain **A** flowers and dust their stigmas with pollen from ripe stamens of strain **B**. Interference by insects was avoided by enclosing the flowers in muslin bags.
(b) has *strongly contrasting phenotypes*, e.g. pea plants are either tall (150–180 cm) or dwarf (20–45 cm); the seeds are either round or wrinkled.

His methods: As parents (P_1, or first parental generation) he chose two contrasting 'pure lines' which 'bred true', i.e. were homozygous. These he mated by cross-pollination. The offspring (F_1, or first filial generation) were allowed to self-pollinate. This gave the F_2, or second filial generation.

Results from one such experiment:
P_1 Tall × Dwarf
F_1 All Tall

Conclusion 1: factor for Tall is dominant to factor for Dwarf.

F_2 Ratio of 3 Tall: 1 Dwarf

Conclusion 2: factor for Dwarf was not lost (as it seemed to have been in the F_1). This suggested that 'factors' were particles of hereditary material which remained unaltered as they were handed on at each generation.

We now know that 'factors' are genes, and that the material of genes is DNA in chromosomes.

Table 17.3 Summary of a Mendelian experiment using modern genetical terms

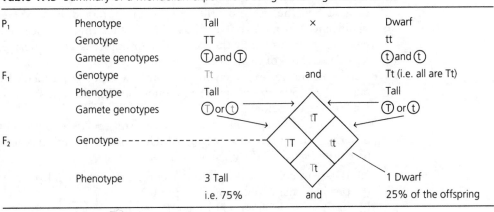

17.5 Hints on tackling genetic problems

When genetics problems are set as questions it is essential that the eight lines of terms relating to the P_1, F_1, and F_2 on the left of Table 17.3 be set out first before the data in the question is inserted in the appropriate places. By reasoning, the rest of the 'form' you have thus created can be filled in. It is vital to remember that gametes are **haploid** (have *one* set of genes) and organisms are **diploid** (have *two* sets of genes). The diamond checkerboard giving the genotypes of offspring is called a Punnett square.

17.6 Test cross test

Test cross test shows whether an organism of dominant phenotype is homozygous (TT) or heterozygous (Tt). The organism is crossed with a double recessive organism.

Table 17.4

Only heterozygotes can give recessive phenotype (dwarf) offspring. Those that do not (homozygotes) can be used as 'pure line' parents in selective breeding.

17.7 Ratios of phenotypes

Tables 17.3 and 17.4 state certain ratios of offspring: 75:25 and 50:50. These are only *expected* ratios. The ratios *obtained* in a breeding experiment are rarely identical with those expected. Thus Mendel obtained 787 Tall:277 Dwarf in the F_2 of the experiment explained in Table 17.3, a ratio of 2.84:1. Likewise a coin tossed 1000 times is *expected* to give 500 'heads' and 500 'tails' – but rarely does so. Scientists apply a 'test of significance' to ratios obtained to see whether they are near enough to the expected ratios to be regarded as the same. For example, is 26:24 near enough to 25:25 to be regarded as 50% of each?

Note: you are not expected to know the 'test of significance'. But if you were given a ratio of, say, 505:499 offspring in a question, you must first *explain why* you assume this is a 50:50 ratio before proceeding.

Mendel used *large numbers* of organisms in his experiments to obtain ratios of offspring that were meaningful. Much modern genetical knowledge has come from breeding *Drosophila* (fruit fly) which

(a) is easy to culture (in small bottles on banana paste and yeast);
(b) produces many offspring (100 per female);
(c) has a short development time (10 days from egg to adult).

Investigating the genetics of slow-breeding species (e.g. cows, Man) is less easy. Experiments are lengthy and costly, and in Man's case not allowed. Information must come from herd, family or hospital records.

17.8 Sex determination in mammals

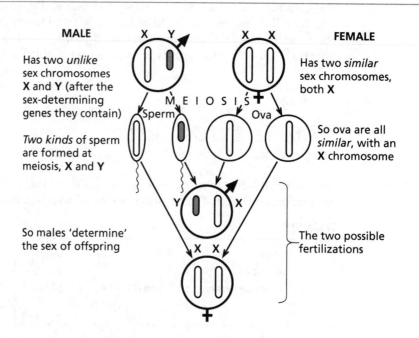

Fig. 17.4 Sex determination

Thus males and females are born in approximately equal numbers.

17.9 Sex linkage

Sex linkage: the appearance of certain characteristics in one sex and not the other (in mammals these appear in the male).

The **Y** chromosome, being shorter than the **X** (see Fig. 17.4), lacks a number of genes present on the longer chromosome. In a male (**XY**) therefore, these genes are present singly and not in pairs, as in the female (**XX**). All these 'single' genes come from the mother (on the **X**) and express themselves, even if recessive. Examples: red/green colour blindness and haemophilia.

About 4% of males are affected by **red/green colour blindness** (the two colours appear grey). Females can be affected too, since the condition is not lethal.

In **haemophilia** blood fails to clot, so trivial cuts and tooth extractions can be lethal through bleeding. Ordinary blows can cause internal bleeding and extensive bruising and joints may bleed after vigorous exertion. Nowadays, injections of the clotting factor that they lack (Factor VIII) can help haemophiliacs to lead near-normal lives.

Possible types H = normal, is dominant to h = haemophiliac

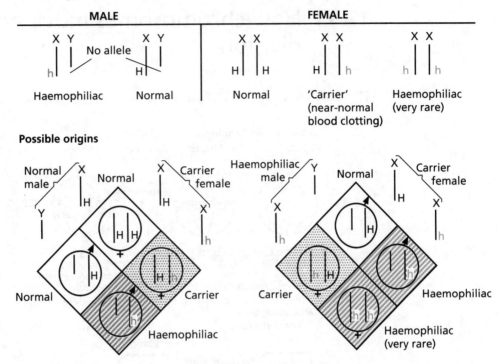

Fig. 17.5 Inheritance of haemophilia

17.10 Mitosis and meiosis in the life cycle

- Most organisms start from a **zygote** cell containing chromosomes in pairs, i.e. it contains a double set or **diploid** number of chromosomes (*2n*). One set comes from each parent.
- The zygote divides by **mitosis** to form new cells, also containing the *2n* number, during **growth**.
- In a multicellular organism these cells **differentiate** (see Unit 16.1) into cells as different as neurones and phagocytes. This happens because although all the cells possess identical genes (see Unit 17.12), they use different combinations of them according to their location in the body. For example, muscle cells do not use their hair colour genes.
- Certain cells in sex organs divide by **meiosis** to become **gametes**. These contain a single set or **haploid** number of chromosomes (*n*).
- At **fertilization**, gametes fuse to form a zygote ($n + n \rightarrow 2n$). Meiosis thus ensures that the chromosome number does not double at each new generation (which it would if gametes were *2n*, i.e. $2n + 2n \rightarrow 4n$; $4n + 4n \rightarrow 8n$ and so on).

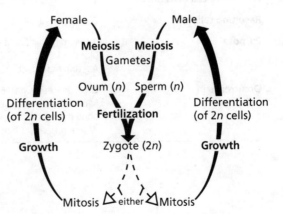

Fig. 17.6 Mitosis and meiosis in a life cycle

Both mitosis and meiosis use similar methods of moving chromosomes; but their *chromosome behaviour* is different.

17.11 How chromosomes move apart at cell division

The stages shown in Fig. 17.7 are all part of a continuous process.

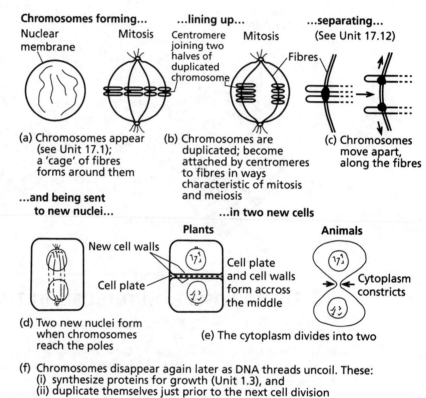

Fig. 17.7 How chromosomes separate at cell division

(a) Chromosomes appear (see Unit 17.1); a 'cage' of fibres forms around them

(b) Chromosomes are duplicated; become attached by centromeres to fibres in ways characteristic of mitosis and meiosis

(c) Chromosomes move apart, along the fibres

(d) Two new nuclei form when chromosomes reach the poles

(e) The cytoplasm divides into two

(f) Chromosomes disappear again later as DNA threads uncoil. These:
(i) synthesize proteins for growth (Unit 1.3), and
(ii) duplicate themselves just prior to the next cell division

17.12 Mitosis and meiosis compared

Table 17.5 Summary comparison of mitosis and meiosis

	Mitosis	Meiosis
Number of cell divisions	1	2
Resulting cells are	Diploid, identical	Haploid, not identical
Purpose	Growth, replacement (e.g. of skin, blood cells) Asexual reproduction	Gamete formation
Occurrence in	Growth areas (Unit 16.1) Replacement tissues, e.g. skin, bone marrow Where runners, tubers form	Gonads, e.g. testes, ovaries; anthers, ovules (Units 15.1, 14.5)

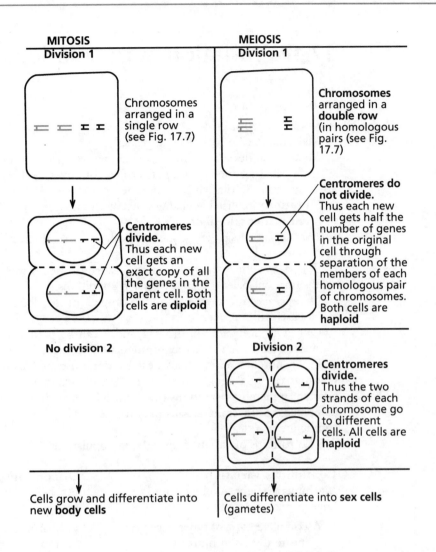

17.13 Meiosis shuffles genes

In addition to halving the chromosome number, meiosis shuffles genes at the stage when chromosomes 'line up' (see Fig. 17.7):

(*a*) **by varying the way they line up:**

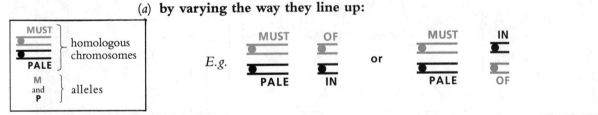

In a human cell with 46 chromosomes (and not 4) this alone makes 2^{22} (over 4 million) different varieties of gamete.

(*b*) **by exchanging material between pairs of chromosomes** ('crossing over')

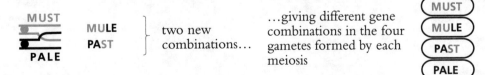

Other combinations are also possible, e.g. MALE, PUST; MUSE, PALT. In a human cell the number of possible combinations is enormous since most of the 23 pairs of chromosomes have hundreds of genes (and not 4 as shown above).

Fig. 17.8 How meiosis shuffles genes to give an enormous variety of gametes

17.14 Variation in populations

Variety arises from

1 Sexual reproduction:
Male and female have *different genes*.
Meiosis shuffles their genes to make *gametes different* (Unit 17.13).
Each pair of gametes fusing at fertilization gives a different *combination* of genes from any other pair. So offspring are unique.

2 Mutation: inheritable changes that are 'new' (see Unit 17.15).

3 Environmental effects
Food supply affects size, e.g. poor soil grows small crops; malnutrition causes obesity or deficiency diseases.
Temperature affects metabolism, e.g. warmth speeds growth; affects colour, e.g. dark moths turn out paler if reared in warm conditions.
Overcrowding affects size through competition for food and water; affects behaviour, e.g. locusts will migrate.

Only variation resulting from **1** and **2** can be passed on (inherited). This can affect evolution (see Unit 18.3). Environmental effects cannot be inherited.

Environmental effects can best be demonstrated using a clone (see Unit 14.2). Cuttings of equal length from a *Tradescantia* plant, rooted in sand, can be grown in different mineral salt solutions (see Unit 5.8). Any differences in growth must be due to differences in the mineral salts present, i.e. environment, since the genes in each plant cutting are identical.

Two patterns of variation are seen in populations:

Continuous variation
E.g. human height, intelligence, fingerprints.

1 A complete *range* of types, e.g. from giants to dwarfs in humans.
2 Phenotype controlled by
  (*a*) *many pairs* of alleles;
  (*b*) environment (may play a major part).

Discontinuous variation
E.g. height of pea plants; human blood groups.

1 Sharply *contrasting* types, e.g. tall and dwarf pea plants.
2 Phenotype controlled by
  (*a*) a *single pair* (or a few) alleles;
  (*b*) environment (plays little part).

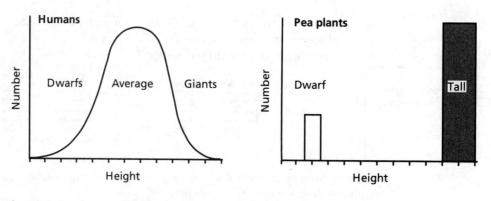

Fig. 17.9 Continuous and discontinuous variation in populations

17.15 Mutation

Mutation: an inheritable change in a cell. The nature of the DNA, or its quantity, alters.

Cause: cosmic rays, ultraviolet rays, radioactive emissions and certain chemicals, e.g. mustard gas, are mutagenic agents (cause mutations). These (and other causes) have effects on:

(*a*) **Genes:** a minute part of DNA once altered, may produce altered proteins in the cell (see Unit 1.3). These may be useless, e.g. *haemophilia* (no Factor VIII for clotting); useful, e.g. *melanism* (black pigment in peppered moths); or a bit of both, e.g. *sickle cell anaemia* (haemoglobin in red blood cells changed) – see Unit 18.2.

(*b*) **Single chromosomes:** through accidents at the separation of chromosomes in meiosis, extra chromosomes reach gametes, e.g. older mothers have a higher chance of producing Down's syndrome babies by this means. These have $2n + 1$ chromosomes, i.e. 47.

(*c*) **Whole sets of chromosomes:** meiosis may go completely wrong and produce diploid ($2n$) gametes. If these are used in fertilization then

$2n + n$ (normal gamete) $\rightarrow 3n$ (triploid chromosome number).

Many apple varieties are $3n$.

Cells with more than 2 *sets* of chromosomes (polyploids) are larger than diploid ($2n$) ones. So Man encourages and selects for these mutations to give bigger crops, e.g. wheat is $6n$.

Man also 'mutates' cells by genetic engineering (Unit 17.16).

Mutations occur constantly in populations. New strains of viruses, e.g. flu, catch human defences unprepared. New strains of bacteria, e.g. syphilis, are resistant to antibiotics. Mutant pest insects, e.g. mosquito, are surviving insecticides. Mutant rats in the UK have become Warfarin (poison) resistant.

17.16 Genetic engineering

Genetic engineering is Man's transfer of useful genes from one organism into another. Two main methods:

1 (*a*) **Bacteria** can be given selected genes using plasmids (Fig. 17.10). Inside the

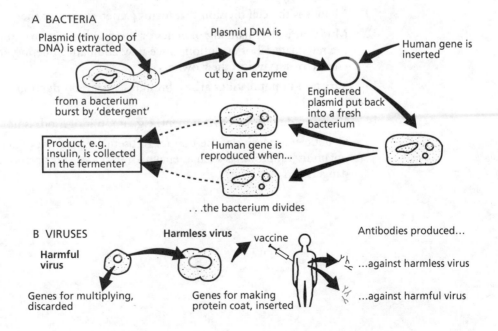

Fig. 17.10 Genetic engineering of bacteria and viruses

bacterium the genes function normally. They are reproduced when bacteria divide. The wanted products (e.g. insulin, growth hormone, vitamins or enzymes) can be extracted in large quantities from the fermenter (in which the bacteria reproduce rapidly – see Fig. 3.12).

(b) **Viruses:** Genes for the protein coat of a harmful virus, e.g. AIDS, can be put into a harmless virus, e.g. cowpox. If this 'engineered' virus is used as a vaccine, the body produces antibodies against the harmful virus. Such ideas are on trial.

2 Fusing two kinds of cells together. Lymphocytes producing particular antibodies (e.g. against measles) can be fused with cancer cells (which divide rapidly). Inside fermenters, these 'engineered' cells both divide rapidly and produce antibodies in very large quantities. The antibodies can be extracted to make vaccines.

Plant cells can also be fused – after removing the cell wall. Attempts are being made to produce a cereal plant with the ability to fix nitrogen (producing its own 'fertilizer').

Summary

1 Genes are lengths of DNA within chromosomes in the nucleus of a cell.

2 Chromosomes are found in pairs. One of the pair came from the sperm, the other from the ovum when they fused at fertilization.

3 Humans have 23 pairs of chromosomes.

4 Genes may be dominant, recessive or codominant, according to whether they express themselves or not.

5 Mendel's experiments with peas determined the basic rules of inheritance of characteristics.

6 Genotypes (genetic make-up) determine phenotypes (observable characteristics).

7 The phenotypes of offspring of a particular pair of parents can be predicted if the parental genotypes are known and a Punnett square is used.

8 Males produce sperm with either an X or a Y chromosome, while all ova have an X chromosome. An XY fertilization produces a boy and an XX fertilization a girl.

9 Certain genes are called sex-linked because they are not present on the shorter Y chromosome. The only genes of this kind in a male have come from his mother on the X chromosome.

10 Mitosis is the cell division of growth and asexual reproduction, and produces identical diploid cells.

11 Meiosis is the cell division that forms gametes, each of them different and haploid.

12 Mutation is the changing of genes or the number of chromosomes in a cell and is the raw material of evolution, since new and better phenotypes give a better chance of survival to their owners.

13 Variation in populations arises through sexual reproduction and mutation, and is inheritable.

14 Variation due to the environment, e.g. amount of food, is not inheritable.

15 Genetic engineering is the transfer of useful genes from organisms into bacteria to obtain useful products such as enzymes, vaccines and hormones. But it has its dangers too.

Chapter 18
Evolution

18.1 Selection of the 'best' from a variety

Organic evolution is the change in a population of a species (over a large number of generations) that results in the formation of a new species. The change is brought about by selection of only the 'best' from the variety of types present in the population.

Variety in a population arises from:

(a) *new combinations of genes* at fertilization (mother and father are different);

(b) *meiosis* (it shuffles the genes to make all gametes different – see Unit 17.13);

(c) *mutation* (which includes the origin of 'new genes' – see Unit 17.15);

(d) *environmental influences* (other than mutagenic agents), e.g. poor soil grows stunted plants.

Note: (a) and (b) are *rearrangements* of existing genes; (c) is the creating of *new* genes; but (d) does not change genetic material at all.

Natural selection occurs when the *environment* permits only those best adapted to it to survive. The survivors are the 'fittest and best' for the particular conditions of the environment at that time (Fig. 18.1). If the conditions change, new kinds of survivors appear since the previous survivors may no longer be the fittest (see Unit 18.2A and E).

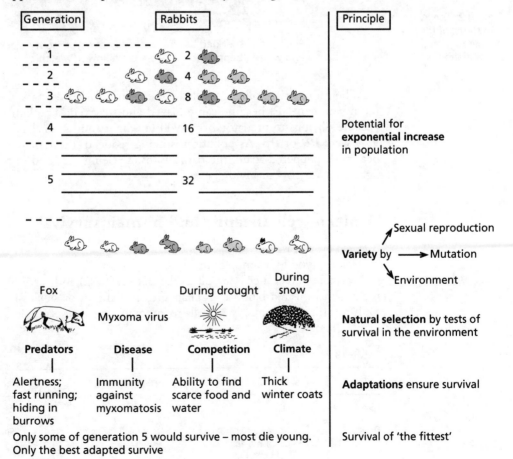

Fig. 18.1 Natural selection results in survival of the fittest

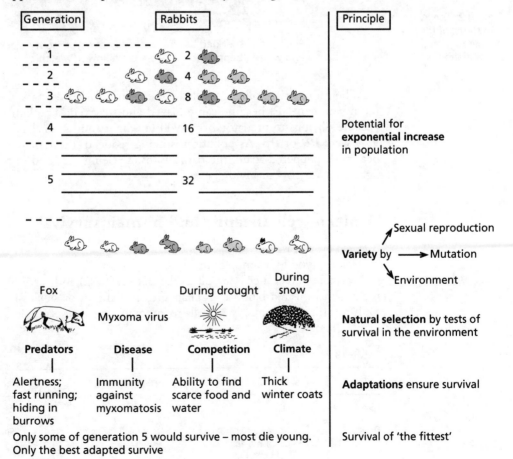Fig. 18.1 diagram text:

Generation	Rabbits	Principle
1	2	
2	4	
3	8	
4	16	Potential for **exponential increase** in population
5	32	

Sexual reproduction
Variety by ⟶ Mutation
Environment

Natural selection by tests of survival in the environment

Fox		During drought	During snow
Myxoma virus			
Predators	**Disease**	**Competition**	**Climate**
Alertness; fast running; hiding in burrows	Immunity against myxomatosis	Ability to find scarce food and water	Thick winter coats

Adaptations ensure survival

Only some of generation 5 would survive – most die young. Only the best adapted survive

Survival of 'the fittest'

An **adaptation** is a solution to a biological problem. Adaptations may be *structures*, e.g. wings for flying; *chemicals*, e.g. antibodies against diseases; *features of the life history*, e.g. high reproductive rate; and even *behaviour*, e.g. phototaxis in fly adults (see Unit 12.13). The majority of adaptations are *inherited*.

Artificial selection occurs when *Man* selects, for his own purposes, certain varieties of organism. These are frequently 'unfit' for survival in the wild, being suited only for the special conditions he puts them in, e.g. farms, greenhouses, gardens and homes (see Unit 18.5).

18.2 Examples of natural selection

A Industrial melanism

Peppered moth *Biston betularia*
Selection by: predatory birds, e.g. thrushes
Adaptation: camouflage

Before 1840 the light-coloured (peppered) moth survived by camouflage on lichen-covered tree trunks in unpolluted woods (Fig. 18.2). Dark mutant moths did not survive predation – they were easily seen.

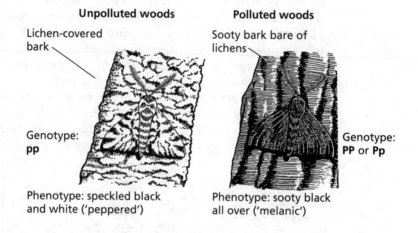

Fig. 18.2 The two forms of the peppered moth, camouflaged

When industrial pollution killed lichens and blackened bark the dark mutant moths (dominant gene, **P**) became camouflaged and survived. The light-coloured moths (**pp**) became obvious to predators. By 1900 few light moths survived in industrial areas and 98% were **PP** or **Pp**. As pollution is being reduced, these mainly dark populations are becoming peppered again; the dark moths are being predated in the cleaner woods and light ones are now surviving better.

B Sickle-cell anaemia and human survival

Selection by: disease
Adaptation: type of haemoglobin

Normal red blood cells are plate-like (see Unit 8.2) and carry O$_2$ well. If haemoglobin is abnormal the red blood cells change to half-moon or sickle shapes in capillaries; and O$_2$ is not supplied properly to cells. A mutant gene is responsible for this fatal condition (Table 18.1).

Table 18.1

	Normal person	Sickle-cell trait	Sickle-cell anaemia
Haemoglobin	Normal	Nearly normal	Abnormal
Diseases	Not anaemic but can die of malaria	Very mildly anaemic and malaria resistant	Severely anaemic (dies)
Genotype	*HH*	*Hh*	*hh*

Thus the homozygote *HH* is at a slight advantage in countries without malaria, and the heterozygote *Hh* is at an advantage in malarial areas.

C Foxes at different latitudes

Selection by: climate – temperature
Adaptations: fur, ears
Arctic foxes: are insulated so well that they tolerate sitting in snow at −40 °C. Ears small to retain heat (and not freeze).
Red foxes: fur can keep bodies warm in European winters. Ears medium size.
Kit foxes: fur not very thick – keep cool from desert heat in burrows. Ears large – radiate heat (and hear well at night).

D Red deer and sexual selection

Selection by: sexual competition
Adaptations: antlers and powerful bodies
Males (stags) push each other, antlers against antlers, to fight for a group of females (hinds) to mate with. The strongest gain most mates, so passing on their genes; the weakest do not mate.

E Shortage of food

Deer on the Kaibab Plateau, Arizona
Selection by: competitors for the food
Adaptation: ability to get enough food (including standing up on hind legs to browse trees)
In 1900, about 4000 well-fed deer roamed the plateau. Predators, e.g. wolves and pumas, kept deer numbers steady. In 1907, the majority of the predators were killed by Man. Unchecked, the deer population rose to over 100 000 in 20 years. Severe competition for food on an over-grazed plateau resulted in a rapid fall in population.
Note: Before 1907, deer able to outwit predators had been selected. The new conditions of 1907–1927, however, selected for deer able to compete successfully for the scarce food.

F Pesticides and medicines

These (produced by Man) are also agents of 'natural' selection (see Unit 17.15). Certain mosquitoes in South America are now adapted to surviving five major insecticides, and many kinds of disease bacteria have become resistant to certain antibiotics.

Note how mutation and new combinations of genes in all the examples A–F provide the basis for adaptation (and thus survival).

18.3 Evolution by natural selection

Tests of natural selection	1 The environment provides tests of survival. These include climate, soil type, predation, disease and competition (see Unit 18.2).
Variety	2 Of the variety of types in a population, only certain types will survive these tests.
Survival by adaptation	3 These 'selected' types survive because they are adapted to the environmental conditions. They breed, passing on their genes for these adaptations.

Mutation (*'new genes'*)   **4** Any mutation which helps an individual organism to survive also gives it a better chance to breed.

Mutants survive and multiply   **5** By breeding, these new genes are spread in the population.

6 The numbers of mutant organisms (those having the genes helping survival) rises. So the population as a whole changes its characteristics, i.e. it evolves (see Unit 18.2A).

Distinct varieties...   **7** In two *different* environments, the mutations that help survival are also likely to be different (see Fig. 18.3). So two main varieties arise as they gather their own, different, mutations and become more and more different.

...interbreed less   **8** As the two populations become increasingly different, less and less successful interbreeding between the two marked varieties occurs. (Any hybrids (crosses) tend not to be as well adapted to the two environments as the two specialized varieties, so they do not survive.)

Barriers to interbreeding   **9** Any breeding barrier (e.g. the Pyrenees mountains between France and Spain) that prevents intermixing of genes between two populations speeds up the process of varieties becoming increasingly different.

New species   **10** After many generations, the differences between the varieties become so great that they cannot interbreed. Two new species have been formed.

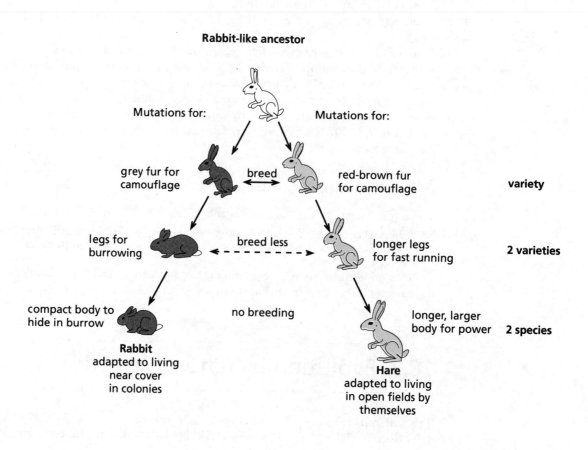

Fig. 18.3 Accumulation of different mutations in two populations over a large number of generations leads to the evolution of new species

18.4 Charles Darwin (1809–82)

As naturalist on *HMS Beagle* (1831–36), Darwin collected much evidence around the world of 'modification of species by descent' (see Unit 18.3).

In 1839, Darwin read *An essay on the principle of population* by the Reverend T. Malthus. This suggested that:

(*a*) the human population could increase exponentially (e.g. 2, 4, 8, 16, 32);

(*b*) but the resources, e.g. food, for it could only increase arithmetically (e.g. 2, 3, 4, 5, 6). As the population's needs could not be met by the resources, there would be a struggle to survive. Famine, disease and war would control the population, unless 'moral restraint', e.g. late marriage, were practised (whose modern equivalent could be contraception).

This idea of struggling to exist provided Darwin with the idea that in similar circumstances in nature the fittest organisms would survive. Darwin's ideas on the 'Origin of Species' are summarized below:

Observation 1	All organisms could, theoretically, increase in numbers exponentially, i.e. **organisms produce more offspring than could possibly survive.**
Observation 2	Populations of organisms, in fact, remain reasonably constant.
Deduction 1	Organisms must have to **struggle for survival** against factors that check their increase in numbers.
Observation 3	In any population there is a variety of types. Much of this variation is inherited by future generations.
Deduction 2	Those best adapted to their environment will survive, i.e. **survival of the fittest**.
Observation 4	Some species have more than one distinct variety.
Observation 5	Anything hindering interbreeding between two varieties will tend to make them even more different because each variety will accumulate mutations, many of which will be different between the two varieties.
Deduction 3	New species arise when **divergence of the two varieties** is great enough to prevent interbreeding between them.

Darwin recognized that evolution is a *branching* process. Modern types of ape, e.g. gorillas, did *not* give rise to Man, but both Man and gorilla are likely to have had common ancestors in the distant past (Fig. 18.4).

Fig. 18.4 Origins of Man   Impossible   Possible

18.5 Artificial selection

Selective breeding by Man has produced:

Plants

by *cross-breeding* strains with desirable characteristics;

by increasing the *mutation* rate in stamens, using radioactive materials;

by vegetative propagation of new strains thus obtained;

by *genetically engineering* microorganisms (see Unit 17.16).

- Climate-adapted crops, e.g lettuce for cool and for hot conditions.
- Disease-resistant crops, e.g. strawberries resistant to viruses.
- High-yielding crops, e.g. rice plants that do not blow over in wind, so spoiling the rice grains (they also grow fast enough to allow two or three crops per year instead of one); wheat and apples (see Unit 17.15).
- Nutritious crops, e.g. maize strains containing *all* the essential amino acids, so helping to fight kwashiorkor (see Unit 4.6).
- Purpose-selected organisms, e.g. yeasts for brewing, for baking and for SCP; bacteria 'engineered' to make insulin (see Units 3.12 and 17.16).
- Attractive plants, e.g. roses, chrysanthemums and appetizingly coloured fruits.

Animals

by breeding from selected useful strains and from interesting mutants:
- Dogs as different as bulldogs, dachshunds, St Bernards and Afghan hounds.
- Horses such as Shetlands, shires, racehorses and mules.
- Cattle for milk (Jerseys), for beef (Herefords) and for resistance to trypanosome diseases in Africa (Zebu × Brahmin);

and by improving not only genetic stock but also the means of feeding and care:
- Hens laying more eggs per year (180 in 1920, 280 in 1980).
- Cows producing more milk per year (2500 kg in 1920, 4500 kg in 1980).

18.6 Evidence for evolution: fossils

Fossils are the remains of organisms from the distant past whose hard parts are preserved in sedimentary rocks. Fossils are rare finds, since most dead organisms disintegrate by decay. Ancient organisms (buried by early sediments) are below more recent organisms (buried by later sediments). By huge compression these layers of sediments are turned to rock.

In the sides of the Grand Canyon, USA, the sedimentary rocks reveal invertebrates at the lower levels and the range of vertebrates shown in Fig. 18.5 above them. Fish are lowest down, amphibia above them and so on.

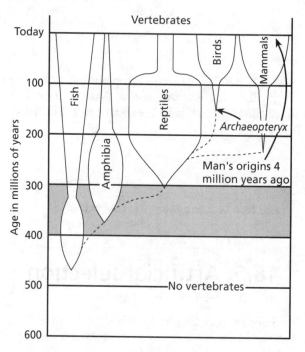

Fig. 18.5 Selected features of the fossil record. Width of areas representing groups named relates to increase or decrease in abundance

The fossil record shows that:
- The variety of life today did not arise all at once – as told in *Genesis* ('special creation').
- First life was aquatic; terrestrial life came later.
- As each new 'improved' kind of vertebrate evolved, the older, less well adapted, groups declined in importance, and many became extinct (e.g. dinosaurs).

Some particular fossils give clues as to how new groups evolved. *Archaeopteryx* (now extinct) had mainly reptile features like those of a lizard. However, its body was covered with feathers and its 'arms' were wings that allowed gliding, but not flapping. It had advantages over reptiles but became extinct when birds with flapping flight evolved.

18.7 Other theories of evolution

① **Lamarck** suggested that ancestors of giraffes (with short necks) achieved longer necks by striving to reach up to the foliage of trees. This change, he said, was passed on to offspring. Conversely humans achieved their vestigial tail (coccyx) by failing to use it enough. Weissmann prevented mice from using their tails for one hundred generations by cutting their tails off at birth but the one-hundred-and-first generation had tails as long as the first.

The theory of use and disuse is *wrong*: organisms inherit genotypes, not phenotypes.

② **Biblical views** (added to by theologians)

- The variety of organisms was specially created, all at once – Bishop Ussher (17th Century) put the date at 4004 BC. Fossil evidence disproves this.
- Man was regarded as the supreme creation, quite separate from and 'lord' over all animals. Now, even the Roman Catholic encyclical of 1951 recognizes the animal origin of man.
- The 'Creation' was regarded as the product of a grand 'Design' by a 'Designer'. Science emphasizes that *chance* events largely shape biological progress. Mutations and meiosis, the first meeting of your parents, and which two of their gametes fused to form your first cell – all events with a strong element of chance in them – these have shaped your destiny.

If the biblical view of the design of the organisms for special purposes is correct, it is indeed surprising that the 'Designer' should have made so many mistakes (extinction) or created half-way houses such as *Archaeopteryx* (see Unit 18.6).

A very few Christians ('fundamentalists') today believe the account of the origin of species exactly as it appears in the book of *Genesis* in the Bible. However, the neo-Darwinian theory is still only a theory and requires further evidence to convince some people.

Summary

1   Evolution is the change in a species that leads to the formation of new, different, species over a large number of generations.

2   Those organisms in a species that are best adapted to the environment will survive, breed and accumulate new advantageous mutations that ensure change to new variants.

3   When new variants can no longer breed with other varieties in the species, a new species has been formed.

4   Charles Darwin was the originator of the ideas behind the 'Origin of Species' through 'Natural Selection'.

5   Fossils provide evidence that organisms evolved.

6   Artificial selection is selection by Man (and not nature) of variants in crops and animals that he wishes to use.

7   Lamarck's theory that use or disuse of parts of organisms was responsible for evolution has been disproved.

8   The theory of special creation – that the various kinds of organisms were created all at one time – is disproved by the evidence of fossils.

Chapter 19
Ecology

19.1 The biosphere – its limits and organization

Ecology: the scientific study of organisms in relation to their environment.
Environment: the influences acting upon organisms. Two kinds:
(*a*) **biotic:** other organisms such as predators, competitors, parasites.
(*b*) **abiotic:** nonliving influences, such as climate, soil structure and water currents.
Habitat: the particular type of locality in an environment in which an organism lives, e.g. among weeds in a pond (stickleback) or among rotting leaves or wood in woodland (woodlouse).

Usually every species of organism exists as a **population** in its environment and not just as a single individual. Together, all the populations of all the species interact to form a **community** within their ecosystem. The role each species plays in the community is its **niche**, e.g. an earthworm's niche is to affect soil fertility by its activities (see Unit 19.12) and provide food for shrews, moles and some birds.

Ecosystem: any area in which organisms interact both with each other *and* with their abiotic environment, to form a self-sustaining unit (Fig. 19.1).

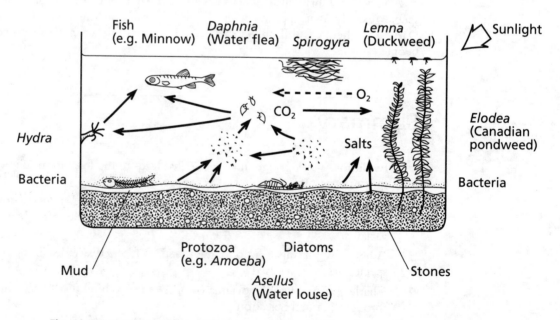

Fig. 19.1 A simple pond ecosystem in an aquarium (arrows represent feeding)

Examples of ecosystems: ponds, jungle, ocean or even a puddle. Ecosystems are not actually distinct, they interact with others. Thus dragonfly nymphs in a pond emerge as flying predators which catch their insect prey over both pond and meadow, so linking both these ecosystems. Even ecosystems in the UK and Africa are linked – by the same swallows feeding on insects in both areas according to the time of year.

Biosphere: the earth's surface that harbours life – a very thin layer of soil and the oceans, lakes, rivers and air (Fig. 19.2). The biosphere is the sum of all the world's ecosystems and is isolated from any others that may exist in space. However, other celestial bodies influence it:

(*a*) life depends on solar energy (from the sun);
(*b*) other radiations (e.g. cosmic rays) from various sources cause mutations;
(*c*) gravitational fields of sun and moon cause tides;
(*d*) at least 200 tonnes of cosmic dust arrive on earth daily.

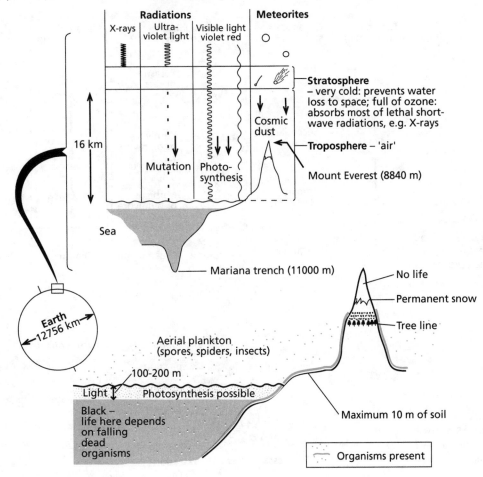

Fig. 19.2 The biosphere in relation to the earth

19.2 Food chains, food webs and food cycles

Food chains, webs and cycles are units composing a community.

① Food chain: a minimum of three organisms, the first always a green plant, the second an animal feeding on the plant, and the third an animal feeding on the second (Fig. 19.3).

All life depends on green plants (**producers**). They alone can trap sunlight *energy* and make organic *food* from water, carbon dioxide and mineral salts. Animals (**consumers**) get their energy and materials for growth from the food that producers make.

Every transfer of food up the chain results in a great loss in mass (**biomass**) – anything up to 90 per cent (Fig. 19.4). This is because a lot of food consumed by animals is lost owing to respiration, excretion and indigestibility (faeces), and never reaches the next member of the chain. Thus food chains can be expressed quantitatively as **pyramids of numbers** or, more usefully to farmers and game-wardens, as **pyramids of biomass** (Fig. 19.3). Such considerations of quantity (of organisms) explain why:

(*a*) the number of species in a food chain rarely exceeds five;

(*b*) the biomass of each species is limited by the capacity of producers (plants) to produce food;

(*c*) an omnivore gains more food by being a vegetarian than by eating meat. Man would do better to eat grain rather than eat cattle fed on the grain (assuming first class protein needs are met – see Unit 4.6).

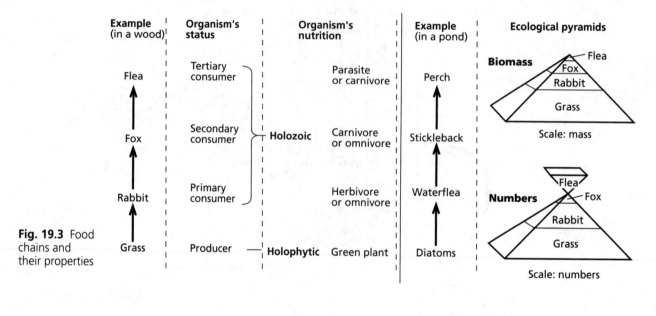

Fig. 19.3 Food chains and their properties

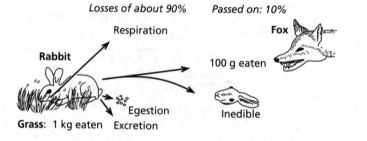

Fig. 19.4 Loss in biomass at each step in a food chain

② **Food web:** a number of interlinked food chains. In an ecosystem that includes foxes and rabbits, the diet of consumers is usually more varied than a food chain suggests. Foxes eat beetles, voles, chickens and pheasants as well as rabbits; and rabbits eat a great variety of green plants (Fig. 19.5).

Fig. 19.5 Food web: a number of interrelated food chains

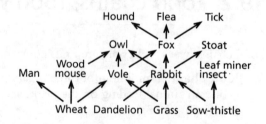

③ **Food cycles:** food chains with **decomposers** added –

(*a*) *Detritivores:* animals which eat dead and decaying organisms, e.g. water louse, woodlouse, earthworms, springtails.

(*b*) *Saprophytes:* fungi decay plant materials; bacteria decay protein especially. Thus, dead organisms and excreta (organic matter) are turned into mineral salts and CO_2 (inorganic matter) – which producers need for food but could not otherwise obtain.

④ **Energy chain:** the passage of energy from the sun along a food chain and on to decomposers. Energy is *not* cycled (Fig. 19.6). It is progressively lost along the chain, e.g. as heat from respiration.

The units making up the biosphere may be summarized as in Fig. 19.7.

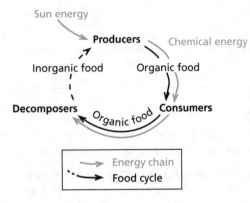

Fig. 19.6 The energy chain in a food cycle

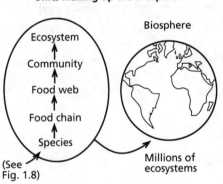

Fig. 19.7 Units making up the biosphere

19.3 Feeding relationships between species

❶ **Predation:** a *predator* is usually larger than its *prey*, an organism it kills for food, e.g. fox kills rabbit; heron kills perch. *Note:* Both organisms are animals, never plants.

'Symbiosis' is now used to describe the very close association of individuals of two different species, principally for reasons of feeding. Symbiosis includes parasitism and mutualism.

❷ **Parasitism:** a *parasite* is an organism living on or in another organism called its *host*, from which it gets its food, usually without killing it.

Examples: mosquito (see Unit 21.12), greenfly (ectoparasites); liverfluke (see Unit 21.15), leaf-miner caterpillar (endoparasites).

❸ **Mutualism:** a *mutualist* and its partner (also a *mutualist*) live very closely together, mutually helping each other. Examples:

Mutualist	Nitrogen–fixing bacteria	Mycorrhiza fungi (around roots)
Exchange	Give nitrates ↓ ↑ Give sugars	Phosphate ions absorbed from soil ↓ ↑ Sugars
Mutualist	Legumes, e.g. clover (See Fig. 20.2)	Trees, e.g. oak, pine (See Fig. 19.11)

④ **Competition:** occurs between two organisms (*competitors*), both attempting to obtain a commodity which is in *short supply* in the environment. Examples:

Commodity	Competitors (may be members of *own* species; or of *different* species)	
Light	Waterlilies out-shade diatoms	Oaks out-shade hawthorns
Food	Stickleback and minnow	Squirrels and wood pigeons
	(for water fleas)	(for acorns)
	Water fleas (for diatoms)	Tits (for caterpillars)
Nesting sites	Sticklebacks for nest materials	Tits for tree-holes
	(Unit 21.16)	
Mates	Frogs	Blackbirds

See also Unit 18.2D – mates – and Unit 18.2E – food.

The planting density for crops is determined so as to minimize competition between individual plants. Weeds are successful competitors of crops.

⑤ **Commensalism:** a loose relationship between two organisms in which the *commensal* (smaller) benefits by feeding on scraps of food wasted by the *host* (larger) – who is neither harmed nor helped, e.g. sparrows feed on Man's discarded bread. Commensals have alternative food, so the relationship is not obligatory.

Table 19.1 Summary comparison of feeding relationships between organisms (+ = benefits, – = harmed, ○ = unaffected; A > B means A is larger than B)

	Organisms		Size relationship
	A	B	
Predation	Predator	Prey	A > B
	+	–	
Parasitism	Parasite	Host	A < B
	+	–	
Mutualism	Mutualist	Mutualist	Any
	+	+	
Competition	Competitor	Competitor	Any
	–	–	
Commensalism	Commensal	Host	A < B
	+	○	

19.4 Stable and unstable ecosystems

Stable ecosystems

(*a*) The numbers of organisms rise and fall (according to season) but a **more or less constant average population level** is maintained. As light and temperature increase from early spring:

1 the numbers of producers increase until early summer when herbivores help to check the increase (Fig. 19.8);
2 the numbers of herbivores increase until midsummer when carnivores begin to check their numbers;
3 carnivores only begin to increase in numbers when their prey is sufficiently abundant.

As light and temperature fall to autumn levels, numbers of organisms begin to fall towards early spring levels. Fewer producers means less food for herbivores; fewer herbivores means less food for carnivores. Deaths by freezing and starvation, and the dying down of leaves before perennation, provide decomposers with food – which is converted to mineral salts.

(*b*) On land, a **dominant plant species** emerges, e.g. oak, which cannot be out-competed. At this stage a *climax community* exists.

Ponds are always potentially unstable. They may silt up, becoming marshes, then dry land.

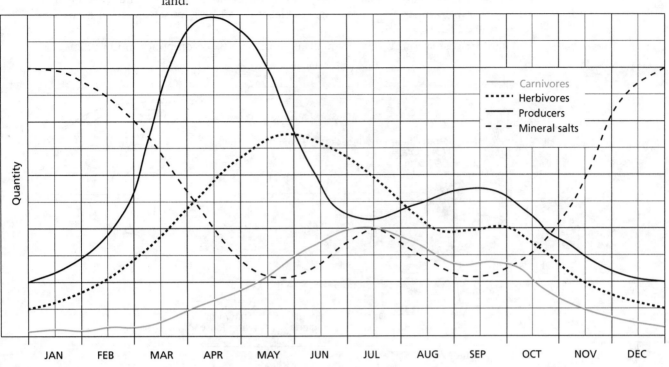

Fig. 19.8 Rise and fall of quantities of food in a pond ecosystem during a year

Unstable ecosystem

Large changes in numbers of most species owing to a changing environment. Examples:

(a) *Succession* – one dominant group of species out-competes another group, and changes its environment.

E.g.   **pond**   **marsh**   **oakwood**

(with *Elodea, Spirogyra, Daphnia*) $\xrightarrow{\text{silting}}$ (with bullrush, *Iris*) $\xrightarrow{\text{drying}}$ (with oaks)

(b) *Pollution or disease* – may disrupt the food web by causing the death of important organisms, e.g. sooty smoke from industry kills lichens (see Unit 18.2A), Dutch-elm disease kills elms, or sewage causes eutrophication (see Table 20.3).

Some causes of instability

(a) *Removing a member of the food chain* affects the whole chain, e.g. shooting foxes kills their fleas; allows rabbits to increase; and grass will become over-grazed.

    Thus an effect on one organism has an effect on all.

(b) *Simple ecosystems* (i.e. with few food chains), e.g. the terrestrial Arctic or Man's monocultures on farms, can most easily be upset by removal or addition of species. Complex ecosystems are more stable, e.g. tropical forest, owing to a great variety of alternative foods.

(c) *Erosion of soil*, e.g. by deforestation on sloping ground, removes the basis for plant growth and thus destroys whole ecosystems (see Unit 20.7).

(d) *Pollution of air and land* often affects water by drainage, e.g. acid rain, insecticides (see Unit 20.6).

19.5 Pond ecosystem

Although Fig. 19.9 shows some features of ponds, you are unlikely to see them all. Figure 19.10 suggests how a class study may be carried out, but you may not have a flat-bottomed boat or pier to work from.

Much useful information can be got by using a dipping net (wide mesh) from the bank and establishing an aquarium with mud and plants in week 1, and representative animals (not fish) in week 2. Fish, e.g. stickleback, can be kept separately in their own aquarium and fed separately.

There are suggestions for experiments of your own based on ponds in Unit 22.9.

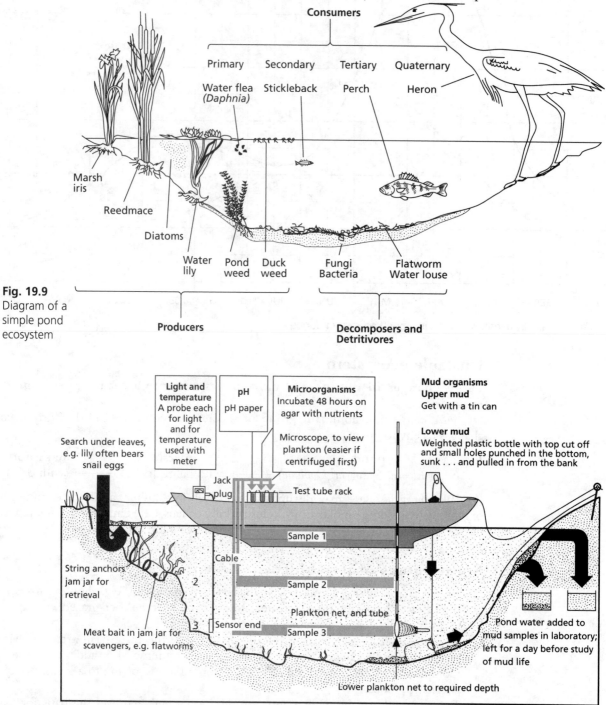

Fig. 19.9 Diagram of a simple pond ecosystem

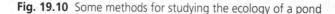

Fig. 19.10 Some methods for studying the ecology of a pond

19.6 Woodland ecosystem

Figure 19.11 gives some idea of the general structure of a wood, but the one you study will have differences. A wood is really two related ecosystems: woodland above and soil below. Figures 19.12–19.14 suggest how you may set about a class study of a wood. In Unit 22.9 are suggestions for experiments of your own.

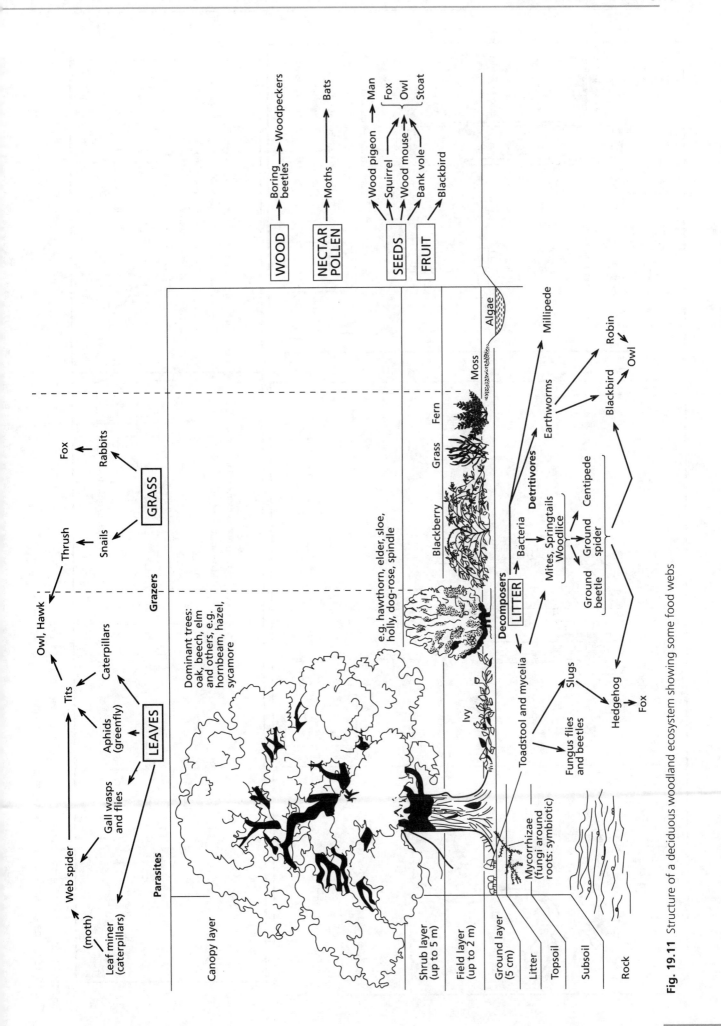

Fig. 19.11 Structure of a deciduous woodland ecosystem showing some food webs

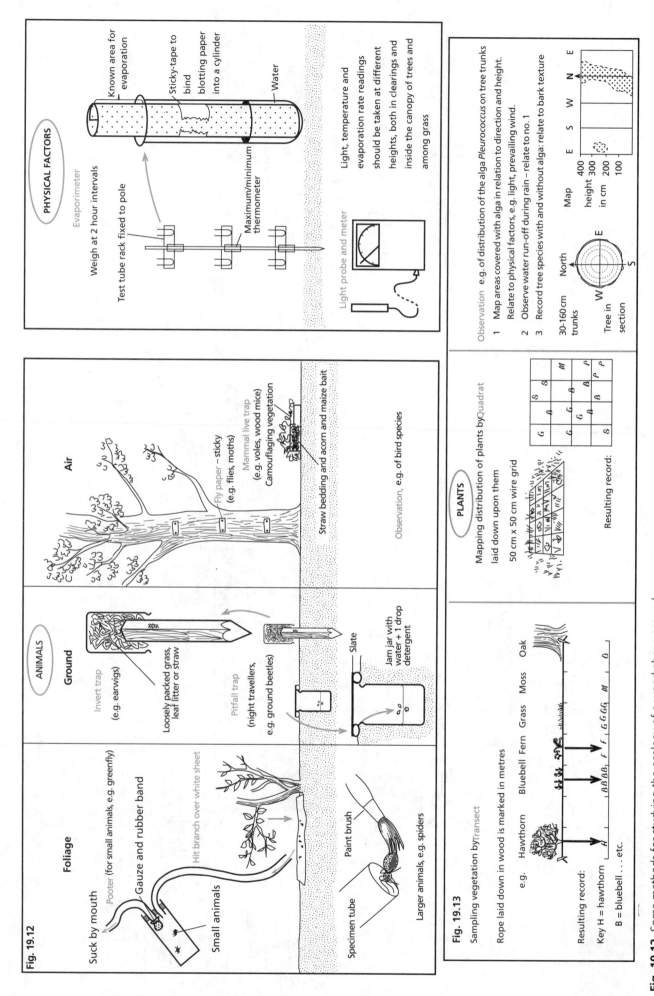

Fig. 19.12 Some methods for studying the ecology of a wood above ground
Fig. 19.13 Some methods for mapping vegetation in a wood

19.7 Soil ecosystem

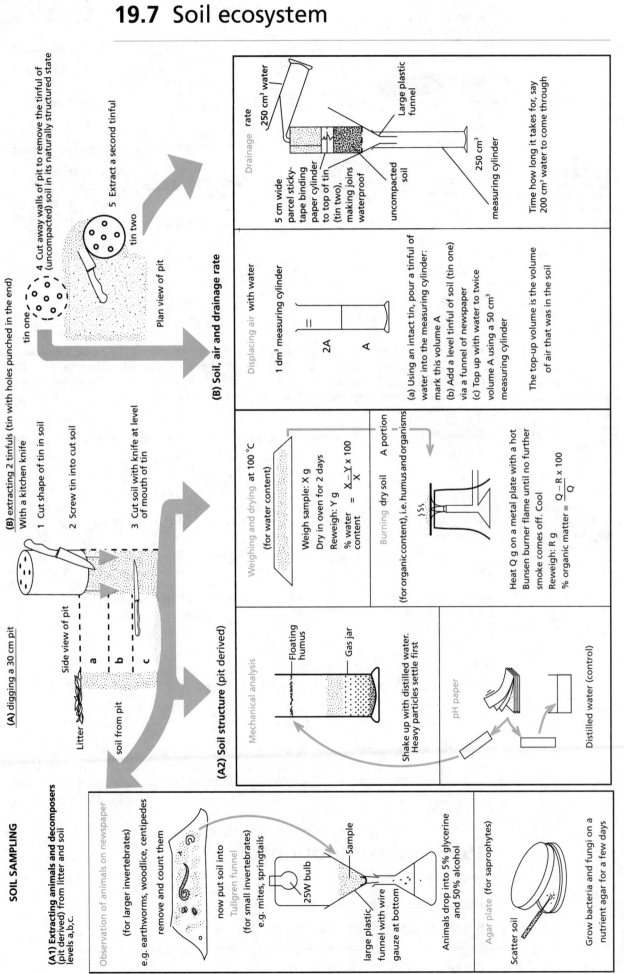

Fig. 19.14 Some methods of studying soil

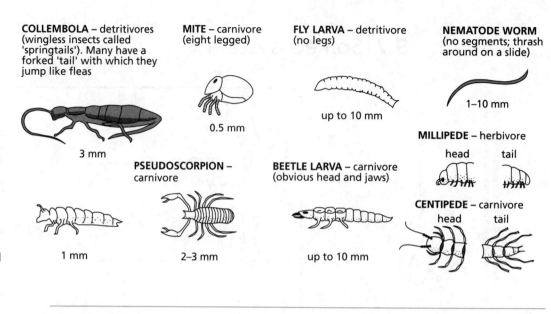

Fig. 19.15
Organisms commonly extracted by Tullgren funnel

19.8 Keys

Keys are a means of identifying organisms in *local* situations, e.g. in a pond or woodland. The user of the key selects one of two *contrasting* descriptions, choosing the one that fits the organism being identified. The chosen description leads to a number, alongside which are further descriptions from which to choose. The final choice leads to the organism's name.

Example: Choose one of the organisms in Fig. 19.16 and use the key below the diagram to identify it.

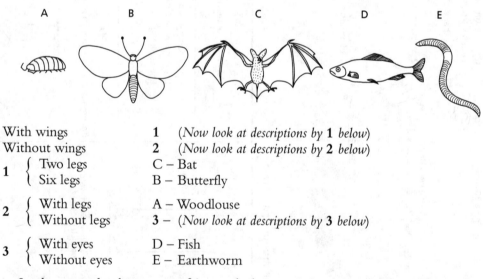

Fig. 19.16
A variety of organisms

| With wings | **1** | (*Now look at descriptions by* **1** *below*) |
| Without wings | **2** | (*Now look at descriptions by* **2** *below*) |

1 { Two legs — C – Bat
Six legs — B – Butterfly

2 { With legs — A – Woodlouse
Without legs — **3** – (*Now look at descriptions by* **3** *below*)

3 { With eyes — D – Fish
Without eyes — E – Earthworm

In the example above, use of internal characteristics (e.g. vertebrae) or confusing ones (e.g. hairiness) would delay identification – some butterflies are as hairy as bats!
Your key of the organisms above could be different but still be 'correct' – if it works.

19.9 Soil components

Soil: the layer of earth that contains organisms. Consists of

1. rock particles
2. air
3. water
4. mineral salts
5. humus
6. organisms.

Table 19.2 Comparison of sandy soil and clay soil

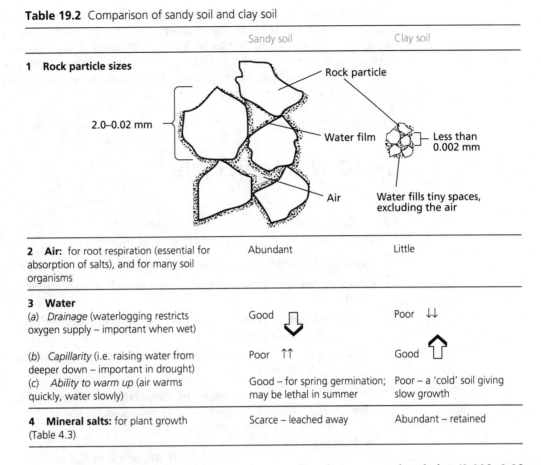

	Sandy soil	Clay soil
1 Rock particle sizes		
2 Air: for root respiration (essential for absorption of salts), and for many soil organisms	Abundant	Little
3 Water		
(a) *Drainage* (waterlogging restricts oxygen supply – important when wet)	Good	Poor ↓↓
(b) *Capillarity* (i.e. raising water from deeper down – important in drought)	Poor ↑↑	Good
(c) *Ability to warm up* (air warms quickly, water slowly)	Good – for spring germination; may be lethal in summer	Poor – a 'cold' soil giving slow growth
4 Mineral salts: for plant growth (Table 4.3)	Scarce – leached away	Abundant – retained

Thus a **silty soil**, with its particle size intermediate between sand and clay (0.002–0.02 mm) 'averages out' their properties, giving near-ideal conditions for plant growth.

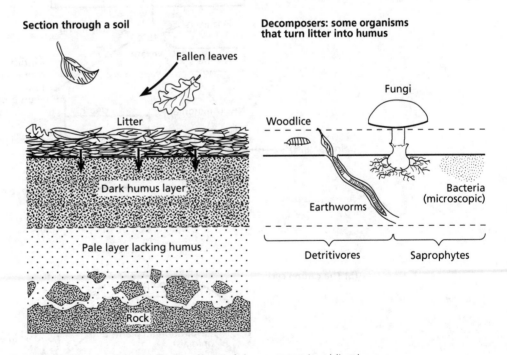

Fig. 19.17 Structure of soil and the effects of decomposers in adding humus

5 Humus – dead organic matter in soil. Mostly decomposing *litter* (fallen leaves) *or manure*. Improves soil by: (*a*) providing mineral salts from decay; (*b*) providing air spaces (improves clay); (*c*) retaining moisture (improves sand); (*d*) improving crumb structure (prevents soil from being blown away); (*e*) encouraging earthworms (see Unit 19.12).

6 Organisms: assist circulation of elements. **Decomposers** in soil are particularly important, turning dead organic matter (unusable by plants) into inorganic food for them, e.g. salts and CO_2. **Bacteria** have special roles in the circulation of nitrogen and carbon in nature (Fig. 19.18). Roots of **plants** bind soil, preventing erosion. Deforestation, particularly on slopes, allows rain to wash soil away; over-grazing, especially by goats, allows wind or rain to remove soil.

19.10 Nitrogen cycle

Green plants need nitrates for protein synthesis.
Nitrates are available to green plants from four sources:

1. **man-made fertilizers**, e.g. ammonium nitrate;

2. **lightning** – causes oxides of nitrogen to form in the air; these become nitric acid in the rainfall.

3. **nitrogen-fixing bacteria** – the only organisms capable of converting nitrogen gas into compounds of nitrogen;

4. **nitrifying bacteria** – oxidize ammonium compounds to nitrites and then nitrates, if there is air for them to use.

Nitrates are turned into nitrogen by **denitrifying** bacteria if the soil lacks air, as in waterlogged conditions. Nitrogen gas is useless to green plants.

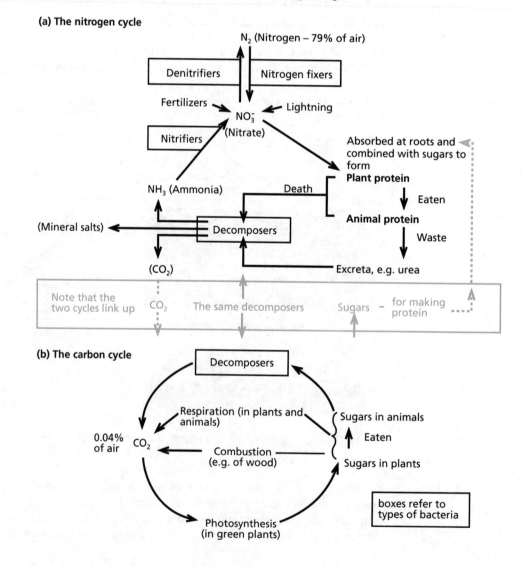

Fig. 19.18
(a) The nitrogen cycle, (b) the carbon cycle

In green plants, nitrates and sugars form amino acids; these become proteins. Animals convert plant proteins into their own, but in doing so waste some, e.g. as urea, which is excreted.

Decomposers break down dead organisms and their wastes. Nitrogen compounds in them, e.g. proteins, end up as ammonia and then ammonium compounds.

19.11 Carbon cycle

Green plants *photosynthesize* CO_2 into sugars. Most other organic molecules are made using sugar; e.g. cellulose in wood, or proteins and oils in seeds and leaves. When these are eaten by animals, the digested products are turned into animal carbohydrates, fats and proteins.

This variety of organic molecules is returned to air as CO_2 during respiration in plants and animals, in bacteria of *decay*, or by *combustion*.

Fuels include wood and the 'fossil fuels' coal, petroleum and natural gas. Fossil fuels were formed by the partial decay and compression of plants by earth-forces millions of years ago.

19.12 Earthworms and soil

Earthworms (*see also* Unit 21.4):
(*a*) *aerate* and *drain* soil by tunnelling;
(*b*) *fertilize* soil by:
  (i) pulling litter down into tunnels for bacteria to decompose
  (ii) excreting urine
  (iii) decomposing when dead;
(*c*) bring *salts*, leached to lower layers, up again to roots (in worm casts);
(*d*) *neutralize* soil acidity by secreting lime into it (from gut glands);
(*e*) *grind* coarse soil finer in gut (in gizzard).

These activities are exactly what a farmer aims to do to make a *loam* (cultivated soil, with all six soil components – see Unit 19.9 – in proportions suitable for good plant growth).

19.13 Water cycle

In the *water cycle* most of the water circulated does not go through organisms (Fig. 19.19). It has long been suggested that cutting down forests decreases rainfall in that area.

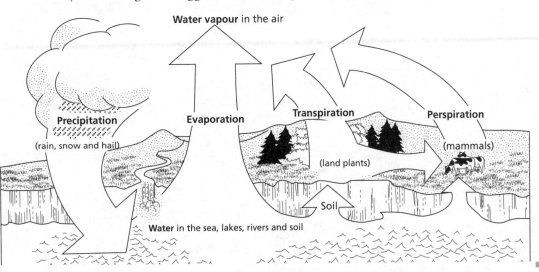

Fig. 19.19 The water cycle

Summary

1 An ecosystem is the interaction between the community of organisms and its non-living environment.

2 The biosphere is the total world ecosystem.

3 Feeding relationships in an ecosystem are represented by a food web.

4 The parts of a food web are food chains. Each food chain starts with a green plant, which provides food for a herbivore, which is then eaten by a carnivore. This is the simplest possible food chain.

5 Food chains can be expressed as pyramids of numbers or of biomass to give an idea of quantity.

6 Food in an ecosystem is cycled from plants to animals and from their dead bodies to saprophytes – which return inorganic food to plants by their decay activities.

7 The cycling of the elements carbon and nitrogen is particularly important to life.

8 Types of feeding relationship include predators, parasites, mutualists and competitors.

9 Stable ecosystems are characterized by a dominant set of plants that are maintained – the climax community.

10 In unstable communities, the vegetation is changing through a 'succession'.

11 Man is making natural ecosystems unstable by his activities, e.g. deforestation and pollution.

12 Studies of natural ecosystems should include measurement of abiotic factors, e.g. temperature and pH, and estimation of the numbers and distribution of species of organisms in the area studied.

13 Species can be identified by means of keys.

14 Ponds, woods and the soil are complex ecosystems, each requiring their own special methods of study.

Chapter 20
Man and his environment

Man has two environments: that outside his skin and the other inside it. He must manage both if he is to stay alive as an individual and as a species.

MAN'S EXTERNAL ENVIRONMENT

Man produces more food for himself than nature alone could provide, by farming the land. Farming depends on producing a fertile soil (see Unit 19.9), on breeding good plant and animal food-species (see Unit 18.5), and on reducing pests and diseases (see Unit 20.4).

Agricultural practices
1 Ploughing
2 Liming
3 Manuring (= fertilizing)

4 Crop rotation
5 Pest control

20.1 Ploughing

1 Aerates and drains soil by creating ridges and furrows (thus discouraging denitrification);

2 brings leached salts up to near the surface for roots;

3 brings pests, sheltering deep down, up to the surface for frost to kill;

4 allows frost to break up the ridges of soil;

5 turns organic matter, e.g. wheat stubble, into the ground to decay.

20.2 Liming and fertilizing

Liming – addition of powdered $CaCO_3$:
(*a*) neutralizes acidity;
(*b*) allows efficient application of fertilizers (see Fig. 20.1);
(*c*) flocculates ('clumps') clay particles together into larger groups ('crumbs') with air spaces between them.

Fertilizing – restoring mineral salts to the soil which have been lost by taking the crops and animals grown there off to market.

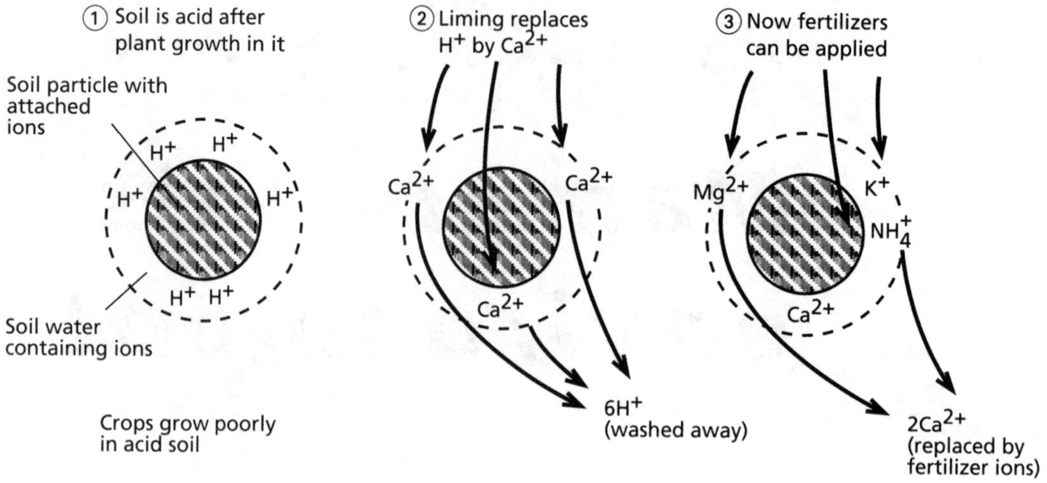

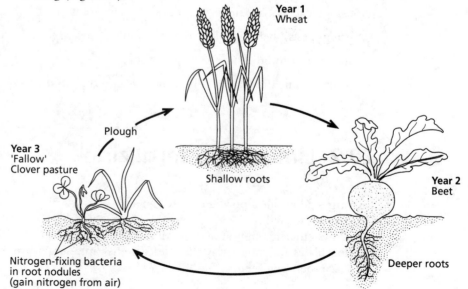

① Soil is acid after plant growth in it

Soil particle with attached ions

Soil water containing ions

Crops grow poorly in acid soil

Fig. 20.1 Liming and fertilizing – chemical effects

② Liming replaces H⁺ by Ca²⁺

6H⁺ (washed away)

③ Now fertilizers can be applied

2Ca²⁺ (replaced by fertilizer ions)

Table 20.1 Comparison of organic and inorganic fertilizers

	Organic: e.g. clover ploughed in to decay and animal dung + urine	**Inorganic:** factory products, e.g. $(NH_4)_2SO_4$ or wastes, e.g. basic slag
Cost	Cheap	Expensive
Application	Difficult (bulky, sticky)	Easy (powders, granules)
Action	Slow but long-lasting	Quick but short-lasting
Soil structure	Improved (see 'humus')	Not improved
Earthworms	Encouraged	Can harm them

Excessive use of fertilizers can pollute freshwater with nitrates. These may
(a) kill freshwater animals by eutrophication (see Table 20.3);
(b) cause gut cancers if drunk (EC safety level is 30 mg nitrate per dm³ water).

20.3 Crop rotation

Crop rotation – growth of different crops on the same land in successive years without manuring each year. The two harvested crops have different mineral requirements and often obtain them from different soil depths. In the 'fallow year'
(a) **legumes**, e.g. clover, are sown to restore *nitrogen compounds* to the soil when the plants decay after being ploughed in. Other minerals (removed in crops) are restored by fertilizing (Fig. 20.2).

Year 1 Wheat

Plough

Shallow roots

Year 2 Beet

Deeper roots

Year 3 'Fallow' Clover pasture

Nitrogen-fixing bacteria in root nodules (gain nitrogen from air)

Fig. 20.2 Rotation of crops

(*b*) **parasites**, e.g. rust fungi, hiding in soil die (no host plants available).

20.4 Pest control

Pest organisms, e.g. locusts, termites and weeds, reduce Man's agricultural efforts or other interests. It was *Man* himself who created pests by providing organisms, normally held in check in their ecosystems, with unusual opportunities for increase in numbers in a monoculture (e.g. of corn, cotton or cows).

Chemical control – expensive. May eliminate pests but also kills harmless organisms. Examples: DDT (insects); 2–4D (weeds) (see Table 20.3).

Biological control – cheap. Use of a natural enemy of the *specific* pest to *control* numbers (some damage must be expected), e.g. guppy fish eat mosquito larvae in ponds (see also Unit 21.12).

20.5 Human population crisis (problems)

Man's population growth has been *exponential*:

Year	Population	
1630 (estimated)	500 million	} 200 years
1830	1000 million	}
1930	2000 million	} 100 years
1975	4000 million	estimated to rise to 6000 million by 2000 (see Fig. 16.10)

This has occurred because of improvements in:

1. **Agriculture:** more food per hectare owing to improved strains of crops and livestock (see Unit 18.5), mechanization and fertilizers.
2. **Sanitation:** disposal of excreta, finally via sewage farms.
3. **Water supply:** filtration, finally chlorination.
4. **Medicine:** inoculation, drugs, antibiotics, aseptic surgery.

} reduced death rate from disease

Consequences

Bacteria on an agar plate show exponential growth in population. This leads to exhaustion of food and self-pollution resulting in mass death (crash phase, see Fig. 16.8). Similarly, Man's exponential growth in population is resulting in both pollution of the biosphere and reduction of its resources. Unlike bacteria, Man has the ability to avoid the crash phase by using a variety of solutions.

20.6 Pollution

Pollution: waste substances or energy from human activities which upset the normal balances in the biosphere. Anything from noise (aircraft) and heat (atomic power stations) to various substances in excess (sewage, DDT).

Laws: the Clean Air Acts (1956 and 1968) have prevented the sooty smogs of industrial and city areas. Smogs caused death by bronchitis and traffic accidents, and dirtied and damaged stone buildings. Britain (1988) has followed some other EC countries in encouraging widespread use of lead-free petrol.

Table 20.2 Air pollutants

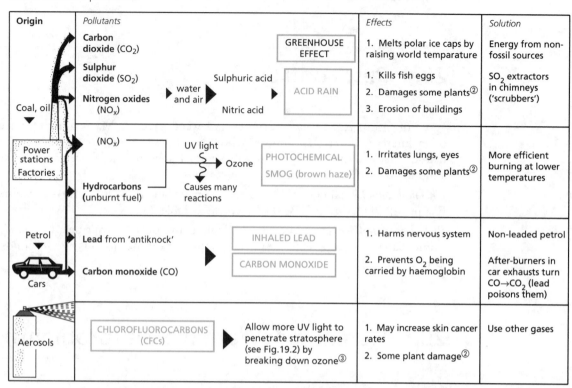

Origin	*Pollutants*				*Effects*	*Solution*
Coal, oil	**Carbon dioxide (CO_2)**			GREENHOUSE EFFECT	1. Melts polar ice caps by raising world temparature	Energy from non-fossil sources
	Sulphur dioxide (SO_2)	water and air	Sulphuric acid	ACID RAIN	1. Kills fish eggs	SO_2 extractors in chimneys ('scrubbers')
	Nitrogen oxides (NO_x)		Nitric acid		2. Damages some plants②	
					3. Erosion of buildings	
Power stations Factories	**(NO_x)**	UV light → Ozone		PHOTOCHEMICAL SMOG (brown haze)	1. Irritates lungs, eyes	More efficient burning at lower temperatures
	Hydrocarbons (unburnt fuel)	Causes many reactions			2. Damages some plants②	
Petrol / Cars	**Lead from 'antiknock'**			INHALED LEAD	1. Harms nervous system	Non-leaded petrol
	Carbon monoxide (CO)			CARBON MONOXIDE	2. Prevents O_2 being carried by haemoglobin	After-burners in car exhausts turn CO→CO_2 (lead poisons them)
Aerosols	CHLOROFLUOROCARBONS (CFCs)			Allow more UV light to penetrate stratosphere (see Fig.19.2) by breaking down ozone③	1. May increase skin cancer rates	Use other gases
					2. Some plant damage②	

① **Greenhouse effect:** rising levels of CO_2 in the air have raised global temperature by slowing loss of heat from earth to outer space. This has melted ice, so raising sea level by about 25 mm in the last 50 years. If this trend continues, large areas (where a third of mankind lives) will be flooded, e.g. Bangladesh, Holland, London, New York. Burning fossil fuels (which produce extra CO_2) and felling tropical forests (which absorb CO_2) are largely responsible (see Unit 20.8, no. 7).

② **Forest damage** in Europe and the US has been blamed on 'acid rain'. This pollution raises aluminium levels (toxic) and removes calcium, magnesium and potassium (nutrients) from soil; but it also kills lichens. Yet trees are severely damaged in some areas where lichens flourish and where SO_2 levels are well below those known to cause damage. In contrast to steadily falling SO_2 levels in Europe, ozone levels are rising and can reach high concentrations in rural as well as industrial areas. Ozone damages chlorophyll. Unknown diseases may be the cause since individual trees flourish in otherwise devastated areas (possibly mutants? – see Unit 17.15). No single cause for tree damage has been established.

③ In Antarctica a progressive **thinning of the ozone layer** (by over 50% in October 1985) has been detected each winter since 1979. The rate of thinning, which occurs in the northern hemisphere too, has been ten times that previously estimated. Rich nations have been alarmed into banning the use of CFCs (in aerosol sprays, refrigerators and foam plastics).

Table 20.3 Land and water pollutants

	Land pollutants	*Origin*	*Effect*	*Solution*
	(a) Insecticides	Crop protection; control of disease vectors, e.g. mosquito	May kill top consumers ①; may lower photosynthesis rate of marine algae	Ban undesirable ones, e.g. DDT, as UK has done ②
	(b) Radioactive wastes	Nuclear reactor accidents and wastes; atom bombs	Mutations	Nuclear waste silos – but some have leaked
	Water pollutants			
	(a) Sewage	Human	Eutrophication ③	Sewage treatment (see Unit 3.12)
	(b) Artificial fertilizers	Excessive agricultural use	Eutrophication ③	Use of organic manures (Unit 20.2)
	(c) Petroleum	Tanker accidents	Oiled sea birds, beaches ④	Effective accident prevention
	(d) Mercury (organic)	Chemical works; fungicides on seeds, wood	Minamata disease (paralysis, idiots born) ①	Effluent purification

① Tiny amounts of pollutants absorbed by producers are concentrated along a food chain into the top consumers. Thus in the 1950s eagles had very high DDT levels and laid thin-shelled eggs that broke easily. Their population fell. Similarly, plankton in Minamata Bay, Japan, absorbed small amounts of mercury waste in a factory's effluent. This was concentrated in predators – crustaceans, then fish – and finally got into the human fish-eating population. Many people died or became paralysed. Mothers gave birth to idiot and malformed children.

② Poor countries cannot afford to do this in the tropics – famine or disease would result. DDT is cheap and effective.

③ **Eutrophication:** enrichment of natural waters with mineral salts.

(a) *Mineral salts* drain off recently over-fertilized fields; or are formed by bacterial breakdown of sewage in the water.

(b) *Algae multiply* exponentially, given this excess of food (water goes green). They crash in numbers as their food runs out.

(c) *Bacteria multiply* exponentially, given an excess of dead algae to decay.

(d) Bacterial respiration sharply *reduces* O_2 in the water – *killing aquatic animals* by suffocation. This worsens the situation as even more bodies decay.

④ **Detergents** have a harmful effect on cell membranes and affect aquatic life seriously. Detergents often harm marine life more than the oil slicks they are used on (to disperse them). Older-type detergents used to release phosphates on break-down – encouraging eutrophication. Modern detergents do not and they break down easily.

20.7 Depletion of resources

Resources are of two types: non-renewable (non-living) and renewable (living).

(a) *Non-renewable*, e.g. **minerals**; and natural gas which will be used up within 50 years (from *known* sources).

Soil is being lost by erosion because of unwise land use, e.g. over-grazing or clear felling of forest (thus removing the binding action of roots), particularly on sloping land, e.g. in Amazonia, Philippines and the Himalayas. New soil takes centuries to form through weathering of rock and the action of organisms (see Unit 19.9). Without fine soil, many producers cannot grow and whole ecosystems may be destroyed.

(b) *Renewable*, e.g. **foods**: herring and whales have been over-fished. Cutting down of forests exceeds planting. Harvesting should not exceed replacement rate.

Destruction of wild-life: Agricultural needs destroy natural habitats; pesticides, poison, and hunting for 'sport' or fashionable items, e.g. skins, ivory, may all lead to extinction of species, e.g. dodo, Cape lion.

Food shortage: Two-thirds of the world population lack either enough energy foods or protein or both in their diet. Poor nations are unable to pay for the surplus food of rich ones.

Reduced living space: Overcrowded populations lead to greater chance of epidemic diseases and social diseases, e.g. vandalism, child abuse, drug-taking, alcoholism. In Britain every year about 10 000 children are registered as abused, of whom about 200 die.

20.8 Human population crisis (solutions)

① **Contraception** (see Unit 15.4) and abortion (removing unwanted embryos) would by themselves reduce the rate of increase in population if used worldwide. Some people object to these practices.

② **Conservation of minerals:** use of substitutes for metals, e.g. carbon fibre plastics; reversing the throw-away mentality by making durable products, e.g. cars that last; recycling metals in discarded items (see also Unit 3.12).

Note: These policies would lead to lowered industrial production (and fewer jobs).

③ **Conservation of wildlife and natural scenery:** strict guardianship of nature reserves; acceptance that minerals in a mountain may be less valuable than the beauty it affords. Man's need for recreation and enjoyment of nature is as necessary for health as meeting his material needs. Reclamation of gravel pits and of mining tips by suitable planting and landscaping can provide amenity areas, e.g. for sailing and as parks. Endangered species can be bred in zoos and, when they have been re-educated to live in the wild, can be reintroduced into suitable areas.

④ **Conservation of genes:** wild animals and plants may not be of direct use to Man but can provide useful genes for introduction into his breeding programmes, e.g. genes for disease resistance from the small inedible potato of South America, genes for hardiness in Soay sheep, and genes for high vitamin C content in wild tomatoes.

⑤ **Conservation of renewable resources:** by never taking more than can be replaced (by reproduction). Reforestation is thus a priority worldwide. Meanwhile recycling paper helps reduce tree-felling.

⑥ **New sources of food:** greater dependence on microorganisms, e.g. 'SCP' and mycoprotein (see Unit 3.12), and soya bean meat-substitutes. Farming wild animals on their natural land supplemented by cattle feedstuffs produces high quality lean meat quickly, e.g. red deer (Scotland), wildebeeste (Africa).

⑦ **Finding new (acceptable) energy sources,** e.g. solar, wind and tidal power. Fast breeder nuclear reactors will produce very much more dangerous waste than conventional reactors – a possible mutation hazard. But using fossil fuels (coal, oil) to a greater extent raises CO_2 levels in air causing a *greenhouse effect*. Biomass from fast-growing willow or poplar clones is a cheap and environmentally sound energy source. The CO_2 produced from burning the chipped wood in high-efficiency burners is simply recycled by growing new trees. To produce the same energy from coal costs almost three times, and from oil four times, as much. To recycle metals, produce substitutes for them, and make artificial fertilizers is very energy-consuming.

MAN'S INTERNAL ENVIRONMENT

Hormones and nerves (see Unit 12.11) help to stabilize the body's internal environment (achieve homeostasis). Any change from normal is called **disease**.

20.9 Types of disease in Man

① **Genetic:** since these diseases are inherited, they are *incurable*.
Examples: **haemophilia** – a gene mutation; **Down's syndrome**: baby has an extra chromosome, i.e. 46 + 1, owing to abnormal meiosis in the mother. Person has retarded development and usually dies before the age of 40 (see Unit 17.15).

② **Diet deficiency:** curable by eating a balanced diet.
Examples: lack of vitamin C (**scurvy**, see Unit 4.5); or protein (**kwashiorkor**, see Unit 4.6).

③ **Hormonal:** curable by artificial supply of hormone.
Examples: lack of thyroxine (**cretinism**) or insulin (**diabetes**) (see Unit 12.10).

④ **Pathogenic:** entry of parasites (pathogens) into body which upsets its metabolism.
Examples: viruses (see Unit 3.1), bacteria (see Unit 3.2), protozoa (see Unit 3.11).

Infectious diseases are those passed on from one individual to another by touching (contagious) or by other means, e.g. 'catching' 'flu. Malaria is not infectious – a vector passes it on (see Unit 21.13).
(*a*) For **prevention** (better than cure):
　(i) **kill vectors,** e.g. mosquitoes carrying malaria, or intermediate hosts, e.g. snails carrying bilharzia;
　(ii) **prevent access** of parasite by hygiene, water chlorination, cooking food or protective measures, e.g. mosquito nets;

   (iii) employ **preventive medicine** (prophylaxis) using immunization (see below) or drugs, e.g. mepacrine for malaria;

   (iv) **quarantine** those who are ill (isolate sources of infection).

   (*b*) A **cure** requires:

   (i) **hospitalization:** rest and good food assist body's own defences;

   (ii) **medicines:** drugs, antibiotics, kill pathogens.

5. **Environmental:** often preventable by wise precautions.
Examples: skin cancer (excessive sunbathing), industrial chemicals (not wearing face masks).

20.10 Natural defences of the body against pathogens

1. **Skin:** keratin; sweat (which is antiseptic) (see Unit 10.10).

2. **Blood clotting:** provides a temporary barrier before wound heals (see Unit 8.2).

3. **Phagocytes:** ingest microorganisms (see Unit 8.2).

4. **Lymphocytes:** make antibodies (see Unit 8.2) to kill pathogens or neutralize their poisons (with antitoxins), thus making the body immune (protected). There are two methods of immunization:

Table 20.4 Comparison of active and passive immunity

	Active immunity (*body participates*)	Passive immunity (*body passive*)
Method	Weakened or dead strain of pathogen introduced, e.g. polio **vaccine**	Antibodies made by another organism, e.g. horse, or genetically engineered, are injected (see Unit 3.12)
Protection	(*a*) long-lasting ('boosters' prolong protection, e.g. anti-tetanus every 3 years) (*b*) takes weeks to develop	(*a*) short-lived (body destroys the foreign antibodies) (*b*) immediate protection

20.11 Notable contributors to health and hygiene

- **Edward Jenner** (1749–1823): practised *vaccination*. He scratched cowpox material (spots on cows caused by the vaccinia virus) into the skin of humans. The patients also developed mild spots, but became protected against the disfiguring or lethal disease smallpox. Smallpox has now been eliminated from the world.

- **Louis Pasteur** (1822–1895): father of *bacteriology*. Discovered the bacterial nature of putrefaction and many diseases. Saved silk industry (pebrine disease of silkworms), brewers ('ropy' beer), poultry farmers (chicken cholera) and cattle farmers (anthrax) from severe losses by developing sterile techniques and vaccines. Finally, developed a rabies vaccine to protect humans.

- **Joseph Lister** (1827–1912): developed *antiseptic surgery*. Used fine phenol spray to kill bacteria during operations, dramatically reducing hospital deaths. Today *aseptic* surgery is used – sterilization of all equipment before use, in autoclaves (see Unit 3.5).

- **Alexander Fleming** (1881–1955): discovered lysozyme (natural antiseptic in tears and saliva) and the *antibiotic* penicillin (see Unit 3.9).

Drugs, antibiotics, disinfectants and antiseptics

- **'Drugs'** are chemicals made by Man or organisms. Some are harmful and possession of them is illegal, e.g. LSD – which has no medical purpose. Others (in the right doses) assist medically, e.g. sulphonamides for curing bacterial infections, aspirin for headaches, and belladonna for helping people with ailing hearts. The term 'drug' is thus too vague to be very useful.

- **Antibiotics** are chemicals secreted by bacteria or fungi and extracted by Man for his own use in killing microorganisms (but not viruses) in his body. *Examples:* penicillin, aureomycin. Accurate choice of antibiotic to treat an infection depends on taking a swab (see Unit 3.6).

- **Disinfectants** are chemicals made by chemists to kill microorganisms, e.g. neat 'Dettol' in toilets.

- **Antiseptics** are chemicals used in such a dose that they kill microorganisms but *not* human cells with which they make contact. May be diluted disinfectants, e.g. weak 'Dettol' for gargling or bathing cuts.

20.12 Options for a human future

There is considerable confusion between the *fact* of variation and the *idea* of equality in human societies; and between the *rights* of individuals and their *duties* to others:

(a) Variation and equality

Human races are different; so are individuals, males and females. Biologically speaking each individual has different adaptations, i.e. potential. Yet in the Declaration of Independence of the United States (1776) there is the statement 'We hold these truths to be self-evident, that all men are created equal'.

(b) Rights and duties

Humans like to have the freedom to 'do their own thing' – to show their natural variation through behaviour. When humans live close together this is not entirely possible – whether in a family, a town or in a family of nations. A large human population in the world has the consequence that actions by some people strongly affect others. Such actions would probably have gone unnoticed in the past when the population was small since the effect was small, e.g. the discharge of sewage into rivers.

As the population rises, the **rights** of individuals become reduced because their **duties** to others (to preserve *their* rights) increase. The 'right' to manufacture goods or to provide energy must be balanced by the 'duty' to minimize pollution (see Unit 20.6). If necessary, governments are forced to impose laws restricting the 'rights' of some to preserve the 'rights' of others. The 'right' to have as many children as a couple wishes may have to be taken away in some countries – as it has been in China.

Here are some options for humans to think about:

1. **Voluntary population control** (see Unit 15.4)
   With sensible population size in each country, demands for food, materials and energy would be reasonable, and pollution could be controlled. Humans could live in balance with the biosphere.

2. **Continued population increase**
   This might result in
   - famine: through misuse of land for agriculture;
   - disease: through greater likelihood of epidemics, breakdown of health services;
   - war and civil unrest: see point 3.

The fate of deer on the Kaibab plateau (see Unit 18.2E) is warning enough of what might happen to a population too large for available resources.

③ Preparation for success in competition

Countries or races may decide to compete for the available resources – a return to the laws of natural selection and a breakdown of human society. In nature, a high rate of reproduction is an adaptation for survival and success, e.g. rabbits, locusts. With human societies it is a recipe for disaster – the population remains in poverty and is technologically underdeveloped. The technological means of eliminating competitors (weaponry) has gone far beyond the club and spear: in a war involving nuclear or biological weapons, this may affect survivors as well.

Malthus (see Unit 18.4) predicted that point 2 above would control human population. He also hoped for a solution by point 1, but he had no knowledge of modern means of contraception.

Which is to be the human solution?

Summary

1. Agriculture involves keeping the soil in good condition and providing water and mineral salts for plant growth.

2. It also requires selection of good plant or animal stock and the reduction of their competitors, diseases and species feeding on them to maximize production in this artificial ecosystem.

3. Soil needs ploughing, liming and fertilizing.

4. Crop rotation prevents 'exhaustion' of soil and helps control pests.

5. Pests may be kept in check by biological or chemical control – each with its own advantages.

6. Pollution is the spilling of harmful substances or energy into the environment.

7. Pollution knows no national boundaries: the greenhouse effect, thinning of the ozone layer and acid rain are of concern globally.

8. Air, land and water are being polluted by industry, agriculture and power generation.

9. World resources are finite and must be used wisely and where possible recycled, if non-renewable, e.g. minerals.

10. Renewable resources must be harvested at a rate that allows replacement, e.g. forests and fish.

11. Wildlife is being destroyed wantonly. Not only its beauty but its usefulness as a source of drugs and of genes for introduction into domestic breeds should be conserved.

12. There are various kinds of disease each with its own problems for control.

13. Natural defences of the body include the skin, blood clotting and blood cells, but antibodies are particularly useful.

14. Medicines, antibiotics, disinfectants and antiseptics all play their part in controlling diseases.

15. Vaccination enhances the body's protection against disease, before exposure to pathogens.

Chapter 21
A variety of life

21.1 Algae

See also Units 2.3 and 3.10.

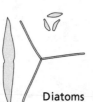

Diatoms

Flagellates (they swim)

Eaten by 'filter-feeders', e.g. *Daphnia*, mosquito larvae and pond mussels

Colonies of algae

Fig. 21.1 A selection of algae commonly found in freshwater as plankton

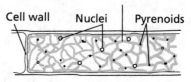

Chloroplast (net-like)

Cell wall Nuclei Pyrenoids

Fig. 21.2 Part of a cell of *Cladophora*, a *branching* filamentous alga forming dense green 'blankets' in ponds – compare *Spirogyra* (Unit 3.10)

Nucleus Chloroplast

Cell wall Cytoplasm

Fig. 21.3 *Pleurococcus*, 'green dust' on the wettest side of tree-trunks, posts, etc.

21.2 Mosses and ferns

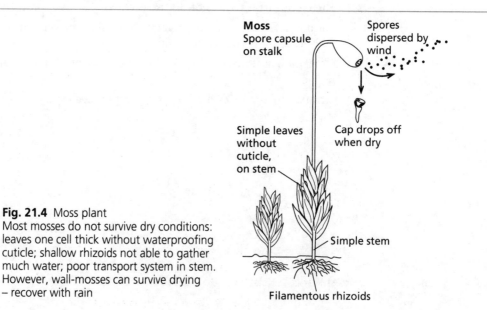

Moss
Spore capsule on stalk

Spores dispersed by wind

Simple leaves without cuticle, on stem

Cap drops off when dry

Simple stem

Fig. 21.4 Moss plant
Most mosses do not survive dry conditions: leaves one cell thick without waterproofing cuticle; shallow rhizoids not able to gather much water; poor transport system in stem. However, wall-mosses can survive drying – recover with rain

Filamentous rhizoids

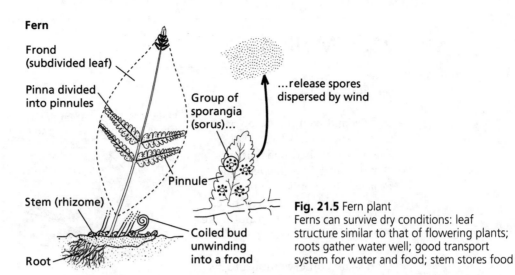

Fern

Frond (subdivided leaf)

Pinna divided into pinnules

Group of sporangia (sorus)...

...release spores dispersed by wind

Pinnule

Stem (rhizome)

Coiled bud unwinding into a frond

Root

Fig. 21.5 Fern plant
Ferns can survive dry conditions: leaf structure similar to that of flowering plants; roots gather water well; good transport system for water and food; stem stores food

Both mosses and ferns require wet conditions for sexual reproduction. Sperms swim in water to reach eggs. Thus neither group can colonize very dry habitats.

21.3 Flowering plants

See also Units 5.5 (leaf), 7.9 (stem and root), 14.5 (flowers), 14.10 (fruits) and 16.4 (seeds).

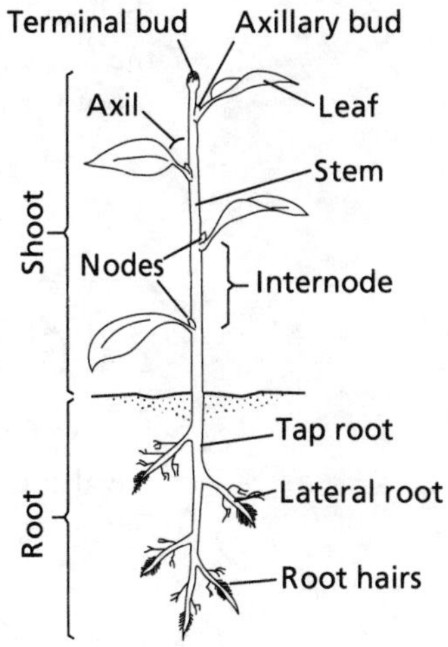

Terminal bud   Axillary bud

Axil

Leaf

Stem

Shoot

Nodes

Internode

Tap root

Lateral root

Root

Root hairs

Fig. 21.6 General structure of a dicot plant

21.4 Annelids

See also Units 2.4, 13.12 (movement) and 19.12 (decomposer). The earthworm is a scavenger (detritus feeder) in soil (see Unit 19.7).

Eaten by many birds (e.g. thrush), hedgehogs, foxes.

In ponds, *Tubifex* worms (about 1 mm in diameter) live in masses in tubes that they make in the mud. When water has less O_2, e.g. in warm weather, the worms partly emerge, actively waving around in the water like moving hair to get O_2. Also a detritus feeder.

Eaten by fish.

Both earthworms and *Tubifex* have haemoglobin in their blood to assist oxygen uptake in their relatively airless habitats.

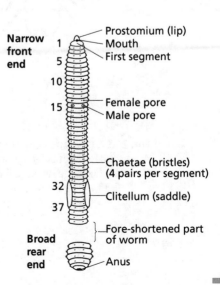

Narrow front end

Prostomium (lip)
Mouth
First segment

1

5

10

15

Female pore
Male pore

Chaetae (bristles) (4 pairs per segment)

32

Clitellum (saddle)

37

Fore-shortened part of worm

Broad rear end

Anus

Fig. 21.7 Earthworm (*Lumbricus*)

21.5 Molluscs

See also Unit 2.4.

The land snail is a herbivore, feeding on ground-layer plants. Eaten by thrushes, hedgehogs.

Pond snails, e.g. *Limnaea* and *Planorbis*, have only one pair of tentacles, with eyes at their base.

Water snails help transmit fluke diseases (see Unit 21.15).

Land snails conserve moisture by:
1 *Activity* only in damp or shady conditions (or at night).
2 *Mucus* (slime) to slow down evaporation.
3 *Lung* to reduce water loss (compared with gills).
4 *Aestivating* in dry conditions: animal withdraws into its waterproof shell and seals the opening with mucus. This hardens into a water-proof membrane (the epiphragm).

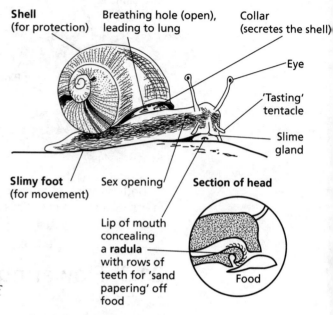

Fig. 21.8 Land snail, e.g. *Helix* (garden snail) or *Cepaea* (woodland and grassland snail)

21.6 Crustacea

See also Units 2.4 and 13.13 (movement).

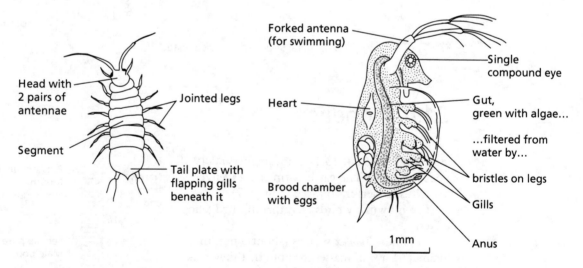

Fig. 21.9 *Asellus* (water-louse)
A scavenger (detritus feeder) in freshwater, like the woodlouse on land. Eaten by fish.

Fig. 21.10 *Daphnia* (water-flea)
A herbivore; part of the plankton in freshwater. Feeds on diatoms and other algae. Eaten by fish.

21.7 Insects

Insect characteristics

As insects are **Arthropods** (Unit 2.4), they also have:

1. an exoskeleton of chitin;
2. discontinuous growth – see below (compare humans, Unit 16.3);
3. many-jointed legs;
4. segmented body.

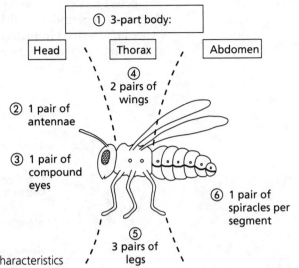
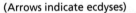

① 3-part body:

Head | Thorax | Abdomen

④ 2 pairs of wings

② 1 pair of antennae

③ 1 pair of compound eyes

⑥ 1 pair of spiracles per segment

⑤ 3 pairs of legs

Fig. 21.11 Six insect characteristics

Growth is discontinuous. The exoskeleton does not grow. It has to be shed (**ecdysis**) from time to time.

To do this the old skeleton is partly digested away and finally split open. The insect emerges with a new soft exoskeleton, which it expands before it hardens at a larger size, within an hour. So the size of an insect increases in bursts (Fig. 21.12). Each stage between ecdyses is called an **instar**.

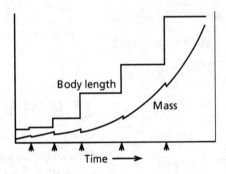

(Arrows indicate ecdyses)

Body length

Mass

Time →

Fig. 21.12 Discontinuous growth pattern of an insect

Metamorphosis is the change from a young to an adult form. Young stages in insects have no *wings*, nor can they *reproduce*.

Two kinds of life cycle:

1 Incomplete metamorphosis

Examples: locust, cockroach, dragonfly

Growing stage: **nymph** (similar to adult, lacking only wings and ability to reproduce). Last ecdysis gives adult.

2 Complete metamorphosis

butterfly, bee (most insects)

larvae (so unlike adult that reorganization into an adult must be achieved as a **pupa**).

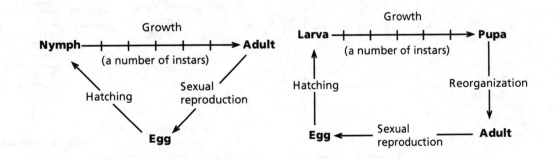

Fig. 21.13 Two kinds of life cycle in insects

Nymph —— Growth —— → Adult
(a number of instars)
Hatching | Sexual reproduction
Egg

Larva —— Growth —— → Pupa
(a number of instars)
Hatching | Reorganization
Egg ← Sexual reproduction — Adult

21.8 Locust

The desert locust (*Schistocerca gregaria*) – found from North Africa to India (Fig. 21.14). Devastates vegetation of all kinds, both as 'hopper' (nymph) and adult. Controlled by laying bran, soaked in insecticide, in the path of hoppers. If necessary, flying swarms of adults must be sprayed with insecticide from planes.

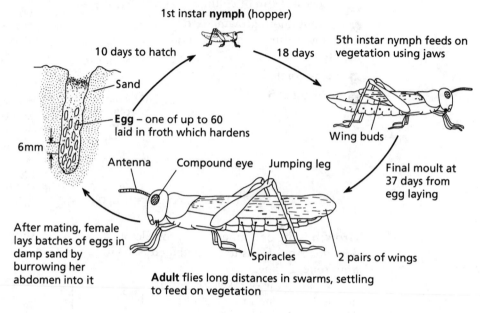

Fig. 21.14
The locust, *Schistocerca gregaria* (showing incomplete metamorphosis)

21.9 Housefly and blowfly

Housefly (*Musca domestica*): Adults transmit diseases (e.g. dysentery, certain worms) by visiting faeces and then human food. Here they deposit the infecting organisms via their feet or saliva (see Fig. 6.1) or by their own droppings ('fly-spots'). Flies are controlled by good garbage disposal and sanitation (removes breeding sites) and insecticides. In tropics: use muslin or wire gauze fly-screens to cover food and drink.

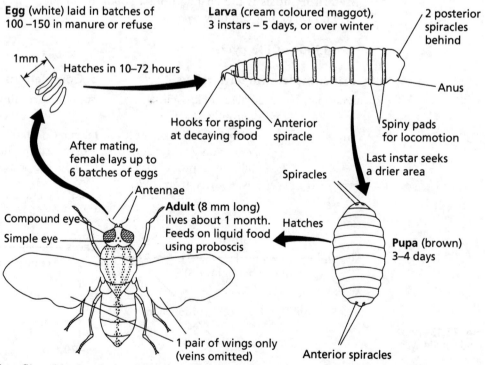

Fig. 21.15
Housefly, *Musca domestica* (showing complete metamorphosis)

Blowflies (bluebottles and greenbottles) have similar life cycles but the larvae feed on the meat of dead animals.

21.10 Large cabbage white butterfly

Large cabbage white butterfly (*Pieris brassicae*) eats cabbage–family plants. Controlled by insecticides and a parasitic 3 mm black wasp (*Apanteles glomerata*). The wasp's eggs, injected into caterpillar, hatch into larvae feeding on caterpillar's tissues, thus killing it. Pupates within bright yellow cocoons on caterpillar's skin.

21.11 Honey-bee

Honey-bee (*Apis mellifera*) (Fig. 21.16).

Organization in the hive

No individual bee can live for long without assistance from the others. Thus the hive, with its 5000–100 000 bees, is comparable to a socially organized unit, e.g. a town.

The queen is the only fertile female (*a*) laying eggs and (*b*) secreting 'queen substance', which is passed from bee to bee by mouth and keeps the colony working together.

Drones are fertile males that mate with the queen in the air, do no hive work, are fed by workers and driven out to die in the autumn.

Workers are infertile females with a sequence of duties as they get older. Their duties include:
(*a*) nursing – look after larvae, feeding them 'royal jelly' (from head glands), honey and pollen;
(*b*) hive maintenance – make honeycomb (from wax secreted by abdomen) and store pollen and honey in it; sealing sections of hive with propolis (from plant buds);
(*c*) foraging – gather nectar from flowers and turn it into honey in crop;
(*d*) defending (by sting) and ventilating (by wing-beating) the hive.

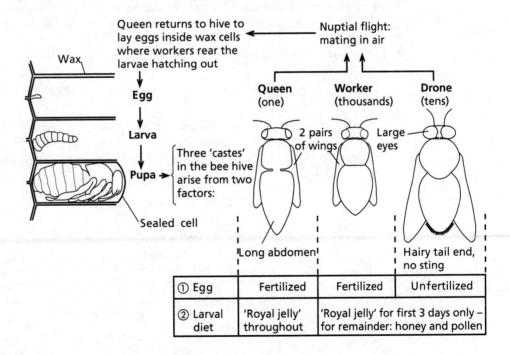

Fig. 21.16 Life cycle of the honey-bee, a social insect

21.12 Mosquito

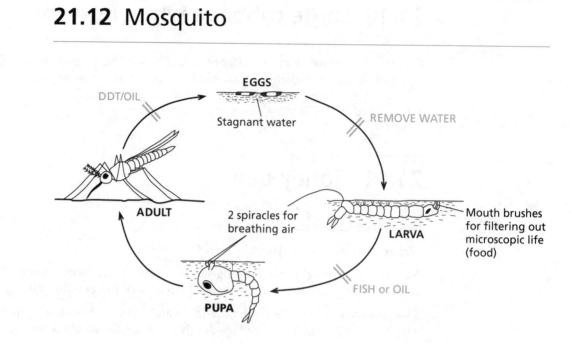

Fig. 21.17 Life cycle of the Anopheline mosquito and methods of controlling it (in green)

The mosquito lays its eggs *on* stagnant water. The aquatic larvae breathe air through spiracles at the surface of the water; so do the pupae. The adults may emerge within a week after egg-laying in tropical countries. The females need a meal of blood to ensure proper egg development before fertilization. They tend to 'bite' humans at night, sheltering by day in dark places in houses. These habits give opportunities for **controlling mosquitoes**:

- drain marshes or otherwise remove stagnant water (prevents egg laying);
- spray light oils containing insecticide on water that cannot be removed (oil blocks spiracles, suffocating the aquatic stages; the insecticide kills females landing to lay eggs);
- introduce 'mosquito fish', e.g. *Gambusia* or guppy, into the water (to eat larvae and pupae);
- spray walls of houses with long-lasting insecticides, e.g. DDT (kills adults sheltering there).

Mosquitoes only transmit **diseases**, e.g. malaria, if they are given the opportunity to suck up the parasites of an infected person. When mosquitoes 'bite' they inject saliva to prevent the blood clotting. It is with this saliva that the parasites enter healthy people.

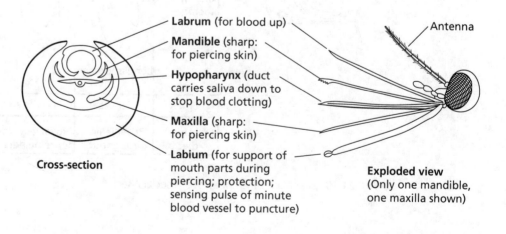

Fig. 21.18 Mouthparts (proboscis) of female mosquito – for piercing skin and sucking blood

21.13 Malaria and other mosquito-borne diseases

Despite precautions, millions of people are affected by **malaria** in the tropics. Millions die of the high fevers it produces. Those with sickle-cell anaemia trait (see Unit 18.2B) survive better.

Drug–resistant strains of *Plasmodium* and insecticide-resistant strains of mosquitoes arise by mutation (see Unit 17.15), making control of malaria a continuing problem.

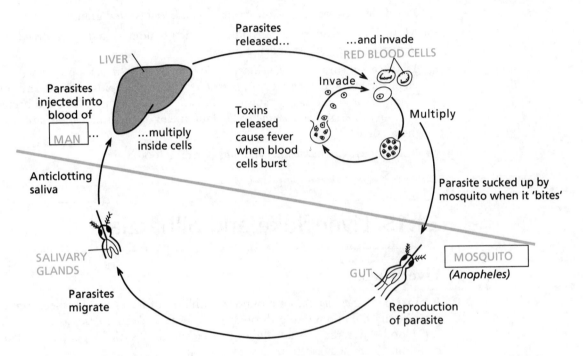

Fig. 21.19 Life cycle of *Plasmodium*, the malaria parasite

Modern methods of malaria control include:

1. Controlling the mosquito (Unit 21.12).
2. Regularly taking drugs which kill the parasites that do get injected (prophylaxis, Unit 20.9).
3. Quarantine (isolating) those who become diseased, away from other people and under mosquito nets (to prevent infecting mosquitoes).
4. Curing diseased people with Artemisin (to which *Plasmodium* is not resistant).
5. Impregnating mosquito nets with Permethrin, which both repels and kills mosquitoes.
6. Vaccinating against *Plasmodium* at present gives 50–75% protection in trials in Colombia and Venezuela.

Various mosquito species also infect Man with:

- **Elephantiasis:** enormous enlargement of limbs caused by blockage of the lymph vessels by millions of tiny worms (nematodes). Incurable.
- **Yellow fever:** severe jaundice (yellow skin) caused by liver damage from a virus which may cause death.

21.14 Importance of insects to Man

Helpful

1. **Bees: pollinators** (without which orchard fruit yields are greatly reduced) and **suppliers of honey** (sweetener) and **beeswax** (for high-grade polishes and lipstick).

2. **Biological control** of pests, by *ladybirds* (eat aphids, mealy-bugs and scale insects in garden, coffee and citrus plantations); *Cactus moth* caterpillars (eat prickly-pear cactus invading agricultural land).

Harmful

1. **Food destroyers,** e.g. *locust* (crops), *grain weevil* (stored grain).

2. **Material destroyers,** e.g. *termites* (wooden buildings), *cotton boll weevil* (cotton flower), *clothes moth* (woollen clothes).

3. **Disease vectors,** e.g. *mosquitoes* (yellow fever virus, malaria protozoan and elephantiasis nematode worm), *tsetse flies* (human sleeping sickness and similar sicknesses in domesticated animals), *housefly* (dysentery protozoa and bacteria), *fleas* (plague bacteria), *wood-boring beetle* (Dutch elm disease fungus), *aphids* (plant virus diseases).

4. **Nuisances,** e.g. *cockroaches* and *ants* (spoiling food).

21.15 Liver fluke and bilharzia

Liver fluke

Importance: *Fasciola* causes around £5 million of losses in UK sheep production per year. Young flukes migrating through liver tissue can cause *death* as they suck in tissues and blood ('liver rot'). Adult flukes in the bile duct suck blood (about 250 in a duct consume 50 cm³/day), causing severe *anaemia*.

Fasciola can also infect cattle, horses, goats, deer, pigs, rabbits and hares – providing a wide reservoir for sheep infection.

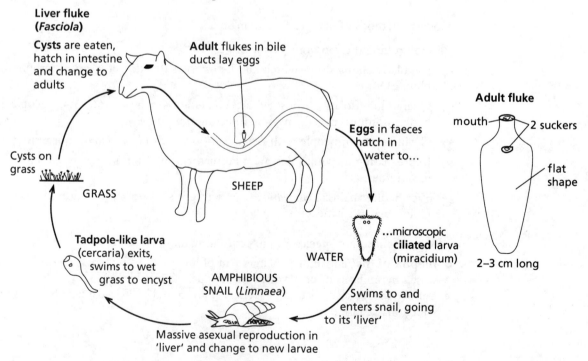

Fig. 21.20 Life cycle of liver fluke of sheep, *Fasciola hepatica*

Adaptations to parasitism:

1. Two suckers to attach to bile duct walls.
2. Large surface area for absorption, excretion and secretion.
3. Lack of sense organs (not needed), but do have muscles for movement.
4. Specialized larvae for infecting hosts.
5. Synchronized life cycle: miracidia hatch in June, the peak month for hatching of snail eggs, so infecting the maximum number of snails.
6. Very high rate of reproduction (to ensure transfer to new hosts, despite huge wastage).
7. Skin secretes substances cancelling effects of sheep antibodies and lymphocytes that are trying to get rid of the flukes.

Control measures:

1. Drain wet pastures (difficult for larval stages and snail to survive).
2. Dose sheep with Fasinex to kill flukes.

Molluscicides are no longer used (cost and environmental reasons), but ducks and geese eating the snails (biological control) have been used in Russia.

Schistosoma

Importance: *Schistosoma* causes schistosomiasis (bilharzia) in most of Africa, northern South America, Japan, China and the Philippines. The worms cause fevers, bleeding into faeces or urine, and damage to spleen. Anaemia often results. Spread of the disease is encouraged by irrigation schemes. In China, the problem is made more serious because water buffalo are a reservoir for infection.

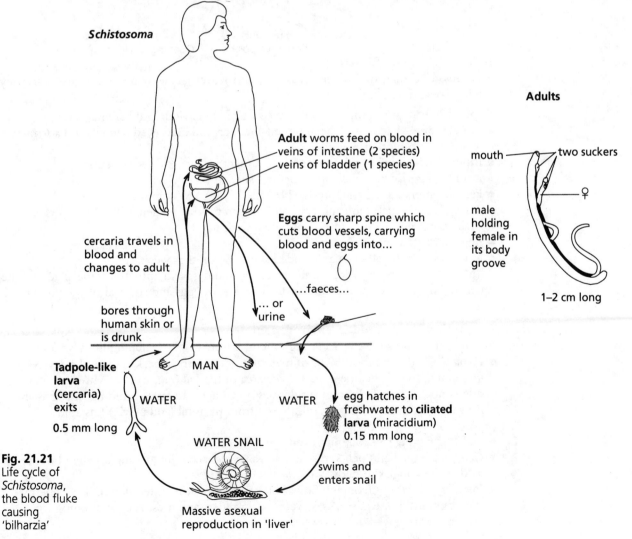

Fig. 21.21
Life cycle of *Schistosoma*, the blood fluke causing 'bilharzia'

Control measures:

1. Good sanitation to prevent faeces and urine reaching fresh water.
2. Educating the young not relieve themselves into water, nor to drink or play in water where snails are present in the open.
3. Use molluscicides to kill snails in waters used by humans, i.e. locally.
4. Filter water for drinking, then chlorinate it (to kill larvae). Water tanks should be kept snail-proof.
5. Use drugs to kill adult worms in humans, e.g. Praziquantel.

21.16 Bony fish

See also Units 2.4 and 9.7 (respiration).

The three-spined stickleback (*Gasterosteus aculeatus*).

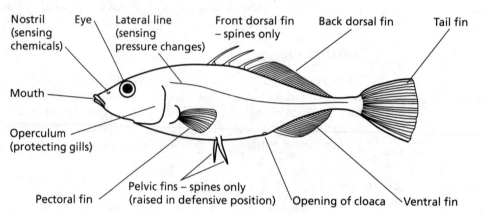

Fig. 21.22
Three-spined stickleback

A carnivore feeding on worms, crustacea and insect larvae at pond margins. Eaten by perch, pike and heron.

Reproduction: has complex *instinctive* courtship behaviour and parental care:
- In February–March, *males* become red-breasted and blue-eyed and take up a *territory* (defended from other males).
- Build a *nest*-tunnel of water-weeds stuck together by a kidney secretion.
- Lead fat, egg-laden females by a *zig-zag dance* to the tunnel.
- Female enters tunnel and, prodded by male, lays a few *eggs*; she then leaves.
- Male enters tunnel, squirting eggs with sperm to *fertilize* them.
- Male *aerates* nest by fin movements and *defends* it.
- Eggs *hatch* after about a week.
- Male keeps *fry* together in a defended shoal for another week.

(Most bony fish lay large numbers of eggs and sperm into the same place in the water, trusting to luck that sufficient fertilization of eggs and survival of the young will take place.)

Adaptation to an aquatic environment
- *Shape:* streamlined. Skin, secreting mucus, covered by overlapping bony scales.
- *Propulsion:* sideways movement of muscular body exerts a backwards and sideways force on the water via the large surface area of the *tail* (Fig. 21.23). Muscles on either side contract alternately to give sideways movement. In fast swimming, side fins are kept flat against body. When still, thrusts from pectoral (and pelvic) fins adjust position.
- *Stability: fins* prevent roll, pitch and yaw (Fig. 21.24).
- *Control:* pectoral and pelvic fins act as *hydroplanes* according to angle; when both are held at right angles to body, act as *brakes*.
- *Buoyancy: air bladder* (contents adjustable) keeps fish at required depth. Saves energy (cartilaginous fish, e.g. sharks, have no air bladders and must keep swimming to prevent sinking).
- *Gills:* for gaseous exchange (see Unit 9.7).

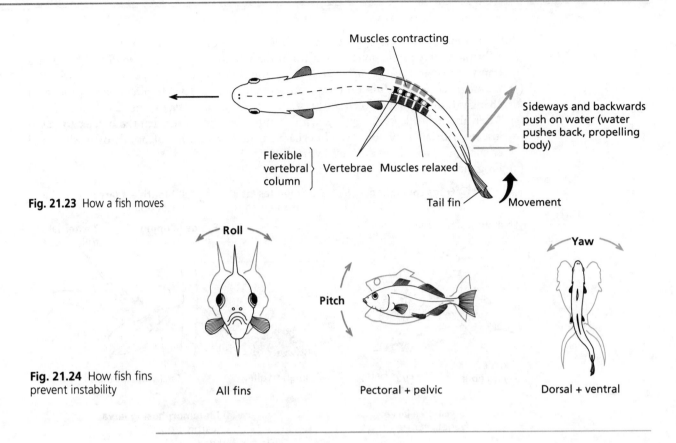

Fig. 21.23 How a fish moves

Fig. 21.24 How fish fins prevent instability

21.17 Amphibia

See also Unit 2.4.
The frog (*Rana temporaria*).

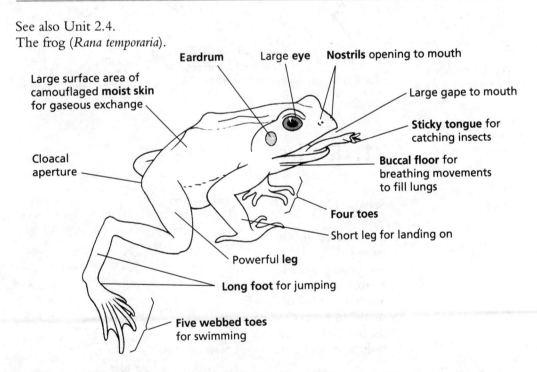

Fig. 21.25 Frog, external features

Adult: a carnivore, feeding on insects and worms in damp conditions and at night on land. Eaten by heron and other predators.

Tadpole: a herbivore, scraping algae off stones, plants; later becoming a scavenger on dead animals. Eaten by fish, water-beetle larvae, dragonfly nymphs and heron.

Life cycle:
(*a*) In March, male frogs croak, inviting females into shallow water.
(*b*) Male grips female under arm-pits with swollen black 'nuptial pads' on thumbs.
(*c*) Female lays a few hundred *eggs*; male squirts *sperm* over them as they emerge in a continuous stream.

(d) Sperm must penetrate eggs to cause *fertilization* before albumen swells.

(e) Albumen gives egg *protection* from injury and predators; *camouflage* (by being transparent); and a *large surface area* for gaseous exchange.

(f) *Larvae* hatch (depending on temperature) in about 10 days. In a *continuous* process of change (little happens overnight) larvae go through *three stages* (Fig. 21.26).

(g) After about 90 days *young frogs* with stumpy tails hop onto land and start to catch insects with a sticky tongue. Hibernate in mud at bottom of ponds or in sheltered crevices, to avoid freezing each winter.

(h) Frogs are *adult* by their fourth season.

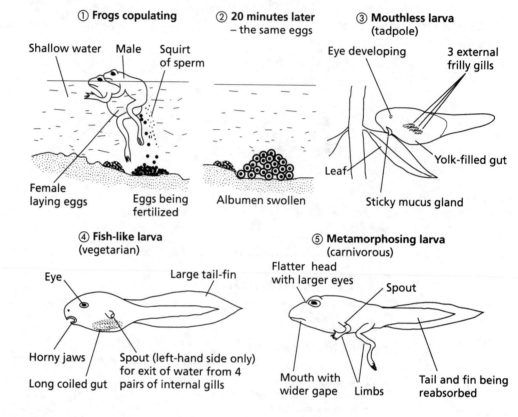

Fig. 21.26 Frog, life history

21.18 Birds

See also Unit 2.4.

e.g. Thrush (*Turdus viscivorus*). An omnivore eating worms, insects and fruits. Snails it smashes on 'anvil stones' to extract and eat the soft body. Eaten by owls, foxes and cats.

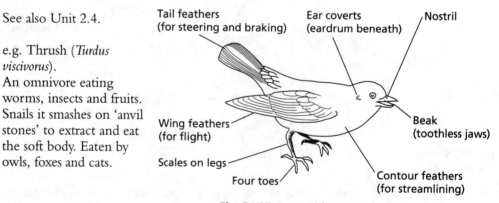

Fig. 21.27 External features of a bird

Adaptations for flight

1. *Light bones* – some air-filled and linked to air sacs; no teeth (heavy).
2. *Streamlined* – general body shape, contour feathers smoothing outline.
3. *Feathered wings* – large surface area to exert force on air. Feathers are light but strong.
4. *Large flight muscles* – on chest, flap the wings.
5. *Large keeled sternum* – for attachment of flight muscles.

⑥ *Special breathing system* and *large heart* – supply food and O_2 to flight muscles at a high rate. Flight requires a great deal of energy.

⑦ *High body temperature* – ensures rapid respiration.

Flightless birds, e.g. ostrich, kiwi, lack some of these adaptations.

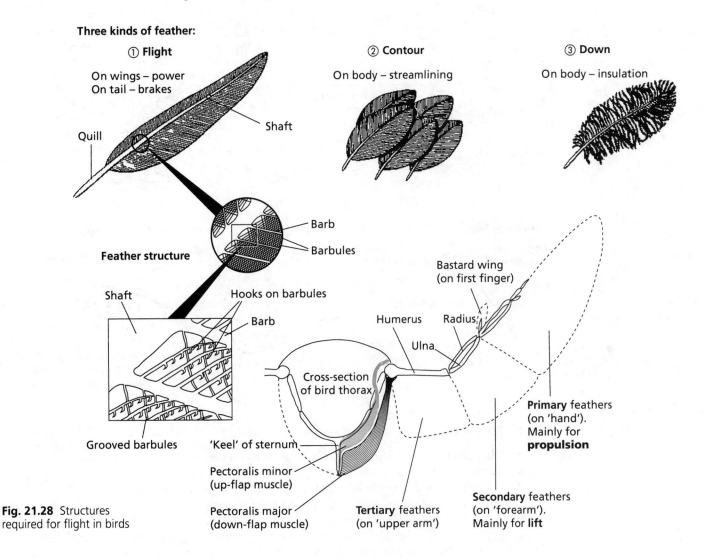

Three kinds of feather:

① **Flight**
On wings – power
On tail – brakes
Quill
Shaft

② **Contour**
On body – streamlining

③ **Down**
On body – insulation

Barb
Barbules

Feather structure

Shaft
Hooks on barbules
Barb

Grooved barbules

Bastard wing
(on first finger)

Humerus   Radius
Ulna

Cross-section
of bird thorax

Primary feathers
(on 'hand').
Mainly for
propulsion

'Keel' of sternum

Pectoralis minor
(up-flap muscle)

Pectoralis major
(down-flap muscle)

Tertiary feathers
(on 'upper arm')

Secondary feathers
(on 'forearm').
Mainly for **lift**

Fig. 21.28 Structures required for flight in birds

Flight

Birds cannot develop buoyancy (compare air-bladder of fishes, see Unit 21.16).
Lift is generated by creating low pressure above wing and higher pressure below it. This requires (*a*) an aerofoil wing and (*b*) movement of air over aerofoil. Movement of air over the wing can be produced in three ways:

① **Gliding:** wing rigid, *air still*; bird moves through air because it is falling.

② **Soaring:** wing rigid, *air moving*, e.g. cliff-side winds or hot up-currents from the ground.

③ **Flapping flight:** *wing moves*, exerting forces on air.

Flapping flight can result in fast, slow and even hovering flight – all modifications of the following essentials:

- **down-flap:** primary feathers overlap giving maximum air resistance as arm is brought down; primaries move forward (giving lift) and downward with ends curled upwards (giving forward propulsion).
- **up-flap:** arm is raised with the wrist *rotated* forward allowing air in between the primaries (like an open venetian blind); this reduces air resistance.

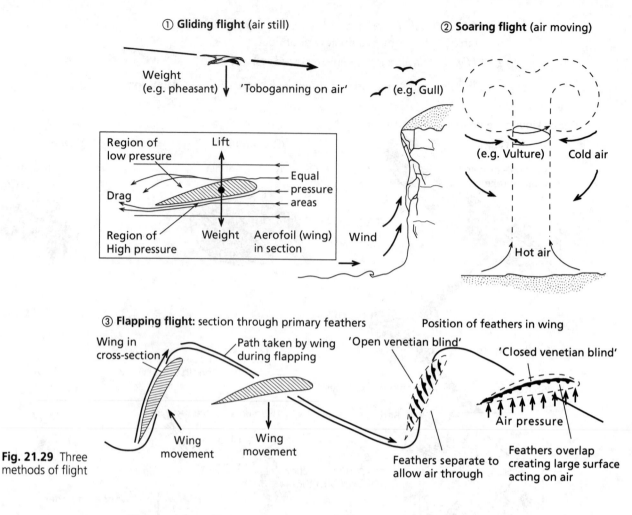

① **Gliding flight** (air still)

Weight
(e.g. pheasant) ↓   'Toboganning on air'

Region of
low pressure   Lift

Drag   ← Equal
pressure
areas

Region of   Weight   Aerofoil (wing)
High pressure   in section

② **Soaring flight** (air moving)

(e.g. Gull)

(e.g. Vulture)   Cold air

Wind   Hot air

③ **Flapping flight:** section through primary feathers

Wing in
cross-section   Path taken by wing
during flapping

Wing
movement   Wing
movement

Position of feathers in wing

'Open venetian blind'   'Closed venetian blind'

Air pressure

Feathers separate to
allow air through   Feathers overlap
creating large surface
acting on air

Fig. 21.29 Three
methods of flight

Reproduction

- Male birds of some species, e.g. robin, take up and defend *territories*.
- Courtship and display leads to *pairing* for the breeding season.
- One or both of the pair build nests in trees, holes or on the ground.
- Further display leads to *mating* and internal fertilization.
- *Eggs* are laid in nest singly, over a period of days, till clutch is complete.
- Eggs gain O_2 through shell from environment, and warmth from female's featherless brood-patches. She also turns the eggs daily, before *incubation* ('sitting').
- Chick *hatches* with help of egg-tooth (discarded after use).
- *Parental care* of young extends to removal of droppings, defence and feeding (instinctive behaviour induced by yellow gape of chick's mouth and chirruping, see Unit 12.6).

21.19 Mammals

See also Unit 2.4.
Mammalian characteristics:

- **Reproduction**
1 *Suckle* their young on milk from mammary glands.
2 *Viviparous* – give birth to young, not eggs (exceptions: echidna and platypus).
- **In the head**
3 *Ear pinna* – external ear.
4 *Four kinds of teeth* – incisors, canines, premolars and molars.
- **Temperature regulation**
5 *Endothermic* (homeothermic) – constant body temperature (birds also).
6 *Hair* – for insulation.
7 *Sweat glands* – for cooling.

● **Respiration**

8 *Diaphragm* – muscular sheet separating heart and lungs from other organs.

9 *Erythrocytes* (red blood cells) – lack nuclei.

Most mammals are **placentals** – embryos are grown inside uterus (womb), nourished via the placenta. Others are **marsupials** – embryos are born early and grow mainly within a pouch, e.g. kangaroo. Two types only (echidna and platypus) lay eggs much like those of reptiles, but then give milk to the hatched young. These egg-layers are the **monotremes**.

Chapter 22

Biology as a science

Biologists are scientists who study life. They are more than people who only do nature-study, observing and describing. Biologists not only observe, they also experiment.

Living things are made of chemicals, and their chemistry is driven by energy. Such beings also have to obey the laws of physics. So a biologist must use the ideas of both physics and chemistry.

When biologists experiment, they make measurements. They use the same units of measurement as physicists and chemists the world over. These are called SI ('Système International') units (see Unit 22.3). Certain non-SI units are still in use, e.g. calories, litres (see Table 22.2 on p. 222).

Having made their measurements biologists often need to present them in a more meaningful way. They may show their results in a bar chart or graph, and they may also need to calculate averages, percentages and ratios. So they need some maths.

This chapter will explain what is meant by the 'scientific method', the range of measurements used in biology and how to present them. It also summarizes the way in which certain common chemical reagents are used in biology. No matter which syllabus you follow you are expected to be familiar with how to use this information.

22.1 Scientific method

Biologists use the *scientific method* to discover new 'facts':

1. They make **observations**, e.g. leaves are green; leaves make starch; greenfly feed on plants.

2. They have an idea or **hypothesis**.
   This may try to explain what has been observed, or it may suggest a connection between two observations, e.g. leaves make starch *because* they are green.
   Hypotheses come easily to mind when the following questions are asked about observations:
   Who or what?   Why?   Where?   When?   How?
   (Try out these questions on the three observations given in part 1 above.)

3. They now **experiment** to see whether the idea is correct.
   Every experiment must have a **minimum of two parts**: the test and the control.
   The **test** is the part where a change is made to the biological material to test a hypothesis. The **control** is identical to the test except that the change is not made. If we were to test the hypothesis 'leaves in the light need carbon dioxide (CO_2) to make starch', leaves that were *denied* CO_2 would provide the test and leaves able to obtain CO_2 would provide the control.
   To do this, certain leaves could be confined in flasks with a CO_2 absorbant, and

others would also need to be put in flasks but with a CO_2 supply (see Fig. 5.3) to *compare* results. If the leaves *given* CO_2 did produce starch and those without CO_2 did not, one can be sure that confinement of the leaves within a flask was *not* responsible for the lack of starch. It must have been the *one* thing that was different that caused the lack of starch: lack of CO_2.

However, if both test *and control* leaves had produced no starch, it might have been possible to conclude that CO_2 is not important for starch-making in leaves – or at least the leaves of that particular plant (a strange result). Could the plant be diseased? It could have been that the leaves had been unable to make starch *in any case*. In other words, lack of CO_2 had not necessarily been responsible for the lack of starch in the test leaves.

Thus, the *control* is essential to an experiment to see whether

(*a*) the biological material is healthy;

(*b*) the apparatus or other conditions (also used in the test) may be playing a part in the results.

A further precaution in experiments is never to rely on results from one test and one control organism.

Experiments should always be done on **as large a number of organisms as possible** – as in an ideal class experiment. This makes sure that biological variation owing to sex, size, age, etc. is not having an effect on the results. For example, only 70% of carrot seed from a packet may germinate. If the conditions needed to germinate carrot seed were being investigated and only single seeds were used for each test and control, it could easily happen that one or more of the seeds chosen was a dead one. This would give misleading results. At least 20 or more seeds should be used in each test and control and the number of seeds germinating recorded as 0/20 or 14/20, etc.

④ The biologist now records his observations as **results**, usually in the form of a table. These must be recorded accurately and honestly. Some very important discoveries in science have arisen by observations that were not expected and even 'unwanted'. For example, Sir Alexander Fleming's observation of a bacterial culture contaminated with a fungus led to the discovery of penicillin.

⑤ The biologist then **concludes** whether the results support the hypothesis. The conclusion is a new 'fact' – for a while at least.

22.2 Reporting your own experiments

You should use the following subheadings, in the order given here, to show that you are using the scientific method:

① **Aim:** 'To discover...' or 'To investigate...' If you start off with 'Experiment to prove...' it makes a mockery of what scientific investigation is all about. This start indicates to those assessing your work that the 'experiments' you did were actually *demonstrations* of something that you knew already – and some examiners may not give you much credit in consequence. So the Aim is a statement of the hypothesis you set out to test.

② **Materials and method:** 'The materials were set up as shown in the diagram' could be the opening sentence. There follows a fully labelled diagram. Only information that the diagram does not explain needs to be added now, e.g. 'The plant used in the experiment had first been de-starched by keeping it in the dark for 48 hours' or, 'The length of the root was measured again after 24 hours'.

Note the use of the impersonal 'was measured'. Professional scientists prefer this to the personal statement '*I* measured'. A list of the materials used is unnecessary. Do not forget to emphasize which was the *test* and which the *control* part of the experiment.

③ **Results:** this should be *brief*, factual reporting of what happened – in both the test and the control. Often the results can best be put into a table. Do *not* write an essay.

If, however, something unforeseen happened you may have to *describe* it and *explain* why it occurred in addition, e.g. 'Some of the germinating peas grew fungus and died'.

④ **Conclusion:** this should be a simple answer to the aim of the experiment. This is a plain statement, not an essay. Thus the aim might have been 'To find out if light is necessary for photosynthesis', and the experiment's conclusion is likely to have been 'Light is necessary for photosynthesis'.

Note that these guidelines cover both GCSE and SCE requirements, but the details on pp. 16–18 should also be consulted.

22.3 Scientific units of measurement

Scientists use SI ('Système International') units and have discarded the older units such as the foot (length) and pound (mass). A descriptive word called a prefix is put before the unit to show how large or small the measurement is. Thus a *kilo*metre (km) is a *thousand* metres and a *centi*metre (cm) is one *hundredth* of a metre – see Tables 22.1 and 22.2.

Table 22.1 Sizes

Sizes	10^{-9}	10^{-6}	10^{-3}	10^{-2}	10^{-1}	Unit 1	10^1	10^2	10^3	10^5	10^9
	(0.000 000 001)	(0.000 001)	(0.001)	(0.01)	(0.1)	1.0	10	100	1000	100 000	1000 000 000
	billionth	millionth	thousandth	hundredth	tenth						
prefix	nano-	micro-	milli-	centi-	deci-	e.g. a metre	deca-	hecto-	kilo-	mega-	giga-
(and **symbol**)	(n)	(μ)	(m)	(c)	(d)		(da)	(h)	(k)	(M)	(G)

Thus, an object 1 metre long, i.e. 1 m, is also 100 cm = 1000 mm = 0.001 km long. The final 'm' in the abbreviation refers to the unit of length, the metre (m).

Mnemonic: Deca, Hecto, Kilo – go and fetch a pillow; deci, centi, milli – doesn't this sound silly

Table 22.2 SI units of measurement

Quantity	Unit		Useful examples Non-SI units also in use are in [ ]
Length	metre	(m)	Virus: 10 nm. Bacterium: 1 μm. Cheek cell: 0.1 mm. Large redwood tree: 120 m high
Area		(m²)	Man's skin: 1.8 m². Lungs, at alveoli: 80 m². 1 hectare (ha) = 10 000 m²
Volume		(m³)	Man's blood: 5–6 dm³ [1 dm³ = 1 litre]
Mass	kilogram	(kg)	1000 kg = 1 tonne. Large elephant: 5 t. Large blue whale: 150 t
Pressure	pascal	(Pa)	Atmospheric pressure at STP = 101 kPa [or 760 mm of mercury]
Energy	joule	(J)	[4.2 J = 1 calorie] 4.2 J raises 1 cm³ water 1 °C. Teenage boy needs 12 MJ/day
Temperature	degree Celsius	(°C)	Human body: 36.8 °C. Boiling point of water: 100 °C. Refrigerator space: 4 °C
Time	second	(s)	[1 minute (min) = 60 s; 1 hour (h) = 3600 s; 1 day (d) = 86 400 s; 1 year (a) ≈ 3.158×10^7 s]

A **solution** is a **solute** dissolved in a **solvent**, e.g. sugar dissolved in water. The *concentration* of the solution can be measured in grams per dm^3. It can also be expressed in moles.

A *molar* solution is the molecular mass of the substance dissolved in 1 dm^3 of solution. Example: the atomic mass of carbon (C) is 12, of hydrogen (H) is 1 and of oxygen (O) is 16. The formula of glucose is $C_6H_{12}O_6$.

The molecular mass of glucose is thus

$$12 \times 6 = 72 \quad (C_6)$$
$$1 \times 12 = 12 \quad (H_{12})$$
$$16 \times 6 = 96 \quad (O_6)$$

The molecular mass of glucose is therefore $\quad\quad 180 \quad (C_6H_{12}O_6)$

A molar solution of glucose is thus made by adding 180 g of glucose to a litre measuring flask and topping it up to the 1 dm^3 mark with distilled water. Glucose will remain as $C_6H_{12}O_6$ molecules in the solution.

Certain other substances will, however, split up into particles that carry electrical charges, called **ions**. Common salt (NaCl) solution contains Na$^+$ (sodium ions) and Cl$^-$ (chloride ions).

The **pH scale** is a measurement of the concentration of hydrogen ions (H$^+$) in a solution. Certain *indicators* show whether solutions are acid (pH 1–7), neutral (exactly pH 7) or alkaline pH 7–14) by changing colour according to their pH (Table 22.3).

Table 22.3 Indicators

Indicator solutions	Very acid pH 1 ←	Acid	→	Neutral pH 7	Alkaline ←	→ pH 14 Very alkaline
Litmus	←	— red		purple	blue —	→
Phenolphthalein	←	— colourless		—	pH 8.4 red —	→
BDH Universal indicator	pH 4 red	pH 6 orange	pH 6.5 yellow	pH 7.0 green	pH 9.0 blue	pH 11 purple

Solutions are all-important both inside cells and also outside them:

1. The 'strength' (concentration) of the solution inside a cell determines its ability to take up water – or to lose it – to a neighbouring solution by osmosis. Plants absorb water in this way (see Unit 7.3).

2. The pH of cells, or the gut, is very important if enzymes are to work properly (see Unit 1.5). If enzymes fail, cells die.

3. Certain ions are used by nerve cells to generate electrical impulses – their method of passing 'messages' (see Unit 12.3).

22.4 Elements, compounds and mixtures

Elements are substances which under normal circumstances cannot be changed, e.g carbon (C), oxygen (O), hydrogen (H) and nitrogen (N). They do not even change their identity when they combine with each other. Elements are made of minute particles of identical mass called atoms, e.g. ^{12}C has an atomic mass of 12.

Certain elements have two or more different types of atom called *isotopes*, each with a different mass, e.g. ^{12}C and ^{14}C. Some isotopes are *stable*, e.g. ^{12}C, but others are *radioactive*, e.g. ^{14}C, and give out radiations that will expose a photographic plate. Normal oxygen ^{16}O has a heavier isotope ^{18}O which is also stable but this too can be detected, using an instrument called a mass spectrometer. Both kinds of isotope can be used as *tracers* to follow chemical reactions in organisms (see Units 5.1 and 7.8).

Compounds are combinations of elements in fixed proportions. The proportions can be written down as a formula which shows the numbers of atoms of each element present, e.g. CO_2 represents one atom of carbon combined with two atoms of oxygen. A single particle of a compound is a **molecule** (Fig. 22.1).

Inorganic molecules are small, simple ones like CO_2, H_2O and $NaNO_3$. They are plentiful outside organisms in non-living matter.

Fig. 22.1 The carbon dioxide molecule

one atom of the element carbon (C)

two atoms (= 1 molecule) of the element oxygen (O)

one molecule of the compound carbon dioxide (CO_2)

Organic molecules are usually large and complex in structure. They usually contain two or more carbon atoms, e.g. $C_6H_{12}O_6$ (glucose). Organisms make organic molecules, examples being carbohydrates, fats (lipids) and proteins (see Units 4.1 and 4.4).

Living things are made up of *mixtures* of water, inorganic and organic molecules. There is no set proportion of elements and compounds in a mixture, so no formula can be written for it.

22.5 Energy

The sun radiates waves of energy to the earth. Some waves have a short wavelength, e.g. X-rays, others have a long wavelength, e.g. radio waves. This range of wavelengths is known as the **electromagnetic spectrum**. Only the shorter waves have any known biological importance (Table 22.4).

The *light* energy trapped by plants is stored as *chemical* energy in bonds of organic compounds, e.g. glucose. As glucose is broken down during respiration, energy is released for movement, so providing *mechanical* energy, but much is wasted as *heat*. Thus, energy that came into living things as light may be converted into a variety of other forms of energy (see Unit 9.13).

Too much heat energy may kill organisms. It may be lost by *conduction, convection, radiation* and by *evaporation* of water. However, too little heat may also kill, so it may be kept in by *insulation* (see Unit 10.7).

Table 22.4

Wavelength		700 nm				360 nm	
Type of wave	Infrared		Visible light			Ionizing radiations	
		Red Orange	Yellow Green	Blue Violet		Ultraviolet X-rays γ-rays	
Effect	Heat		Trapped in photosynthesis			Can cause mutations	
	(see Unit 10.6)		(see Unit 5.1)			(see Unit 17.15)	

22.6 Surface area to volume ratio

As an organism gets larger (in volume) its surface area does not increase in proportion (Fig. 22.2):

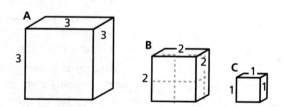

Fig. 22.2 Surface area to volume ratio

	A	**B**	**C**
Surface:	$3 \times 3 = 9$ cm^2 (each face)	$2 \times 2 = 4$ cm^2	$1 \times 1 = 1$ cm^2
	$6 \times 9 = 54$ cm^2 (six faces)	$6 \times 4 = 24$ cm^2	$6 \times 1 = 6$ cm^2
Volume	$3 \times 3 \times 3 = 27$ cm^3	$2 \times 2 \times 2 = 8$ cm^3	$1 \times 1 \times 1 = 1$ cm^2
Ratio = $\dfrac{\textbf{Surface}}{\textbf{Volume}}$	$\dfrac{54}{27} = \mathbf{2}$	$\dfrac{24}{8} = \mathbf{3}$	$\dfrac{6}{1} = \mathbf{6}$

Let us assume that A, B and C are living. In C a volume of one cubic centimetre (cm^3) has 6 cm^2 through which oxygen or food enter, and through which CO_2 and other wastes can leave. But in B each cm^3 has only 3 cm^2 through which these functions can occur. This makes the movement of these materials more difficult. It is not surprising therefore that organs concerned with **absorption** (guts, lungs, leaves, roots) or **excretion** (lungs, kidneys) have large surface areas.

Surface area is equally important where **heat loss** is concerned. Small animals, e.g. shrews, with their large surface area to volume ratio, lose heat very easily. They eat a lot of food to provide heat to make up for this loss. Elephants on the other hand, being large, have the problem of keeping cool since they have a small surface area for their bulk. They resort to bathing, but also use their large ears to radiate heat (see Unit 10.7).

The surface area of **food** is increased by chewing. In Fig. 22.2, if B were a 2 cm cube of food and it were chopped into eight separate 1 cm cubes, the total surface area would increase from 8 cm² to 48 cm². This would give digestive enzymes more area to work on.

22.7 Handling measurements and making them meaningful

A class of 20 pupils gave the information shown in Table 22.5.

Table 22.5

Boys Height/cm	Blood group		Girls Height/cm	Blood group
124	AB		132	O
132	B		129	A
144	O		126	O
129	B		143	A
133	O		141	A
139	A		136	A
138	O		131	O
147	A		121	AB
136	B		134	O
138	B		137	O
____ (total)			____ (total)	

Combined total of boys and girls _____ cm

Height measurements provide a *continuous* range of readings, i.e. each one can differ from the next one by only 1 cm. These results can be expressed as a diagram called a **histogram** (Fig. 22.3a).

However, the blood groups are *discontinuous*, i.e. there are only four types. These can be expressed in a similar diagram called a **bar chart** (= bar graph). The columns in Fig. 22.3(b) are separated from one another.

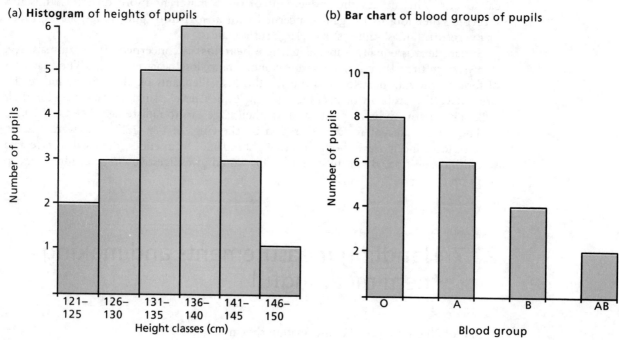

Fig 22.3

Note that it is very important to put in the measurements you are using: *numbers of individuals* on the vertical axis (*y* axis) and *measurement* or characteristic on the horizontal axis (*x* axis). A *title* must be added.

For practice, draw in the histogram for height of *boys*; and the bar chart for blood group of *girls* in Fig. 22.4.

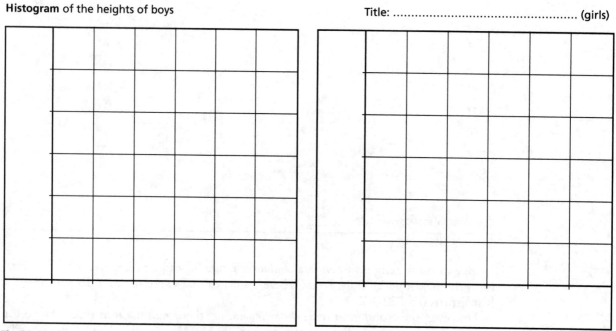

Histogram of the heights of boys

Title: .... (girls)

Fig 22.4

To do this, start by entering a tick on a chart such as that shown on the next page, for each height class you decide upon. The first three boys in the list have been ticked for you already. Do something similar for the girls' blood groups (Fig. 22.5).

Height classes for boys (cm)

121–125	126–130	131–135	136–140	141–145	146–150
✓		✓		✓	

Blood groups for girls

O	A	B	AB

Fig. 22.5   Fill in a tick for each boy   Fill in a tick for each girl

Each tick can now be converted into one of the blocks that make up the histogram or bar graph columns.

Continuous or discontinuous measurements can also be shown as **pie charts**, e.g. blood groups of the class (Fig. 22.6). Try making one for boys only.

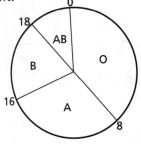

Fig. 22.6 Pie chart of blood groups in a class

Method:
The number of O blood group in the class is 8. There are 20 in the class. A circle has 360°. So O blood group will have 8/20 × 360 = 144° of the 360° pie.
Using a protractor, the appropriate 144° line can be drawn in.

The **range** of heights in the class is given by taking away the height of the shortest person (121 cm) from the height of the tallest (147 cm) = 26 cm.

Calculate the range for boys: _____
and for girls: _____

The **average** (= mean) height is the sum of all the heights (2690 cm) divided by the number of pupils (20): $\dfrac{2690}{20}$ = 134.5 cm

Calculate the mean height of the boys: _____
and of the girls: _____

Histograms, bar charts and pie charts all show measurements in a visual way, which should make them easily understood. You may, however, be asked to use the information mathematically.

The **ratio** of blood group O to blood group AB in the class is 8:2 or, more simply, 4:1 (four to one).

Calculate the ratio of A to B blood groups in the girls of the class: _____

The **percentage** of pupils that are 140 cm or taller in the class refers to the number there would be if the class were 100 strong ('cent' means a 'hundred'). It is calculated by multiplying the ratio by 100. Thus, 4 pupils are over 140 cm tall and the class is 20 strong. The ratio is $\dfrac{4}{20}$. The percentage is $\dfrac{4}{20}$ × 100 = 20%.

You may also be asked to select information more carefully, e.g. what percentage of the class is boys with blood group A: $\frac{2}{20} \times 100 = 10\%$.

Now calculate the percentage for the girls: _____

A **graph** is another visual means of presenting data (scientific measurements). One of its values is to allow predictions to be made from it. Data on the mass of American boys could be presented as a graph (see Fig. 22.7).

Average mass of American boys age 1–10

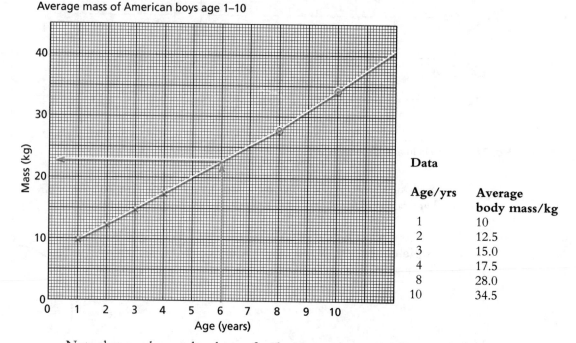

Data	
Age/yrs	**Average body mass/kg**
1	10
2	12.5
3	15.0
4	17.5
8	28.0
10	34.5

Fig. 22.7

Note that a *scale* must be chosen for the measurement (in this case 10 kg = 10 units on the *y* axis; and 1 year = 10 units on the *x* axis). This scale must be a sensible one if the graph is to be fitted onto the graph paper and will therefore depend on the range of measurements given. This range is 34.5–10.0 = 24.5 kg and 10 – 1 = 9 years. However, it is usual to start at 0 for both *x* and *y* axes and to allow a bit extra.

The data are then plotted by putting either a cross × or a ringed dot ⊙ exactly where readings for age and average body mass intersect. These dots or crosses are then joined up.

From the graph, *predictions* can be made:
What is the average mass of American boys at age 6? (see above)
What is the average mass of American boys at age 12 likely to be?
Here the line can be projected (see above) and a reading taken.

Read from the graph what age you would expect a 14 kg boy to be.

22.8 Drawings

It is not easy for some people to record their observations of organisms as drawings. The following may help you:

① Measure the object and then scale it up before you draw on paper (Fig. 22.8).

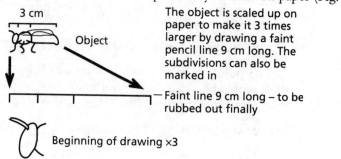

3 cm

Object

The object is scaled up on paper to make it 3 times larger by drawing a faint pencil line 9 cm long. The subdivisions can also be marked in

Faint line 9 cm long – to be rubbed out finally

Beginning of drawing ×3

Fig. 22.8

These marks help you to draw the object in correct proportion.

2 Once drawn in pencil, the drawing should be given a *title* and a *scale* added (in this case '× 3').

3 *Labels* should be added, as required, by ruling lines in biro or pencil, and adding names (Fig. 22.9).

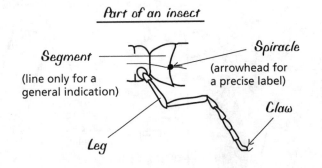

Fig. 22.9

22.9 Ideas for experiments of your own

Below are some ideas for you to choose from in designing your own experiments as part of your Coursework Assessment. Once you have chosen, read Units 22.1 and 22.2, and perhaps 22.8. The suggestions below have a reference to the relevant unit in this book which will give you the background to the idea and often some suggestions as to the apparatus you may wish to use.

How does the vitamin C content of food vary? (ref: Unit 4.5)

(a) Measure the amount of vitamin C in fresh new potatoes and old potatoes, fried potatoes, boiled potatoes and potato water.
(b) Does it matter *how long* the potatoes were stored, or cooked?
(c) Do conditions of light/dark and heat/cold affect (b)?
(d) Measure the vitamin content of cabbage, lettuce or milk (if you can get it fresh from the cow) – bearing in mind (b) and (c).

What conditions affect the rate of photosynthesis? (ref: Unit 5.4)

(a) Measure the rate of photosynthesis in *Elodea* (or other submerged water-weeds). Apparatus B is more accurate – with apparatus A, are all bubbles the same size? Vary (i) the light intensity, or (ii) the CO_2 level, or (iii) the temperature – keeping the other conditions constant.
(b) What effect do (i) muddy water (*how* muddy?), (ii) green water (many unicell algae in it), (iii) depth of water (many water baths in a row) have on the rate of photosynthesis?

Does the rate of respiration of a pond snail change as the pond gets warmer? (ref: Unit 5.6)

Measure the rate of respiration of pond snails at different temperatures. Blow through some stock *red* hydrogencarbonate indicator solution in a test-tube with a straw. When it just turns *pale yellow*, add a rubber bung. This is your colour-reference tube.

1 Warm (or cool) red indicator solution in one stoppered tube; and a snail in a second tube which is left open, in a water bath for a few minutes.

2 Then place the snail in the red indicator tube and re-stopper. Time how long it takes for the red indicator to turn to the colour of the colour-reference tube.

Repeat for other temperatures using the same colour-reference tube, same snail but fresh indicator solution.

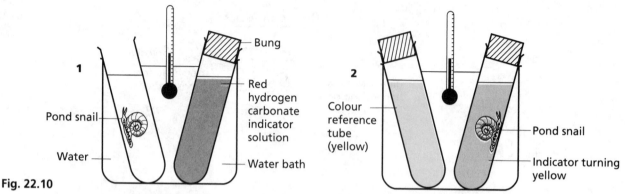

Fig. 22.10

What happens to the heart beat of *Daphnia* as the pond gets cooler? (ref: Unit 21.6)

Measure the heart beat rate of *Daphnia* at different temperatures. With a dropper put a *Daphnia* onto a cavity slide with some water. Place the slide on top of a petri dish containing water at a known temperature. Observe under a microscope.

How much does a supply of mineral salts to seedlings affect their growth? (ref: Unit 5.8)

Measure the gain in mass of batches of seed (e.g. 100 mustard seeds) grown in different mineral salt solutions. Other growing conditions must be the same. Grow batches on weighed blotting paper dipping into the different mineral salt solutions. Harvest and dry the batches in an oven at 100 °C after a few weeks' growth; reweigh.

(a) Use solutions each lacking a different element, e.g. no nitrogen.

(b) Use a full culture solution to which is added extra quantities of an element, e.g. × 1, × 2, × 4 the amounts of nitrogen.

How do the quantities of starch, of hydrogen ions and of salivary amylase affect the rate of digestion of the starch? (ref: Unit 6.3)

Measure the rate of digestion by salivary amylase under constant conditions:

(a) when the *quantity of enzyme* is altered, e.g. tubes with 1, 2, 3 and 4 cm^3 of enzyme solution added to the 5 cm^3 of starch solution in each;

(b) when the *quantity of starch* is altered, e.g. tubes with 5, 10, 15 and 20 cm^3 of starch, to each of which is added 1 cm^3 of enzyme;

(c) when the *pH* is changed, e.g. by adding acid or alkali (see Unit 6.3, Example 2).

How strong is the solution inside rhubarb cells? (ref: Unit 7.4)

Measure the concentration of the solution inside rhubarb epidermis cells. Strip off red epidermis about 0.5 cm wide from rhubarb stalks. Cut off 1 cm lengths from the strip with scissors so that they drop directly into drops of sugar solution of different concentration, placed on separate slides. Add a coverslip to each and observe under the microscope after 2 minutes. Record how many cells out of 20 are plasmolysed or turgid. How does this give you the answer? Do other solutions of the same molarity, e.g. salt or glucose, give the same result? Do cells from wilted rhubarb give a different result from cells of healthy rhubarb?

What makes the pores of a leaf (stomata) open and close? (ref: Unit 7.5)

Discover what factors cause opening or closing of stomata in a leaf. Use the nail varnish technique, having left the leaf in one of the following conditions for 5 minutes: light or dark; warm or cool; with CO_2 (see Fig. 5.3) or without it. While testing one pair of conditions, keep the other conditions, e.g. temperature and CO_2, as constant as possible. Do not use hairy leaves; shiny ones are best.

Do small animals such as beetles and woodlice respire faster when it is warm? (ref: Unit 9.5)

Measure the rate of respiration of a small animal at different temperatures. Allow it to gain the temperature of the water bath with the syringe nozzle pulled out for 3 minutes. Return the nozzle to the bung and suck an ink drop into the capillary tube. Measure how far the drop moves in 5 minutes. Do the animals need to be kept still by a wad of cotton wool?

(a) Use locust, earthworm, woodlouse, etc. (any one).

(b) Do different species of animal differ in their rate of respiration (on a *weight for weight* basis) at a particular warm temperature?

How does ethanol (alcohol) affect a person's coordination? (ref: Unit 12.9)

Measure the effect of alcohol on the nervous system. Test the rate of reaction of your parents or other members of the family before and after they have been to the pub. Record what they have drunk and over what time period.

(a) Place your forearm on a table and your parent's forearm on a chair. Drop the metre ruler vertically between your parent's forefinger and thumb. Ask your parent to catch the ruler as it falls. Measure the distance the ruler falls.

(b) Play a video game, e.g. 'squash', 'tennis' – anything that requires anticipation and motor skills. Record the scores.

Relate (a) distance fallen, (b) video scores, to amount of alcohol consumed. Do tiredness, time of day or amount of food eaten by your parent affect your experiments?

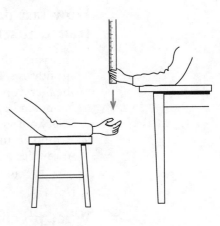

Fig 22.11

How do some weeds defeat the gardener trying to get rid of them? (ref: Unit 14.2)

How large a piece of rhizome (underground stem) is necessary to form a new plant? Use weed species such as ground elder (*Aegopodium*), bindweed (*Convolvulus*) or couch grass (*Agropyron*). Cut the cleaned rhizome into lengths (e.g. 2.5 cm and 10 cm) and weigh them. Plant in damp potting fibre in a warm place. Count those that show a leaf above ground. Unearth all of them to see whether length or mass or presence of a node is the deciding factor. Anything else? Do winter, spring and summer rhizomes behave differently?

What makes pollen germinate? (ref: Units 14.7 and 14.8)

(a) Measure the percentage germination of pollen in water and various concentrations of sugar solution. Place three layers of blotting paper in a petri dish. Add a flat strip

of Visking tubing. Pour sugar solution (e.g. 5, 10 or 15%) onto the Visking until the blotting paper is just flooded. Dust ripe pollen from ripe stamens onto the Visking in each of the dishes; add a lid and leave for 24 hours. Lift the Visking onto a slide with forceps and count the percentage of germinated grains under a microscope.
(b) Does temperature or light affect germination?
(c) Do all flower species germinate best at the same sugar concentration?
(d) Do pollens from wind-pollinated and insect-pollinated flowers die off after a time and at the same rate? Collect pollen from two species of flower in separate tubes. Dust pollen at different times (e.g. collected fresh and after 1, 4 and 8 days' storage) onto Visking as in method (a).

Do seedlings lose weight during their first week of growth, just as new-born babies do? (ref: Unit 16.6)

Measure the change in mass of seeds (e.g. broad beans) as they grow into young plants. Measure both the live (wet) mass and dead (dry) mass at intervals; make a graph of the results; explain what three processes account for the changes in mass.
Example
Weigh five batches of 10 seeds, A–E, and plant 5 cm down in damp potting fibre. Using batch A, reweigh every 2 days and replace in the fibre. Do the last weighing when most seeds have radicles peeping through the testa. Then obtain batch A's dry mass after drying the batch in an oven for 24 hours at 100 °C.

Measure wet and dry mass of other batches as follows –
B, 4 days after last weighing of A; C, when half the seedlings are just peeping through the fibre; D and E, when the batch has been above ground in sunlit conditions for 1 and 2 weeks, respectively.

How fast does a population of duckweed grow? (ref: Units 16.7 and 19.3)

(a) Measure the rate of increase in population of duckweed (*Lemna*). Using a paintbrush, transfer 10 healthy (green) duckweed plants from a pond to a 250 cm³ beaker containing 200 cm³ of 'full culture' solution. Cover with pin-holed 'clingfilm' and put in a warm, light place to grow. Count the number of plants every 4 days by transferring them to a fresh beakerful of culture solution.
(b) Compare the rise in population of duckweed placed in beakers with different quantities of solution (e.g. 25, 50, 100 and 200 cm³). Do *not* transfer them to fresh solutions (compare (a) above).

What precisely does the water louse *Asellus* eat? (ref: Unit 19.5)

Discover the food preferences of *Asellus* and their role in decomposition of leaves. Cut measured squares of freshly fallen oak leaves. Soak five in pond water and five in muddy pond water for a week. Leave five dry. Add the three batches of five leaf squares to different jam jars half full of pond water containing five *Asellus*. After a number of days remove the squares and trace their outlines on graph paper.
Do *Asellus* prefer oak to any other species of fallen leaf?
Do the leaves decay better on their own without *Asellus* in the jars?
Does the pH (or the appearance of the water) change during the process?

What food attracts scavengers in a pond? (ref: Fig. 19.9)

Discover the food preferences of pond scavengers. Tie string round the necks of jam jars and anchor the loose ends with stakes to the bank. Put various baits in the jars, e.g. fresh meat or rotting meat, dead snail or rotting snail, fresh chopped or dead chopped leaves, etc. Sink these in water and haul in for study at intervals, e.g. every 20 minutes

or every hour. Count and describe the kinds of organism. This is best done in summer.
Does the position around the pond affect results?
Does the depth of water or type of bottom (e.g. mud or gravel) affect results?

Does it matter how you set up a pitfall trap? (ref: Fig. 19.12)

Discover the differences in pitfall trap catches when set up in different ways. Set up a number as shown in Fig. 19.12; another number dry; another number with 5% formalin; another number with baits, e.g. a small piece of meat. Leave overnight, collect in the morning and observe carefully *everything* in the jar.
Do the following affect your results: the vegetation around each jar; the amount of leaf litter; the weather beforehand? This is best done in the autumn.

How do the small animals in the soil react to rain – or the lack of it? (ref: Fig. 19.14)

Discover the effect of rain on the distribution of invertebrates in the soil. Take horizontal layers of soil (e.g. 5 cm thick) from the same area and extract the invertebrates by Tullgren funnel. Do this after heavy rain, a few dry days later and after a dry spell. This is best done in September.

Hints for candidates taking biology examinations

Showing the examiner what you know, understand and could do (by experiment)

Students should not be entered for an examination that is beyond their ability. Success in examinations for which you have been entered (which assumes that you *do* have the ability) lies in good 'examination technique'. Your teacher will usually advise you on the type of examination you will sit by showing you past question papers (see also specimen questions on pp. 239–272). But certain principles of technique apply to all methods of examination:

1. **Come fully equipped** with pen, pencil, rubber, ruler, calculator, watch and coloured pens or pencils.

2. **Read the exam instructions carefully.**

3. **Plan your time for answering** according to the marks allocated. If you are given 40 minutes to complete 50 multiple choice items, you can calculate that you have 48 seconds per item. More usefully, you can work out that you should at the very least have reached Question 25 after 20 minutes in the exam room.

4. **Do the maximum number of questions.** Usually, modern exams allow you plenty of time to complete all the questions. But always check your answers right through for any that you may have missed.

   Where you have left an answer-space blank you can be certain of one thing: a *blank* scores *no* marks. So look again at the question and write *something*. That 'something' has a better chance of scoring you marks than a blank. Think positively!

5. **Understand what the question asks.** Never twist the examiner's words into a meaning that was not intended. It is no use answering a completely different question from that written on the examination paper. If someone asks you how to mend a bicycle puncture and you reply with an excellent description of how to raise the saddle, you have not answered their question, nor have you given them any help! In an examination, mis-information of this kind earns you no marks. You may know the correct answer all along. But if you fail to show the examiner that you know, how can you succeed?

6. **Plan before writing** your essay, paragraph and experimental answers. Organize key words into a *logical order* or pattern. This is particularly important when you have been asked to design an experiment. Use *short*, clear sentences, each one explaining a single step in the procedure. See the section below and Unit 22.2.

⑦ **Use large labelled diagrams** in your answers if they make your answer clearer. Descriptions of experiments are almost always clearer, and certainly much shorter, when diagrams are used. Diagrams save words.

⑧ **Set out your work neatly.** An examiner is human. If your written answers are neatly set out he is much more likely to give you the benefit of the doubt where your answers are not entirely clear.

⑨ **Check your spelling, punctuation and grammar.** This carries marks.

⑩ **Keep a cool head.** You can only do this by getting plenty of sleep and some exercise over the examination period. You will reason better if you do *not* stay up all night revising.

Tackling various types of examination question

1 Multiple choice questions

These are sometimes called fixed response or objective questions. At first sight these questions seem to be comparatively easy because answering them is simply a matter of choosing one correct answer from the possible answers given. However, the questions are designed to test how well you understand specific topics and students do not always obtain as high a mark as they expected. But providing you know or can work out each answer (see below), the multiple choice questions in an examination should not be troublesome.

If four choices of answer are offered, usually two are very obviously wrong. You now have a 50% chance of being right even if you don't know the answer. Don't leave the odds at 25% by a blind guess.

Suppose the question requires you to *reason* from facts you should know. Say the question is 'Which gas(es) are produced by a green plant's leaves in the dark?' and the answer choices are: (*a*) CO_2, (*b*) N_2, (*c*) CO_2 and O_2, (*d*) O_2. From these (*b*) can be eliminated because nitrogen gas is neither used nor produced by green plants on their own. 'Leaves' readily suggests photosynthesis, a by-product of which is oxygen. But *light* is needed for photosynthesis and the question states that the leaves are in the *dark*. So (*c*) and (*d*) must be wrong because both include oxygen. That leaves (*a*) as the answer. There are also other types of 'choice' questions which are more testing.

2 Essay and paragraph questions

Most essay questions today are 'structured' into sections which require paragraph answers. The principles for writing essays or paragraphs are the same. The examiner is looking for a number of points that you should be remembering as key words – just how many is often suggested by the mark allocation. On rough paper write down the key words and join these by lines into a pattern-diagram where necessary. Number the key words according to the order in which you are going to use the facts in your answer. In this way your facts will be presented logically, and nothing will be left out. If *examples* make your answer clearer, use them.

Take the following example of a structured question:

'(*a*) Why are enzymes frequently referred to as "biological catalysts"? (4)

(*b*) What are the effects of changing (i) pH, (ii) temperature upon the rate of action of any **named** enzyme?' (7)

(There followed a third section to complete the question.)

The way to go about planning your answers is illustrated on the following page:

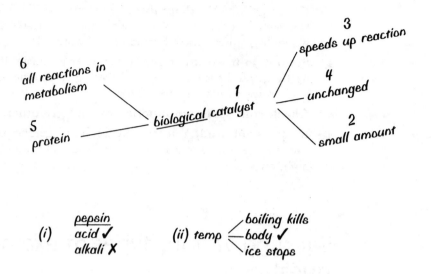

Notice that this student used the key words from the question to build up this pattern-diagram. From this pattern-diagram, done in a minute or two, might come a written answer like:

(a) *Catalysts are substances which in small amounts can greatly increase the rate of certain chemical reactions. Catalysts remain unchanged at the end of the reaction. Enzymes, unlike catalysts used in chemical works, are proteins. They control the rate of reactions in living things, e.g. in respiration and digestion.*

(b) (i) *Pepsin digests proteins in the stomach where conditions are acid. It will not do so if conditions are alkaline.*

(ii) *Pepsin works best at body temperature. If it is boiled it is destroyed and stops working. If it is cooled by ice it will also stop working but it is not destroyed.*

- **'State'** and **'explain'** questions: **'state'** or **'list'** means put down as simple facts – nothing else. **'Name'** is a similar instruction: no explanations are required.

- **'Explain'** requires not only the facts or principles but also the reasons behind them. When you are thinking out the answer to an 'explain' question, ask yourself 'which?', 'what?', 'where?', 'why?' and 'when?' about the subject. These questions will help you to avoid leaving out information that you know. You *must*, however, only give the information that is asked for – for example 'which?' and 'when?' may be irrelevant (unnecessary) in a particular question.

- **'Calculate'** usually means not only give the answer but *show your working*.

- **'Deduce'** usually means reason out an answer and *state your reasoning*.

- **'Compare'** and **'contrast'** questions: **'contrast'** means pick out the *differences* between. If you are asked to do this you must use such words as 'whereas…' and 'however…'. It is not sufficient to give two *separate* accounts of the two organisms or processes to be contrasted.

- **'Compare'** means pick out not only *differences* (contrasts) but also *similarities*. Thus your answer will include not only 'whereas…' and 'however…' statements but also 'both…'.

   In planning such answers it is vital to write down on rough paper, in three columns, the features to be compared or contrasted and, alongside, the comparison you have made mentally.

Feature, or characteristic	Organism, or process A	Organism, or process B
1 ... **2** ... etc.	Differences (i.e. *contrasts*)	
1 ... **2** ... etc.	Similarities	

} *Comparison*

Such questions are usually only found in papers taken by those of higher ability.

3 Graph, diagram and experiment questions

● **Graphs:** If you are asked to put information onto a graph, it is vital that on both axes you state the relevant *units*, e.g. 'g' or 'cm³/h' or 'numbers of live insects'. Usually the title of the graph is supplied by the question – but sometimes it is important that *you* should provide it. All plots must be precise and ringed. You will avoid wrong plots by using a ruler to lead your eye to the precise spot. Join each plot with a *straight* line to the next one.

● **Diagrams:**
  1 *Draw in pencil* – in case you need to use an eraser.
  2 *Draw large* – for clarity and easy labelling; then put down your pencil.
  3 *Rule your labelling lines* in biro, avoiding crosses. Biro does not smudge against the ruler. Neither can the straight biro labelling lines be confused with being part of the detail of the drawing (which is in pencil).
  4 *Label* in ink or biro neatly and add a *title*.
  If you follow the drill *in sequence* you will save time. And time is often marks!

● **Experiments**
  Experiments must be written up in a logical order under subheadings. The account usually includes a diagram which *saves* words. Do not duplicate the information in a diagram by also giving a *written* account of what it shows. Only write what the diagram does *not* say.
  Questions asking you to *describe* experiments are usually of two types:
  1 Coursework assessment of an experiment that you have carried out. Below is a reminder of the way that such an account should be set out (see also p. 221).
  2 Examination questions which often restrict themselves to asking you to *design* an experiment. These answers require only the 'Materials and Method' part of the sequence outlined below (see also Unit 22.2).

Introduction: origin of the idea you want to test; prediction of the outcome of your particular experiment.

Aim: you should start with 'To discover...' or 'To investigate...' – never 'Experiment to prove...'. State the hypothesis (idea) you are testing in your experiment.

Materials and method: start with 'The materials were set up as shown in the diagram below'. Now draw a fully labelled diagram of your experiment. The 'test' and the 'control' parts must be clearly indicated. Finally, give any *extra* information not shown by the diagram. For example, 'The seeds were reweighed every two days. On day 10 they were crushed and tested with Benedict's solution and with iodine.'

Results: write a plain statement of what happened in both test *and* control – no discussion. Record your results in a table if at all possible.

Discussion: this should include some ideas on how your experiment could have been *improved* to give a more trustworthy result. The results themselves could perhaps have been more accurately obtained; if so, state how.

Conclusion: end with a simple answer to the question posed in the Aim. For example, the aim 'To discover whether chlorophyll is necessary for photosynthesis' is likely to be answered by the conclusion 'chlorophyll is necessary for photosynthesis' – and nothing more. However, there may be more than one interpretation of your results; if so, say so, explaining why.

Too often students score poor marks by giving rambling accounts which leave out important details. Accounts which are organized into a logical sequence always score better.

4 Relevance in answers

Sadly, a large number of reasonably knowledgeable students do not do themselves justice because they write irrelevant answers. Sheer length of an answer will not gain any marks. It is only the key facts and principles that the examiner is looking for, *whatever* the length of the answer. So do not 'pad out' your answers.

The length of answer required is often suggested either by the marks awarded to it in the mark scheme (usually stated alongside the question), or by the space allocated to it on an answer sheet. If your answer is about to be either much shorter or much longer than these two indicators suggest, think again. Re-read the question – and your underlining of the important words in it.

Practice in answering examination questions

The following questions are all taken from actual exam papers or are recent specimen questions produced by the exam boards (specimen questions are marked with an asterisk *). They have been carefully selected:

(a) to give as wide a range of subject matter as possible,

(b) to illustrate the range of question types,

(c) to illustrate the way in which examiners mark answers – see answers section, pp. 273–9.

The answers given are the author's own, to help your understanding. They are not necessarily the only ones that would gain marks.

The purpose in providing both questions and answers is to give you some practice. Answer the questions after you have revised each topic. Only then check your answers against the answers given in the book. If you find any questions difficult, refer back to the appropriate chapter before attempting the question again.

Chapter 1

1   Complete the list below of the characteristics of living organisms.

    1   Reproduction
    2   Sensitivity
    3   Nutrition
    4   ....
    5   ....
    6   ....
    7   ....

(4)

NICCEA 1993

2   (a) The list below gives the names of parts of a cell.

cell membrane	cell wall	chloroplast
chromosome	cytoplasm	nuclear membrane
nucleus	large vacuole	

Which of the parts named above fits the following descriptions?

   (i) The outer layer of plants cells.
   (ii) Consists of a string of genes.
   (iii) Carries out photosynthesis.
   (iv) Contains cell sap.

(4)

(b) The shape overleaf represents the outline of a plant cell.
On the diagram draw and label the structures that distinguish plant cells from animal cells.

(3)

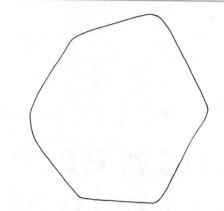

(c) Complete the following table:

Organ system	Organ	Function of organ
Excretory		Filters blood
	Heart	
Respiratory		

(5)

NICCEA 1993

3 Organisms are made up of cells, organs, systems and tissues. In the table, list these four terms in order of increasing size. Write down an example of each term next to its name. The first one has been done for you.

Term	Example
1 Cell	Cheek cell
2	
3	
4	

(5)

ULEAC 1992

4 The diagram below shows DNA in the process of replication.

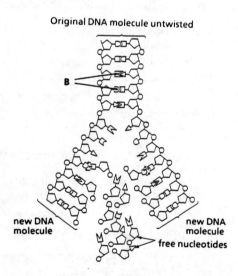

(a) What is a gene? (1)
(b) Use the diagram to help describe how DNA replicates. (4)
(c) What is the significance of the order of the structures labelled B in the diagram? (2)

NICCEA★

Chapter 2

5 Look at these diagrams of plants and animals.

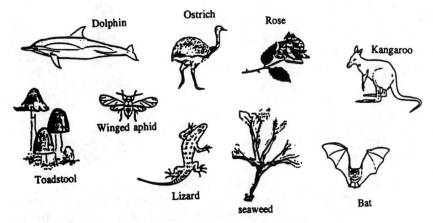

(a) (i) Name *one* animal shown which lives in water.   (1)
(ii) Write down *one* way in which *this* animal is suited to life in water.   (1)
(b) Name *one* plant shown which grows under water.   (1)
(c) (i) Write down *one* way in which the bat is suited to flying.   (1)
(ii) Name *one* other animal shown in the diagrams which can fly.   (1)
(d) The table shows the groups to which some of the plants and animals in the diagrams belong. Fill in the spaces.   (5)

Name of plant or animal	Group
Ostrich	
	Flowering plant
	Reptile
	Mammal
	Insect

SEG★

6 The table below gives some characteristics of four animal groups.

Group	Example	Reproduction	Characteristics
Fish	Cod	External fertilization Many eggs laid in water	Fins Scales
Amphibia	Frog	External fertilization Many eggs laid in water	Moist skin Lungs in adult
Reptiles	Snake	Internal fertilization Small number of eggs laid on land	Scales Lungs
Birds	Robin	Internal fertilization Small number of eggs laid on land Parental care	Lungs Beak

Use the information in the table to help answer the questions below.

(a) Give *two* ways in which amphibians are similar to fish: (2)
(b) Give *three* features of reptiles which help them live on land. Give an explanation for each.   (6)
(c) Name another feature, not given in the table, which is characteristic of each of the fish and bird groups.   (2)

NICCEA 1993

7 The diagram below shows a fern plant.

(a) On the diagram label root, stem and leaf.   (3)
(b) Give *two* ways in which ferns are similar to mosses.   (2)
(c) Give *two* ways in which ferns are different from mosses.   (2)

NICCEA 1992

Chapter 3

8 An experiment was carried out to assess the sensitivity of a bacterial strain to certain antibiotics. Paper discs, each impregnated with a different antibiotic, were placed on a medium previously inoculated with the strain. The appearance of the culture, after a 24-hour period, is shown below.

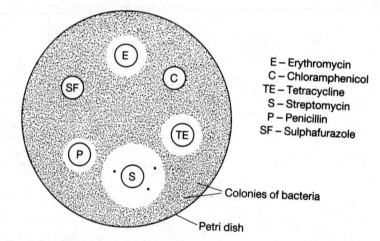

E – Erythromycin
C – Chloramphenicol
TE – Tetracycline
S – Streptomycin
P – Penicillin
SF – Sulphafurazole

Colonies of bacteria

Petri dish

(a) The effectiveness of antibiotics is normally assessed by measuring the diameter of the clear zone around each antibiotic disc. What problem might this create for the experimenter, in dealing with this set of results?
(b) What conclusions can you draw about the sensitivity of this bacterial strain to the different antibiotics?
(c) From your conclusions, what generalized statement could you make concerning the action of antibiotics on bacteria?
(d) The three colonies growing near the Streptomycin disc were thought to be resistant to this antibiotic. Describe how you would test for this hypothesis.

SEB

9 The diagram below shows part of a biological filter from a sewage works.

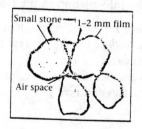

Small stone
1–2 mm film
Air space

The watery film contains aerobic microbes and the animals shown in the diagram below.

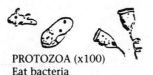

PROTOZOA (x100)
Eat bacteria

BACTERIA (x1000)

MITE (x10)
Eats larvae

FLY LARVA (x10)
Eats bacteria and protozoa

(a) (i) Construct and label a pyramid of biomass for the organisms which live in the watery film.

(ii) What is the function of the aerobic microbes in the filter bed?   (1)

(iii) Explain why the protozoa and larvae are useful inhabitants of the film of water.   (2)

(b) The table below shows a monthly analysis of the effluent from this filter bed.

Month	Organic matter (mg/l)	Ammonium ions (mg/l)	Nitrate ions (mg/l)
Jan	35.0	11.2	3.6
Feb	42.0	12.4	4.0
Mar	44.0	14.4	3.8
Apr	29.5	7.2	8.4
May	27.0	7.6	10.7
Jun	29.5	5.5	10.2
Jul	21.5	5.6	13.4
Aug	25.5	7.7	14.8
Sep	25.5	6.7	9.9
Oct	31.0	11.4	7.9
Nov	34.5	13.5	5.7
Dec	32.5	9.9	4.9

The sewage works should not discharge effluent containing more than 30 mg/l of organic matter into a river.

(i) During which months does the organic matter from the filter bed exceed this limit?   (1)

(ii) Describe what might happen to the river if this excessive amount of organic matter from the filter bed was passed into it during these months.   (2)

(iii) Explain why the amount of organic matter from the filter bed exceeds the limit during these months.   (2)

(iv) Describe how the effluent from the filter bed should be treated before being passed into the river during these months.   (2)

(v) Explain the relationship between the concentration of ammonium ions and nitrate ions.   (3)

WJEC★

10 Describe how you would make a compost heap. Include in your description the conditions which are needed for successful decay. You will be awarded up to *two* marks for the clear way in which you express your answer.   (7)

SEG★

11 Explain what is meant by the term 'biotechnology'. Describe *one* method by which the production of food is made more effective.   (6)

MEG 1993

Chapter 4

12 (a) The table shows some of the major vitamins, a rich source of each and what happens when they are not in a diet. Complete the table by filling in the blank spaces. (4)

Vitamin	Rich source	What happens when it is not in a diet
B_1		
A		
		Poorly formed bones
	Citrus fruits	

(b) The table gives information about a breakfast cereal. It shows the energy content and the amount of some food substances in 100 g of the cereal.

Item	Amount per 100 g
Energy	1650 kJ
Protein	12 g
Carbohydrate	54 g
Fat (lipid)	13 g
Dietary fibre	15 g
Calcium	0.1 g
Iron	0.07 g

(i) Which *two* substances in the table would most likely be used to supply energy? (2)

(ii) Name *one* substance in the table which is important in forming red blood cells. (1)

(iii) State *one* reason for including dietary fibre in a healthy diet. (1)

SEG★

13 Doctors and insurance companies use graphs to decide if a person is a suitable weight for their height.

The graph below is an example.

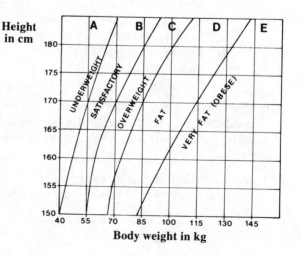

(a) John and Sarah both weigh 70 kg.
   John's height is 180 cm. Sarah's height is 150 cm.
   (i) Use the graph to decide which of the bands, A, B, C, D or E, John and Sarah are in. (2)
   (ii) How much weight would Sarah have to lose to place her in band B? Show your working. (2)

(b) Doctors recommend a balanced diet and plenty of exercise for a healthy life.
   They encourage people to 'watch their weight' and to try to stay in 'Band B'.
   People who are very fat (obese) are much more likely to suffer from health problems. Some of these may shorten their life.
   Use this information, together with your own biological knowledge, to answer the following questions.
   (i) Explain what is meant by 'a balanced diet'. (5)
   (ii) Suggest *one* health problem which might result from being very fat. (1)
   (iii) How does exercise help a person to lose weight? (2)

   ULEAC 1993

14 The amounts of carbohydrate, lipid and protein in 28 g portions of six foods are shown in the table below.

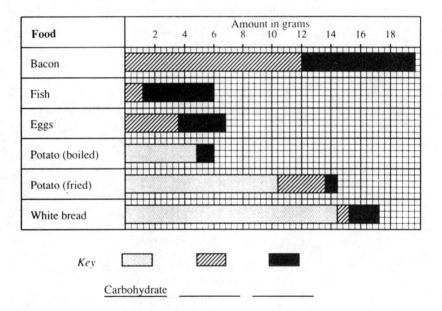

(a) (i) The key for carbohydrate has been done for you. Fill in the key for lipid and protein. (1)
   (ii) Give a reason for your choice in (i). (1)

(b) (i) What is the amount of carbohydrate in 28 g of white bread? (1)
   (ii) 1 g of carbohydrate produces 17 kilojoules of energy.
      How many kilojoules would be produced by the carbohydrate in the 28 g of white bread? (1)
   (iii) What is the combined amount of lipid and protein in 28 g of fish? (1)
   (iv) Which substance, other than carbohydrate, lipid and protein, makes up most of the rest of the 28 g portions of the foods? (1)

(c) (i) Suggest why there is more carbohydrate in 28 g of fried potato than in 28 g of boiled potato. (2)
   (ii) Suggest why fried potatoes are less good for your health than boiled potatoes. (1)

   ULEAC 1993

Chapter 5

15 (a) The diagram overleaf shows the movement of substances into and out of a green leaf during photosynthesis.

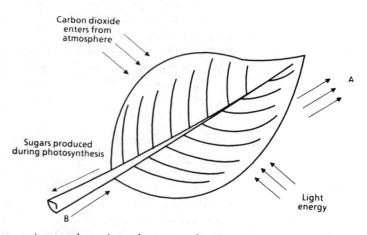

(i) What gas is passed out into the atmosphere at A? (1)
(ii) What raw material, required for photosynthesis, enters the leaf at B? (1)
(iii) State *one* way in which the plant uses the sugars produced during photosynthesis. (1)
(iv) Some plants have leaves which are green in parts and white in other parts. Why does photosynthesis not take place in the white parts? (2)

(b) Two sets of apparatus (A and B below) were used to investigate the process of photosynthesis. Before the apparatus was set up both plants were kept in the dark for 48 hours.

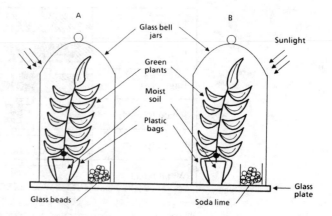

(i) Why were the plants kept in the dark for 48 hours before starting the investigation? (1)
(ii) Which environmental factor necessary for photosynthesis was missing from one of the bell jars? (1)
(iii) Why were two sets of apparatus used in the investigation? (1)
(iv) What chemical substance in the leaves do you usually test for to show that photosynthesis has taken place? (1)
(v) How would the results of this test show the importance of the missing environmental factor to the process of photosynthesis? (2)

NICCEA★

16 Heather plants have narrow leaves. The diagram below shows a section cut across a leaf of a heather plant.

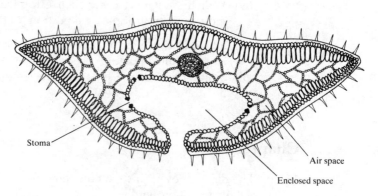

(a) On the diagram label clearly with a guideline:

A the epidermis

B the palisade layer. (2)

(b) Describe how carbon dioxide gets from the air outside the leaf to the cells in the palisade layer. (2)

(c) The leaves are folded so that the stomata open into an enclosed space. Explain how this helps to reduce water loss. (2)

NEAB 1993

17 Below is a label from a package of 'PHOS-TABS PLANT FOOD'

(a) Read the label carefully, then design a fair test to find if the tablets do improve the growth of potted plants. (6)

(b) Explain why plants need nitrogen and magnesium for healthy growth. (4)

PHOSTROGEN HOUSE PLANT FOOD is PHOS-TABS in a handy spike pack. It provides a balanced diet of the nutrients, including vital trace elements, essential for long life and healthy, vigorous growth. Applied at monthly intervals, each tablet releases its nutrients gently to be absorbed by the roots, during normal watering.

These unique tablets are recommended for all flowering **and** foliage varieties, including lime-hating plants. They promote an abundance of more colourful flowers and richer, greener leaves. **No other plant food inserted in the growing medium is as effective, versatile and so very economical.**

1 Peel off sealing band from cap.

2 Take out required number of tablets and replace cap firmly.

PHOS-TABS PLANTOIDS

Large pots: Over 10cms (4 ins). Press one tablet into growing medium just below surface and insert one deep down near roots. Repeat at four weekly intervals. For very large subjects, double this quantity.

Small pots: 5 to 10cms (2 to 4ins). Press one tablet into growing medium just below the surface. Repeat at four weekly intervals.

3 Use spike to make a hole, then push tablet down with tip of spike. Gently re-fill hole.

Large pots

NEAB 1993

Chapter 6

18 Separate test-tubes containing starch suspension and amylase solution were placed in water-baths set at a range of temperatures.

When the required temperatures were reached, the amylase was added to the starch. The mixtures were left in the water-baths at these temperatures for 30 minutes.

Samples were then analysed for the quantity of sugar present.

The results are shown in the table below.

Temperature (°C)	0	15	30	40	50	70
Units of sugar	5	30	60	80	10	0

(a) From the results, state the optimum temperature for this enzyme. (1)

(b) Amylase is **specific** to the substrate starch.

Explain the meaning of the term 'specific'. (1)

(c) What would be the effect on the results at 70 °C, if the starch suspension and amylase solution had been mixed together **before** being placed in the water-bath? Explain your answer. (2)

SEB 1993

19 (a) Complete the table below to show the enzymes in the juices of a healthy human.

Place a ✔ where the enzyme is present and an X where the enzyme is absent. (3)

		Name of enzyme		
		Amylase	Lipase	Protease
Name of juice	Saliva			
	Gastric			
	Pancreatic			

(b) Some people are unable to digest the milk sugar lactose because their intestinal juice does not contain the enzyme lactase.
  (i) What is the substrate for the enzyme lactase? (1)
  (ii) Glucose is a product of the action of lactase on its substrate. Suggest why glucose can be absorbed into the blood but lactose cannot. (1)
  (iii) What features of the small intestine help to increase the absorption of glucose? (2)
  (iv) Describe what happens to glucose when it reaches the liver in a healthy person. (2)

NICCEA 1992

20 The diagram below shows the outline of a section through a canine tooth.

(a) (i) Complete the diagram to show the various parts of the tooth and its surroundings. (2)
  (ii) Label the dentine, enamel, gum, bone, pulp cavity, cement, crown, neck and root. (5)

(b) Write down what happens in the mouth when we eat a food such as bread which contains starch. The functions of the teeth, tongue and saliva should be included in your account. (5)

(c) (i) Which tissue brings about peristalsis in the alimentary canal? (1)
  (ii) Write down *two* functions of peristalsis in the alimentary canal. (2)

ULEAC 1992

21 (a) The cat is a carnivore and the sheep is a herbivore. State *two* ways in which you would expect the teeth of a sheep to differ from those of a cat. (2)

(b) Name the kind of tooth which, in humans,
  (i) crushes food (1)
  (ii) bites pieces of food (1)

SEG★

22 The practice of adding small quantities of fluoride salts to the water supply of a town is controversial. Give *two* arguments *for* and *two* arguments *against* the practice. (4)

MEG 1993

Chapter 7

23 Red blood cells and onion epidermal cells were placed in pure water and left for one hour.

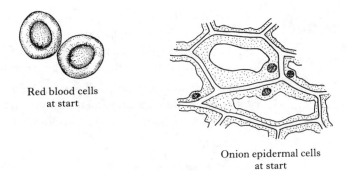

Red blood cells
at start

Onion epidermal cells
at start

(a) What concentration gradient exists when the red blood cells are first placed in the pure water? (1)

(b) Examine each of the statements below. Complete the table using the letter

R if the statement is true for red blood cells only;

O if the statement is true for onion epidermal cells only;

R and O if the statement is true for both types of cell.

Write an F for false if the statement is not true for either cell.

Statement	Letter
The cell walls have prevented the cells from bursting	
The vacuoles have decreased in size	
The cells have burst	
The cells have become turgid	

(3)
SEB 1993

24 (a) Which mineral ion containing nitrogen is absorbed by the roots of a flowering plant from the soil? (1)

(b) Which cells carry out most of this absorption for a flowering plant? (1)

(c) Which tissue carries this ion from the roots to other parts of a flowering plant? (1)

(d) This ion is normally in a lower concentration in the soil than in the cells of the plant. Which process is used to take it in? (1)

(e) Name a molecule formed within the cells of a plant from the nitrogen in this ion. (1)

ULEAC 1992

25 The diagram below shows a cross-section of a plant stem.

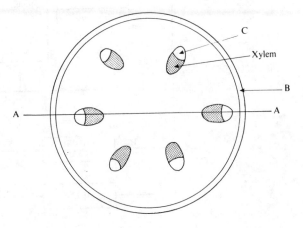

(a) (i) Draw a diagram, to show the stem cut lengthways through A – – – A. (3)
     (ii) Name the parts labelled B and C. (2)
     (iii) Explain how the xylem carries out its function. (3)
     (iv) Give *two* structural differences between the stem and the root of a plant. (2)

(b) Explain how the apparatus, illustrated below, could be used to investigate the effect of increasing air movements on the rate of water uptake by the shoot. (5)

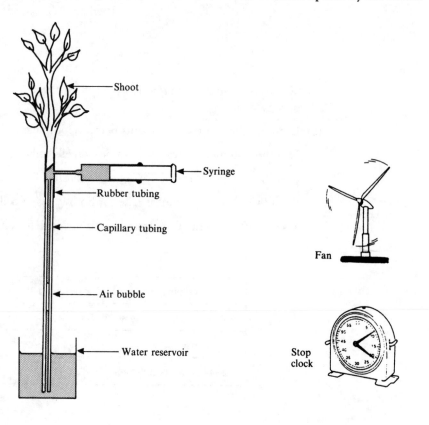

NICCEA 1992

Chapter 8

26 The diagram below shows some of the main blood vessels and the chambers of the heart of a human fetus (developing baby) in the mother's uterus.

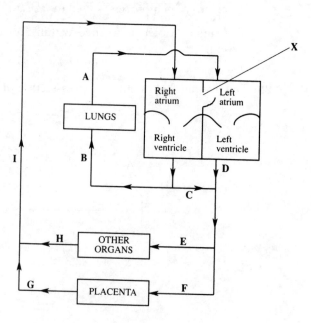

(a) (i) Arteries, veins and capillaries are the three types of blood vessel in the blood system. Which of these is present at A and at F? (2)
 (ii) Write down the letter of the blood vessel which would be the pulmonary vein. (1)

(b) Write down *two* differences in the content of the blood present in G compared with that in F. You must refer to the blood in G and F in each answer. (2)

(c) (i) What structural difference would allow you to tell the right ventricle from the left ventricle in the heart? (1)
 (ii) What is the job of the left ventricle? (2)

(d) At birth C and the gap labelled X between the atria normally close.
 (i) How does this affect the blood flow through the lungs at birth? (1)
 (ii) Sometimes the gap labelled X does not close at birth. If this happens the child may quickly become tired when exercise takes place. Explain why the child quickly becomes tired. (2)

(e) (i) Write down *two* features of capillaries which help materials to be exchanged between the blood and the surrounding tissues. (2)
 (ii) Explain the mechanism by which blood is passed back to the heart from the organs of the body of an active child. (2)

ULEAC 1992

27 The table below shows the volume of blood flowing per minute through some different organs for a person at rest and then during exercise.

Organ	Volume of blood flowing through (cm³ per minute)	
	At rest	During exercise
Brain	700	700
Kidneys	1100	800
Liver	1350	1200
Muscles	750	3000
Skin	300	900

(a) Draw a **bar chart** to show these data. Use the vertical axis for the volume of blood flowing through and the horizontal axis for each organ. (3)

(b) (i) How does the blood flow to the muscles change during exercise?
 (ii) Explain the advantage of this change. (3)

(c) (i) How does the blood flow to the skin change during exercise?
 (ii) Explain the advantage of this change. (3)

(d) Suggest why there is no change in blood flow to the brain? (1)

NEAB 1993

28 Select the correct statement A, B, C or D:

Some white cells in the blood ...

A make antibodies.
B help the blood to clot.
C transport carbon dioxide.
D prevent heart disease.

NEAB 1993

29 Select the correct statement A, B, C or D:

The blood of a person who has breathed in carbon monoxide would ...

A be unable to carry as much carbon dioxide.
B release more carbon dioxide into the lungs.
C move around the body more slowly.
D carry less oxygen round the body.

NEAB 1993

30 Which of the following A, B, C, D, or E contains two *correct* statements?

Red blood cells	White blood cells
A kill germs	have a nucleus
B contain haemoglobin	can change shape
C have a nucleus	carry oxygen
D carry oxygen	contain haemoglobin
E can change shape	kill germs

MEG 1990

Chapter 9

31 (a) Respiration is the release of energy from glucose by living cells.
Complete the following equation for aerobic respiration.

Glucose + ... → Carbon dioxide + ... + energy

(2)

(b) The diagram below shows the apparatus used to compare the amount of carbon dioxide given off by an insect and a green plant.

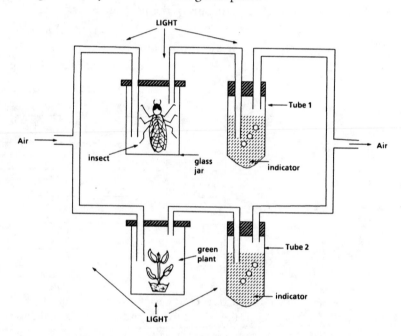

(i) Name an indicator that detects changes in carbon dioxide content. (1)
(ii) After one hour the indicator in Tube 2 had not changed but the indicator in Tube 1 showed the presence of carbon dioxide. Explain these results.
Tube 1 (2)
Tube 2 (3)
(iii) Suggest *one* change to the apparatus shown that would be needed to compare the respiration rates in insects and green plants. (1)

NICCEA★

32 The diagram shows a section through the human chest.

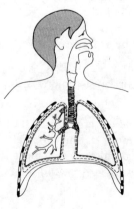

(a) Label the ribs, diaphragm and intercostal muscles on the diagram. (3)

(b) Use the above structures, together with the terms 'volume' and 'pressure', to describe how breathing in takes place. (6)

ULEAC 1993

33 The diagram below shows an alveolus and some blood vessels.

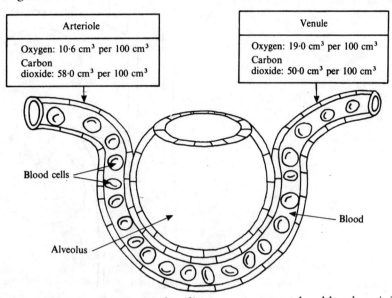

Arteriole
Oxygen: 10·6 cm³ per 100 cm³
Carbon dioxide: 58·0 cm³ per 100 cm³

Venule
Oxygen: 19·0 cm³ per 100 cm³
Carbon dioxide: 50·0 cm³ per 100 cm³

Blood cells

Blood

Alveolus

(a) What evidence, shown in the diagram, suggests that blood arriving at the alveolus contains oxygen? (1)

(b) On the diagram, draw labelled arrows to show the direction of:
   1 blood flow.
   2 oxygen diffusion.
   3 carbon dioxide diffusion. (3)

(c) Explain why the diffusion of oxygen and carbon dioxide occurs. (2)

(d) Give *four* features of an alveolus which make it a good surface for gas exchange. (4)

(e) The diagram shows an alveolus of a nonsmoker.
   (i) Explain how smoking would change the structure of the alveolus.
   (ii) How would this change in the alveolus affect the rate of gas exchange? (2)

NICCEA 1993

34 The diagram shows part of the gas exchange system of an insect.

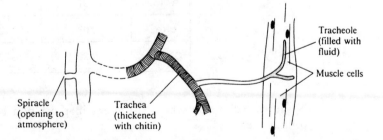

Tracheole (filled with fluid)

Muscle cells

Spiracle (opening to atmosphere)

Trachea (thickened with chitin)

Use the information in the diagram and your own knowledge to answer the following questions.

(a)   (i) Suggest how the structure of the trachea of an insect is similar to that in humans. (1)
      (ii) Write down *two* ways in which the structure of the tracheole of an insect is different from the alveolus in humans. (2)

(b) Suggest how the transport of gases to and from the muscle cells of an insect differs from that in humans. (2)

ULEAC 1993

Chapter 10

35 (a) What is excretion? (2)

(b) The diagram below shows a section through a human kidney and the vessels connected to it.

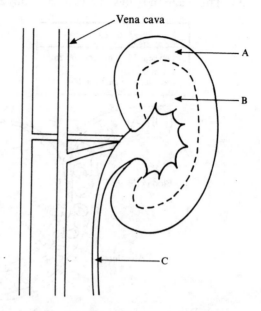

(i) Name the parts labelled A, B and C. (3)
(ii) Name the liquid carried in C. (1)
(iii) To which organ does C lead? (1)
(iv) On the diagram, use the letter D to label the vessel carrying blood into the kidney. (1)

(c) The table below shows the percentage composition of blood and urine.

Chemical	Percentage composition	
	Blood	Urine
Water	92.00	95.00
Protein	7.00	0.00
Glucose	0.10	0.00
Salt	0.37	0.60
Urea	0.03	2.00
Others	0.50	2.40

Name *one* substance which is present in the blood but not in the urine. Explain your answer. (2)

NICCEA 1993

36 Excess proteins are broken down in the body. The waste nitrogen compounds produced from these proteins are excreted.

Describe the processes involved. Your answer should include a description of how and where the waste nitrogen compounds are produced, how they are transported and how they are excreted.

Marks will be given *both* for showing knowledge and understanding *and* for the way in which your account is organized and expressed. (10)

NEAB 1993

37 The diagram shows a kidney machine which is used to return blood plasma to its normal composition.

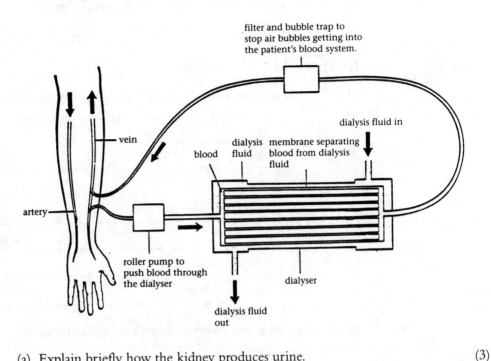

(a) Explain briefly how the kidney produces urine. (3)

(b) (i) Give *one* way in which the dialysis fluid entering the machine would be different from the patient's blood plasma. (1)

(ii) Give *two* ways in which the dialysis fluid entering the machine would be the same as the patient's blood plasma. (2)

(c) Give *one* advantage of having a kidney transplant rather than using a dialysis machine. (1)

*WJEC**

38 The diagram shows a section through human skin.

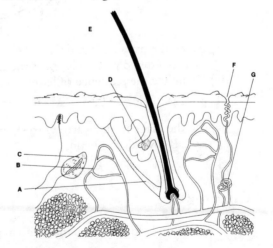

(a) Write down the letter which labels (i) the sweat gland and (ii) the hair erector muscle. (2)

(b) (i) When we get hot after being cold, what happens to the sweat gland and the hair erector muscle? (2)

(ii) Explain how these changes could help to cool the body.
Sweat gland. (2)
Hair erector muscle. (2)

(c) Explain what happens when vasodilation takes place in the skin and explain how vasodilation helps to cool the body. (3)

(d) (i) Explain why a person who comes out of the sea at Brighton can feel cold.

(2)

(ii) Why does shivering warm the person up again?

(2)

ULEAC 1990

Chapter 11

39 Fill in the table to show where, in a human being, various stimuli are sensed:

Stimulus	Sensitive part
Light	
	Cochlea
Temperature (external)	
	Hypothalamus of brain
Glucose concentration in the blood	
Chemicals in the air	

40 The diagram below shows a section through a human eye.

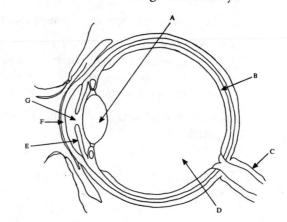

(i) Name the parts A, B and C. (3)
(ii) Which lettered parts help focus the light on B? (2)
(iii) Complete the sequence of letters to show the path of a ray of light from F to B.

F → → → → B (1)

(iv) On the diagram draw arrows to show the route which nerve impulses take from layer B towards the brain.

(2)

NICCEA 1993

Chapter 12

41 The diagram below shows a mammalian neurone (nerve cell).

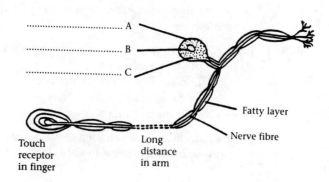

(a) On the diagram, label parts A, B and C of the cell body. (3)

(b) Suggest why the fibre is surrounded by a fatty layer. (1)

(c) The touch receptor is found in the skin of the finger.

  (i) Where would the branches at the other end of the neurone be found? (1)

  (ii) What happens when the receptor is touched? (1)

WJEC★

42 Which *one* of the following shows the correct sequence in the pathway of impulses in a reflex arc?

A receptor → relay neurone → sensory neurone → motor neurone → effector

B sensory neurone → receptor → motor neurone → relay neurone → effector

C receptor → sensory neurone → relay neurone → motor neurone → effector

D receptor → relay neurone → motor neurone → sensory neurone → effector

E receptor → motor neurone → relay neurone → sensory neurone → effector

MEG 1990

43 (a) Label the endocrine glands as shown in the diagram below. (2)

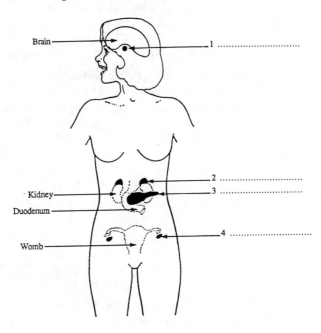

(b) Describe the effect on the body of (i) too much and (ii) too little hormone released by number 3. (2)

WJEC 1991

44 Compare nervous and hormonal communication. In your answer refer to *four* of the following: the nature of the message, the speed of the message, the duration of the effect, the accuracy of the message and the speed of response. (8)

MEG 1993

45 (a) Give three factors which may affect the rate at which seedlings grow. (3)

(b) Young oat seedlings have a single straight shoot. In an investigation of the growth of oat seedlings a student marked shoots with ink at 1 mm intervals. The results are shown in the diagrams below.

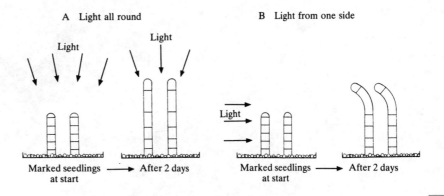

What do these results show about:
  (i) the growth of the shoot?
  (ii) the response of the shoot to light from one side? (2)

(c) (i) Name the response shown by the seedlings to light from one side. (1)
  (ii) Explain why this response is important to the seedlings. (1)

(d) The student then carried out another experiment. She covered the tip of a shoot with a small piece of black paper. She shone light from one side onto the shoot.
The result is shown in the diagram below.

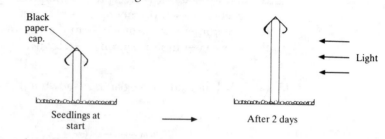

Suggest a hypothesis to explain these results. (2)

(e) The diagrams below show another experiment carried out by the student. She grew more seedlings and coated some on one side with substance X. The result is shown in the diagram below.

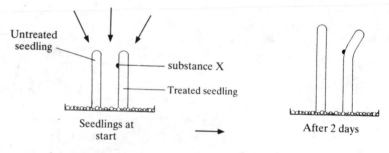

(i) Suggest what substance X is. (1)
(ii) Explain how this substance is involved in the response of shoots to light from one side. (2)

NEAB 1993

Chapter 13

46 The diagram below shows the arrangement of the muscles at the human elbow joint.

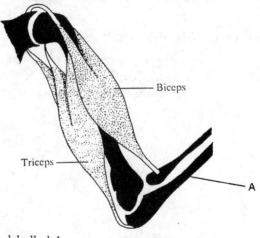

(a) Name the bone labelled A. (1)
(b) What do the biceps and triceps each do to straighten the arm? (2)
(c) Why are two muscles needed to operate the elbow joint? (1)

SEG★

47 (a) Diagram 1 shows the arrangement of fibres and myofibrils in a muscle.
Diagram 2 shows how the filaments of actin and myosin are arranged in a myofibril in a contracted and in a relaxed state.

Diagram 1

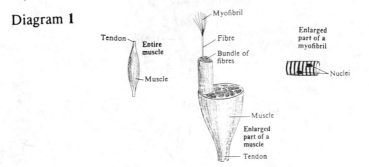

Diagram 2

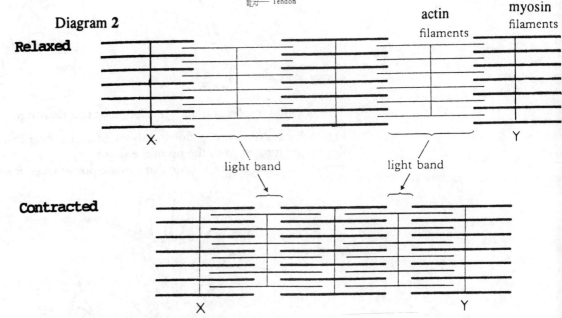

Calculate the percentage (%) reduction between X and Y when the muscle contracts. Suggest show the arrangement of filaments of actin and myosin makes muscle contraction possible. (6)

(b) The diagram shows a cross-section through a wing and the air flow it creates as it cuts through the air.

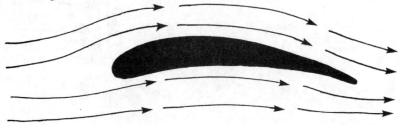

Describe how the sectional shape of the wing and the air flow it creates help to produce lift. (3)

SEG★

Chapter 14

48 The diagrams overleaf show the main stages in taking a stem cutting of a geranium.

(a) Explain why stages 2 and 4 are necessary. (2)

(b) What type of reproduction (sexual or asexual) is involved in
   (i) producing seeds? (1)
   (ii) taking cuttings? (1)

(c) Why do gardeners sometimes take cuttings rather than collect and sow the seeds of a plant such as a geranium? (1)

SEG★

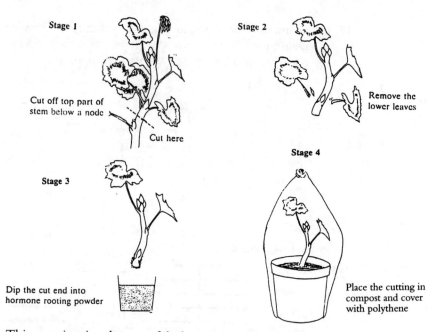

Stage 1 — Cut off top part of stem below a node — Cut here

Stage 2 — Remove the lower leaves

Stage 3 — Dip the cut end into hormone rooting powder

Stage 4 — Place the cutting in compost and cover with polythene

49 This question involves careful observation of two drawings.

Figure 1 is a drawing of a flowing shoot of an Evening Primrose plant. The oldest flowers are furthest from the tip of the shoot.
Figure 2 is a drawing of a section of a single flower taken from the flowering shoot.

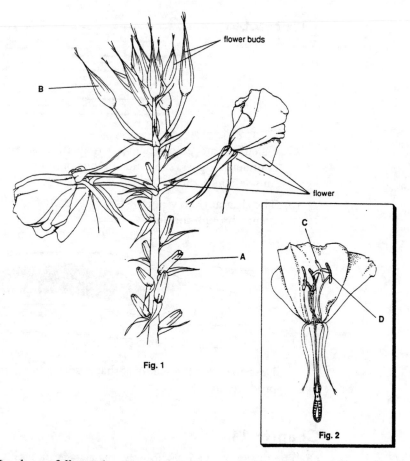

Fig. 1

Fig. 2

(a) Look carefully at the drawings in Figs. 1 and 2 and then answer the following questions.
    (i) Draw a circle around the ovary of an open flower in Fig. 1.   (1)
    (ii) Identify structure A.   (1)
    (iii) Name the small round structures found inside structure A.   (1)
    (iv) 1 Which part of the flower bud does label line B actually touch?   (1)
        2 How many of these structures are present in each flower?   (1)
        3 Describe what happens to these structures as the flower ages.   (3)

(b) (i) Identify structure C. (1)
    (ii) State the function of structure D. (1)

(c) Each Evening Primrose plant typically produces many flowering shoots similar to that shown in Fig. 1. The plant flowers from May through to October. Explain how these features help the plant to compete well with other species of flowering plant. (2)

(d) State *three* differences in structure between the flower in Fig. 2 and a *typical* wind-pollinated flower. (3)

MEG 1993

50 The diagram below shows a wind-pollinated flower.

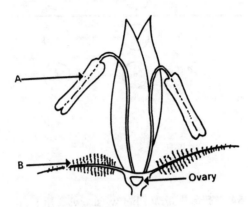

(a) Name the parts labelled A and B. (2)
(b) Give *two* features of wind-pollinated flowers shown in the diagram. (2)
(c) Explain how this flower is cross-pollinated by the wind. (2)

NICCEA★

51 The following events occur during sexual reproduction in a flowering plant. Arrange them in the correct order by writing the appropriate letter in the boxes in the table below.

A meiosis takes place in the anther
B pollen tube grows down into the ovary
C a male nucleus fuses with the ovum nucleus
D anthers split open releasing pollen
E insects transfer pollen from anther to stigma

Order of events	Statement letter
1	
2	
3	
4	
5	

MEG

Chapter 15

52 Select the correct statement A, B, C or D:
In animals, fertilization ...

A is the movement of a sperm towards an egg.
B is the fusion of the nuclei of a sperm and an egg.
C is the production of male and female gametes.
D always takes place inside the body of the female.

NEAB 1993

53 Which one of the following diagrams show the process which will produce identical twin boys?

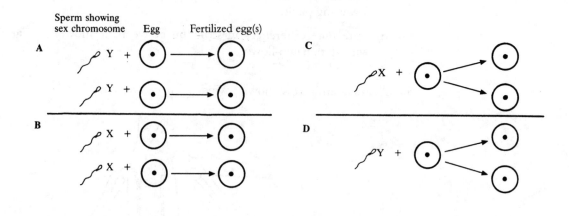

NEAB 1993

54 The diagram below shows a human embryo in the uterus of its mother.

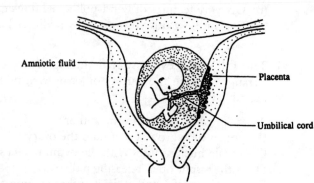

(a) Give *two* different functions of:
   (i) the placenta; (2)
   (ii) the umbilical cord. (2)

(b) Give *one* function of the amniotic fluid. (1)

SEG★

55 The table shows some of the human female reproductive hormones, their sources and one important effect of each.

Name of hormone	Source	Effect
FSH (Follicle stimulating hormone)	Pituitary gland	
LH (Luteinizing hormone)		Stimulates release of egg cell
	Follicle in ovary	Thickens lining of uterus
Progesterone		Vascularizes lining of uterus

(a) Complete the table by filling in the blank spaces. (4)

(b) Describe, briefly, the mechanism by which the levels of FSH and LH are controlled during the menstrual cycle. (2)

SEG★

56 Which *one* of the following methods of contraception prevents the release of an ovum (egg) from the ovary?

    A using a condom
    B having a coil (IUD) fitted
    C taking the 'pill'
    D using a diaphragm
    E vasectomy

MEG 1991

57 Many couples are infertile. Pregnancy can be usually achieved by in vitro fertilization followed by the placing of several of the embryos into the mother's womb. If this operation succeeds one or more of the embryos will become attached to the uterus and develop normally.

This process is illustrated below.

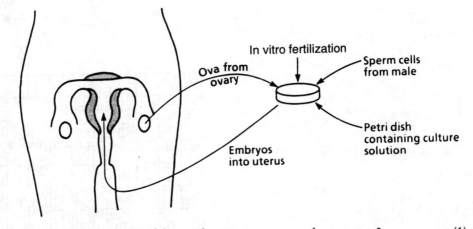

(a) Why should blockage of the oviducts prevent normal pregnancy?   (1)
(b) Outline the process which takes place in the petri dish.   (2)
(c) Give *one* benefit and *one* drawback of giving the infertile woman hormone treatment.   (2)

NICCEA★

Chapter 16

58 (a) Below is a drawing of a seed cut in half. Four parts have been labelled A, B, C and D.

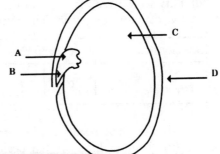

      (i) Name the parts A and B.   (2)
      (ii) Give *one* function of C and D.   (2)

  (b) Complete the diagram below, to show what happens to parts A and B after the seed has germinated.   (2)

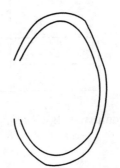

(c) The drawings and graph below show changes in the appearance and dry mass of seedlings during the early growth of a pea plant.

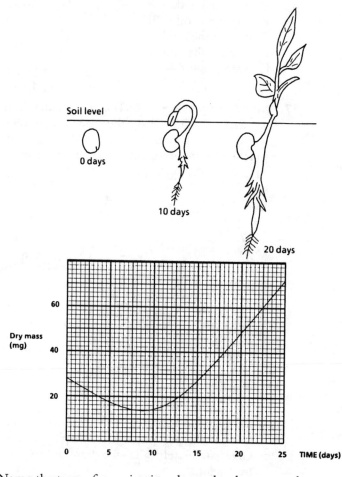

(i) Name the type of germination shown by the pea seed. (1)
(ii) Account for the change in dry mass during the first 10 days. (3)
(iii) Explain how you would find the dry mass of a pea seedling. (3)
(iv) Give *two* conditions that are necessary for the successful germination of seeds. (2)

(d) Fifty seeds were planted and the number which germinated was recorded every five days for thirty days. The results are shown in the table below.

Time in days	0	5	10	15	20	25	30
Number of seeds germinated	0	3	15	35	46	47	47

(i) Plot these results as a line graph.
(ii) Within which five-day period did most seeds germinate? (1)

NICCEA★

59 Table 1 shows the birth rates and death rates for five different countries in a particular year.

	Country				
	A	B	C	D	E
Birth rate %	6.0	5.0	4.5	4.0	3.0
Death rate %	4.0	3.0	2.5	1.5	3.5

Which country A, B, C, D or E had the highest population growth in that year?

MEG 1992

Chapter 17

60 (a) What do the terms **phenotype** and **heterozygous** mean? (4)

(b) Give an example of incomplete dominance (codominance). (1)

(c) What letters are used to represent the sex chromosomes of a human male in a genetic cross? (1)

(d) In humans, brown eye-colour is due to the dominant form of a gene **B**, and blue eye-colour is due to its recessive allele, **b**.

The table contains information about a family.

Person	Father	Mother	1st son	1st daughter	2nd daughter	2nd son
Eye colour	blue	brown	blue	brown	blue	brown

(i) The first son and the second daughter had the same genotype. What was it? (1)

(ii) Complete the checker board.

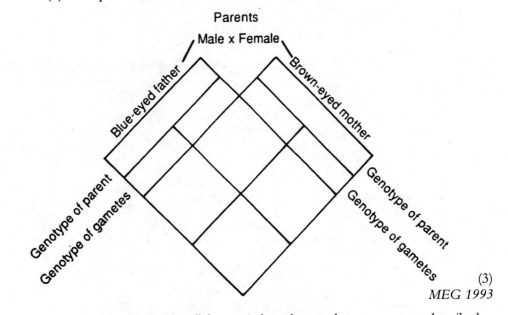

(3)

MEG 1993

61 Characteristics controlled by alleles carried on the sex chromosomes are described as being sex-linked. The alleles only occur on the X chromosomes and do not appear on the Y chromosomes. The pedigree below shows the inheritance of haemophilia, a sex-linked condition, in a family over several generations. The first generation shown in the pedigree has the genotypes $X^H X^h$ (individual 1) and $X^H Y$ (individual 2).

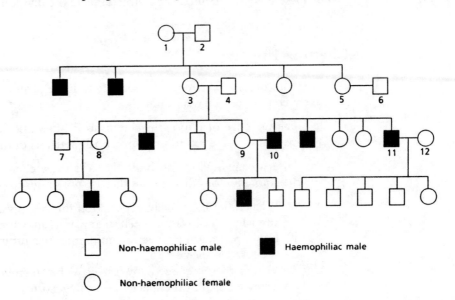

□ Non-haemophiliac male   ■ Haemophiliac male

○ Non-haemophiliac female

(a) What evidence in the pedigree suggests that haemophilia is a sex-linked characteristic? (1)

(b) State how the genotypes of individuals 9 and 12 could differ. Support your answer by quoting evidence obtained from the pedigree. (4)

(c) Females suffering from haemophilia do occur though they are less numerous than male sufferers. Select one marriage from the pedigree and show clearly, by means of a genetic diagram, how a daughter could suffer from haemophilia. (4)

NICCEA★

62 Nuclei may divide either by mitosis or by meiosis. If the chromosome number of a nucleus of a cell was 46 before it divided, which *one* of the following combinations represents the chromosome number of the daughter nuclei after each type of division?

	Mitosis	Meiosis
A	46	92
B	46	23
C	23	46
D	23	23
E	92	46

MEG 1990

63 The diagram below shows a stage in meiosis in an insect cell.

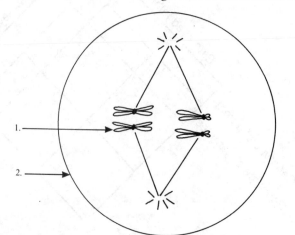

(a) Name the structures labelled 1 and 2. (2)
(b) What is the diploid number of chromosomes in this insect? (1)
(c) Give *one* reason why the type of division shown is meiosis. (1)
(d) Where, in an adult insect, would this division occur? (1)
(e) Describe what would happen to complete the division of the cell. (3)

NICCEA 1992

Chapter 18

64 (a) The colour red is frequently seen in both the plant and animal kingdoms and is used to attract or warn animals.

The presence of poisonous chemicals is often associated with this colour and many insects use red to warn potential predators of their toxic qualities.

The African swallow-tail butterfly lacks these chemicals but closely resembles the coloration of other species that are poisonous to predators.

(i) What is the most likely explanation for the appearance of red colour in an animal when it was not seen in any of its ancestors? (1)
(ii) How may natural selection influence the future success of the African swallow-tail species? (3)
(iii) Why is the existence of variation within members of a species a form of insurance against the species becoming extinct? (3)

(b) Plant breeders have produced a new variety of oilseed rape, a flowering plant with seeds rich in oil which is used in the production of margarine. A good variety should have the following characteristics:

a high yield of oil;

a strong stem to support the seed head; and

fast growth leading to early harvest.

The results below were obtained from trials using two old varieties and the new variety.

Variety	Seed yield (kg/hectare)	Oil content of seed (%)	Strength of stem 1 (weak) 9 (strong)	Time of maturity 1 (early) 9 (late)
Old A	2150	45	4	7
Old B	2100	42	7	5
New C	2500	39	6	2

(i) Use all the given information to support the use of the new variety C in preference to each of the older varieties.
(Show the workings of any calculations used.)
New C versus Old A
New C versus Old B   (6)
(ii) How does the type of selection used in the production of the new variety differ from selection in the wild?   (2)

NICCEA★

65 Scientists have discovered that they can produce animals with identical genes by cloning. One way to do this is to remove the nucleus from an unfertilized egg cell and replace it with a nucleus from a body cell. The egg cell with its new nucleus can then grow into a new individual.

(a) Give the *main* difference in the amount of genetic material between the nucleus which has been removed and the one which has replaced it.   (2)

(b) Early cloning experiments were done on the eggs of frogs and toads. This was done because it was easier than using eggs from animals such as rabbits and sheep. Suggest and explain *one* reason why this was easier.   (2)

(c) More recent experiments have been done by removing the nucleus from an egg cell of a rabbit. A liver cell from another rabbit was used to provide a nucleus which was then placed into the egg. The following diagram shows the main stages in the process.

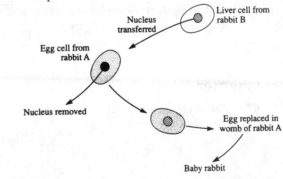

(i) Which rabbit, A or B, will the baby rabbit look like?   (1)
(ii) Explain your answer to part (i).   (2)

(d) Cloning can be used with many different animals. For example, cloning could be used to improve the quality of sheep. The following diagram shows the main stages in the process. Fill in the *four* boxes to briefly describe stages 2, 3, 4 and 5.
                                                                               (4)

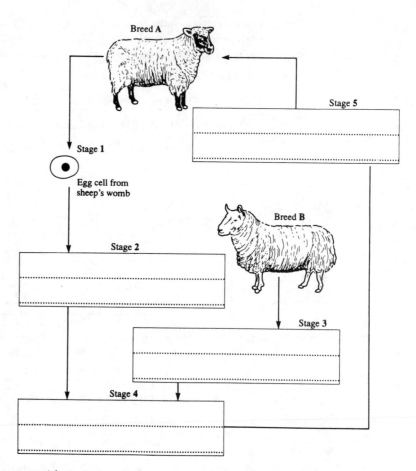

(e) Suggest, with your reasons, *one* advantage and *one* disadvantage of the cloning of farm animals. (4)

(f) Cloning is fairly new way of changing the characteristics of a living thing. However, changes have been taking place amongst the living things on this planet for millions of years due to another process.
   (i) What is this process called? (1)
   (ii) Explain how this process may have caused giraffes to change from a short-necked to a long-necked species. You will be awarded up to *three* marks for the clear way in which you express your answer. (9)

SEG★

66 Man is constantly exploring ways of producing more food of the right type and quality. **Artificial selection** and **biotechnology** can each play a part in helping to solve this problem.

Explain what is meant by artificial selection.

Describe *one* method by which the production of food is made more effective. (6)

MEG 1993

Chapter 19

67 The diagram below shows a food chain in a wood.

Sparrow Hawk

↑

Coal Tit

↑

Lacewing larva

↑

Aphid

↑

Sycamore tree

Use the food chain to answer the following questions:
(a) Name the producer and the secondary consumer. (2)
(b) At which trophic level does the lacewing larva feed? (1)
(c) Explain what is shown by the arrows. (2)
(d) What is the source of energy for the green plants? (1)
(e) What would happen to the number of coal tits if the sparrow hawks left the wood? (1)
(f) Explain why there are only two sparrow hawks in the wood but a large number of lacewing larvae. (3)

NICCEA 1993

68 The diagram below shows part of a food web which exists in the very cold waters of the Antarctic Ocean. Use this information to help you answer some of the questions which follow.

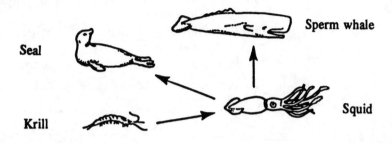

(a) From the web choose the names of the animals which can be used to complete the following sentence. (3)

The .... is the predator of the ....

and the prey of the ....

(b) In the food web, which *one* of the animals would you expect to find in the largest numbers? Give a reason for your answer. (2)

(c) Until recently the Antarctic Ocean has been free from the effects of pollution. However, over the last few years there has been a gradual build up of pollutants in these waters.

Which *one* of the animals shown in the food web above is likely to have the *most* pollutant in its body? Give a reason for your answer. (3)

(d) (i) What would be the effect on the krill population if all the squid suddenly died? Give a reason for your answer. (2)
(ii) The bodies of the dead would, like the bodies of any dead organisms, gradually decay.

(A) Give the name of *one* type of organism, other than mould, which causes decay. (1)

(B) Suggest and explain *one* reason why the bodies of these squid would decay more slowly than the bodies of dead squid in the seas in other parts of the world. (2)

(C) Explain why the decay process is an important part of nature. (2)

(e) Krill are not only an important part of the food chain of many sea animals, but many are now being caught for use as a food for land animals. Scientists are attempting by selective breeding to produce krill which are not only larger in size, but which also mature at a younger age than those krill normally found in the seas.

Suggest *two* advantages of carrying out this work. (2)

SEG★

69 (a) The diagram overleaf shows the connection between some living things and the water cycle.

(i) Fill in the missing words by naming the processes at A and at B. (2)

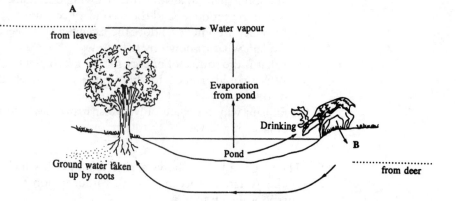

(ii) Suggest *one* way in which water vapour becomes pond water again, completing the cycle. (2)

(iii) Write down *one* way in which the deer in the diagram is well adapted to life in woodland. (1)

(iv) How is this adaptation passed on to the deer's young? (1)

(b) The diagram below shows part of the carbon cycle on land.

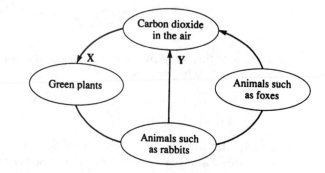

(i) What processes are occurring at X and Y? (2)

(ii) How is the carbon in the green plant passed to the fox? (2)

(iii) What is the effect on the carbon cycle of cutting down a lot of trees? (2)

(iv) The last two diagrams have shown the water cycle and the carbon cycle. Name *one* other element that is cycled. (1)

SEG★

Chapter 20

70 (a) (i) Describe, with full experimental details, how you could compare the percentage of water in a sample of a light sandy soil with that of a heavy clay soil. (8)

(ii) State the likely results of the investigation. (1)

(iii) With reference to the structure of each of the soils, explain why you would expect these results. (3)

(b) The use of artificial fertilizers in agriculture is controversial. Describe *two* arguments *for* and *two* arguments *against* the practice. (4)

MEG 1993

71 (a) (i) Give *one* example of the present day, large scale, human destruction of plant life on this planet. (1)

(ii) Explain how this destruction affects the carbon cycle. (2)

(b) Since the beginning of this century there has been an increasing destruction of plants growing in a natural, uncultivated state. There has also been an increasing use of fossil fuels.

Explain the main reasons why these changes have occurred:

(i) increasing destruction of natural, uncultivated plants; (2)

(ii) increasing use of fossil fuels. (2)

(c) One way in which the biosphere may change is as a result of the greenhouse effect.
  (i) Describe what causes the greenhouse effect. (3)
  (ii) Give *three* possible results of the greenhouse effect. (3)
  SEG★

72 Burning coal often leads to an increase in the amount of sulphur dioxide in the atmosphere.

The following table shows which lichens are found in areas with different levels of sulphur dioxide in the atmosphere.

Lichens	Level of sulphur dioxide
No lichens at all	Very high
Some crusty lichens	High
Orange lichen found on concrete or limestone	Medium
Grey-green leafy lichen on trees	Low
Spiky 'Old man's beard' lichen can survive	Very low

You wish to make a map of a town which shows the amount of air pollution in different zones. Explain how you could use the information in the table to help you. You will be awarded up to *two* marks for the clear way in which you express your answer. (7)
  SEG★

73 The graphs below show the percentage of North Sea cod stock caught annually (Graph A) and the size of the breeding population of cod in the North Sea (Graph B) between 1966 and 1986.

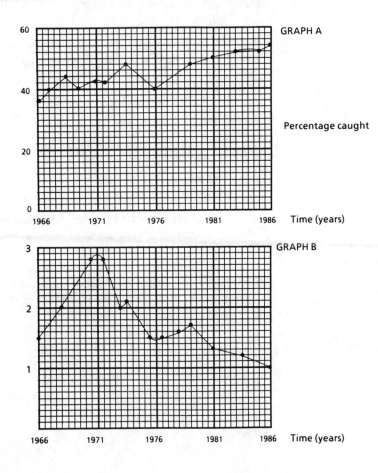

(a) In what year was 50% of the North Sea stock of cod caught? (1)

(b) Suggest why the evidence, provided by the graphs, gives rise for concern for the North Sea cod fishing industry. (2)

NICCEA★

Chapter 21

74 Read the passage below and use this information, together with your own biological knowledge, to answer the questions that follow.

The screw worm fly is a parasite which affects cattle in South America. The female screw worm fly can travel up to 200 km in its search for a new host. The flies lay their eggs near open wounds. The maggots which hatch burrow into the flesh of the cattle. This makes it difficult to kill the maggots.

In 1988 the screw worm fly was accidentally taken to Libya, a country in North Africa. It has been calculated that, if left to spread, 70 000 000 animals would have been affected by the parasite.

To try to control the spread of the screw worm fly, male flies were specially bred and exposed to radiation so they became infertile. Very large numbers of these infertile males were released at intervals of one kilometre.

Infertile males mated with the females so that the eggs failed to hatch.

(a) What is a parasite? (3)

(b) Give *two* reasons why the screw worm fly is such a successful parasite. (2)

(c) How does radiation affect the male flies? (1)

(d) Why is it necessary to release a very large number of infertile male flies? (2)

ULEAC 1993

75 Read the passage and use the information, together with your own biological knowledge, to answer the questions which follow.

An insect pest from Australia which feeds on orange and lemon trees is called the 'cottony cushion'. This insect was accidentally taken to America where it became a very serious pest by causing extensive damage to the orange and lemon trees.

In order to control this pest, scientists visited Australia to see if they could find any parasites or predators of the 'cottony cushion'.

Eventually, a ladybird was found which ate the 'cottony cushion'. Some of these ladybirds were collected and taken to America where they were set free on some of the orange and lemon trees.

The ladybirds bred so successfully that they quickly spread to all of the orange and lemon trees and the 'cottony cushion' almost disappeared.

(a) Give the name of the predator described in this passage. (1)
(b) Give a reason for your answer. (1)
(c) The passage describes an example of 'biological control'. What does 'biological control' mean? (2)
(d) Describe *one* other example of biological control. (2)
(e) Suggest why the 'cottony cushion' was a less serious pest in Australia than in America. (2)

ULEAC 1992

Answers

Key:
/ = alternative answer for 1 mark
; = separate mark
Where 'extended writing', (i.e. prose answers) is involved, marks are built in for good spelling, correct use of biological terms and logical development.

Chapter 1

1 growth, excretion, respiration, movement

2 (a) (i) cell wall
   (ii) chromosome
   (iii) chloroplast
   (iv) (large) vacuole

(b)

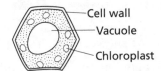

Also possible: starch grains in cytoplasm

(c)

Organ system	Organ	Functions of organ
Excretory	**Kidney**	Filters blood
Circulatory/ Blood	Heart	**Pumps blood**
Respiratory	**Lung/gill/skin**	**Gaseous exchange/ O₂ uptake/ CO₂ removal**

3

	Term	Example(s) (see Unit 1.6)
1	Cell	Cheek cell/Ovum
2	**Tissue**	**Muscle/Nerve**
3	**Organ**	**Kidney/Penis**
4	**System**	**Excretory system/ Reproductive**

4 (a) a section of DNA, which controls formation of a specific protein
  (b) double strand splits; new nucleotides join; by specific base pairing; to form 2 identical strands
  (c) the order of the bases is special; specific for a particular protein (i.e. its recipe)

Chapter 2

5 (a) (i) dolphin
   (ii) fins/streamlined
  (b) seaweed
  (c) (i) wings/skin membranes
   (ii) aphid

(d) | | |
|---|---|
| Ostrich | **Bird** |
| **Rose** | Flowering plant |
| **Lizard** | Reptile |
| **Dolphin/Bat/Kangaroo** | Mammal |
| **Aphid** | Insect |

6 (a) external fertilization; many eggs laid in water
  (b) (i) internal fertilization; avoids need for/ hazards of water or allows less wastage of gametes
   (ii) scales; skin is waterproof/protective/ camouflaged
   (iii) lungs; allow breathing air/more O₂ available than in water or internal and protected
   (iv) eggs; protected by shell/large food supply to give excellent start to young (any 3 of the 4 = 6 marks)
  (c) fish: **gills**; birds: **feathers**

7 (a)

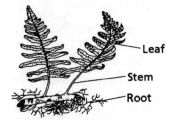

Leaf
Stem
Root

(b) stem/leaves; spores/asexual reproduction/no flowers/no seeds; contain chlorophyll/ green/photosynthesize; need water for sperm to swim in (any 2 similarities)
  (c) mosses have no roots; no vascular/conducting tissue; ferns are larger; moss spores from a capsule/fern spores on leaves (any 2)

Chapter 3

8 (a) although Streptomycin appears best it is ineffective against some colonies. Terramycin and Erythromycin seem equally effective
  (b) it is unaffected by Sulphafurazole and Chloramphenicol but sensitive to the rest
  (c) bacteria are killed by some antibiotics and not others
  (d) subculture the 3 colonies on fresh agar. Add a Streptomycin disc. If no clear zone appears, bacteria are resistant to Streptomycin

9 (a) (i) shape (1 mark)
   organisms in right order (1 mark)

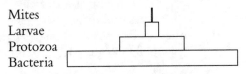

Mites
Larvae
Protozoa
Bacteria

   (ii) decompose organic matter in sewage
   (iii) eat sewage bacteria; eat decomposer bacteria (which could block filter)
  (b) (i) October to March
   (ii) river bacteria would multiply; oxygen depletion due to their respiration

(iii) low temperatures; bacteria relatively inactive

(iv) transfer to activated sludge tank; to complete organic breakdown and/or pass to oxidation pond; to remove mineral salts

(v) when ammonia level high, nitrate level is low (or vice versa); because ammonia (from decomposition) is converted to nitrate (during nitrification); process quicker in warmer months

10 Looking for *design*: e.g. box of wide slats with big gaps between, with wide mesh wire as a bottom, on short legs, placed in a warm shady area. This gives adequate *aeration*; *warmth*; and *humidity* (watering in dry weather) reaching the mowings, weeds, kitchen refuse (i.e. *compostable material*) – all needed for good bacterial decomposition. Note: 2 marks for good prose.

11 The large-scale production of substances useful to Man which have been produced by microorganisms; *example* of food, e.g. bread; *organism* used, e.g. yeast; *raw materials*, e.g. flour, water, sugar; *fermenter* conditions (for bread, conditions needed to rise and bake); *sterilization/treatment* of product (e.g. extraction of penicillin from batch by organic solvents)
(6 marks)

Chapter 4

12 (a) (B1) yeast/legumes/liver, etc.   Beri-beri
   (A) liver oils/egg yolk/   Night
        milk, etc.   blindness/
                     xerophthalmia
   D liver oils/egg yolk, etc.
   C   Scurvy
   (½ mark each)
   (b) (i) carbohydrate; fat
       (ii) iron/protein
       (iii) prevent constipation/bowel cancer

13 (a) (i) John: B; Sarah: D
       (ii) 70 – 55; = 15 kg N.B. 'show working'
   (b) (i) A diet which maintains health for that individual; requires correct proportions; correct quantity; correct quality, e.g. protein quality in vegetable foods is poorer than in animal foods; reference to 7 types of food and calories
       (ii) heart disease/strain on joints and mobility/high blood pressure/late onset diabetes (any 1)
       (iii) exercise needs energy; if energy use exceeds energy intake (food) then fat is used up

14 (a) (i) hatched = fat (lipid); solid = protein (½ mark each)

(ii) no fat in boiled potato, but present in fried potato/more protein than fat in fish
   (b) (i) 14.4 g
       (ii) 14.4 × 17 = 244.8 kJ
       (iii) 6 g
       (iv) water
   (c) (i) frying boils off much of the water; therefore proportion of carbohydrate rises
       (ii) contain fat

Chapter 5

15 (a) (i) oxygen
       (ii) water
       (iii) storage as starch/respiration/in growth
       (iv) no chlorophyll; therefore no sunlight energy can be trapped
   (b) (i) to destarch them
       (ii) carbon dioxide
       (iii) to eliminate the effects of other factors affecting photosynthesis/have a 'control'
       (iv) starch
       (v) A's leaves would have starch, B's would not; showing CO_2 is necessary

16 (a) epidermis: outermost circles; palisade: long cells (N.B. line *touches* cells)
   (b) by diffusion; via stomata; through air spaces; dissolves in film of moisture on palisade cell wall (½ each)
   (c) increases humidity in enclosed space; reduces diffusion gradient; water vapour not blown away; reduced transpiration rate (any 2)

17 (a) One set of plants with Phostab, another set of plants without Phostab
      Same: plant species; size; number (many); ideally all asexually produced to give same genes in all plants; healthiness
      Same: light; water; air, temperature; amount of soil; kind of pot; time to grow; method of estimating growth, e.g. height or number and size of leaves
   (b) nitrogen: amino acid/protein synthesis; for enzymes/metabolism
      magnesium: chlorophyll; to achieve photosynthesis

Chapter 6

18 (a) 40 °C
   (b) will digest only its substrate (here starch) and no other substrate
   (c) there would be some digestion, possibly even complete digestion; because enzyme would digest starch as it warmed, even up to 50 °C

19 (a)

	Amylase	Lipase	Protease	
Saliva	✔	✕	✕	(1 mark)
Gastric	✕	✕	✔	(1 mark)
Pancreatic	✔	✔	✔	(1 mark)

(b) (i) lactose
   (ii) lactose molecule too large to pass through gut membrane, but glucose (half the size) is small enough
   (iii) large surface area of villi; of length of intestine; thin lining; lining is well supplied with capillaries (any 2)
   (iv) glucose stored as glycogen; under control of insulin; or respired; or passed on in circulation to body (any 2)

20 (a) (i) and (ii)

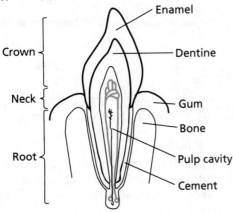

(b) incisors bite morsel; premolars or molars crush it; saliva contains amylase; which digests starch → maltose; tongue mixes saliva with bread; and helps with swallowing (any 5)
(c) (i) muscle
   (ii) passes food along; mixes food with enzymes; helps in egesting food at anus (any 2)

21 (a) sheep: no canines; flat-topped, ridged premolars and molars
   cat: prominent canines; high ridged, smooth premolars and molars
(b) (i) premolar and molar
   (ii) incisors

22 For: hardens enamel/reduces decay of teeth; evidence from areas with high and low levels of fluoride in natural drinking water; preventative medicine is cheaper than fillings/extractions (any 2)
Against: too much causes mottling of teeth/poisonous/bone cancer; additive in water interferes with human rights not to have it; can be taken in through toothpaste instead (any 2)

Chapter 7

23 (a) water concentration high outside → low inside cell
(b) O; F; R; O

24 (a) nitrate
(b) cells at root tip/root hair cells
(c) xylem
(d) active uptake/active transport
(e) amino acid/protein

25 (a) (i)

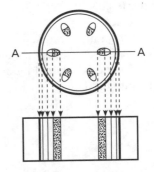

Draw lines vertically down to box to get right *proportions* of epidermis; xylem and phloem; and pith
(ii) B: epidermis; C: phloem
(iii) *transport* water/mineral salts; water loss at leaves/transpiration – draws water through it; or *support*; thick strong lignin walls (either = 2 marks)
(iv) see Fig. 7.10, e.g. *stem* has no root hairs; xylem and phloem in 'outer' position (not central); has pith; bears leaves/buds/flowers (any 2) OR contrasting features of *root*

(b) with fan, without fan; at different speeds; for same time; other conditions the same: light/temperature; measure distance bubble moves per time chosen; syringe used to return bubble to starting point; a number of readings (any 5)

Chapter 8

26 (a) (i) A: vein; F: artery
   (ii) A
(b) F has more food, e.g. glucose than G; G has more CO_2/wastes than F; F has more oxygen than G (any 2)
(c) (i) left ventricle is thicker/has more muscle
   (ii) to pump blood to the body; raise blood pressure
(d) (i) increases it, *all* blood entering the right atrium goes to lungs
   (ii) deoxygenated blood from body mixes with oxygenated; so less O_2 available
(e) (i) large surface area; thin walls; leaky walls (tissue fluid leaves and enters); slow blood flow giving time for exchange (any 2)

(ii) (low) blood pressure in veins; muscles contracting; 'massaging' blood along veins

27 (a) if correct, 3 marks – less 1 mark for each error, organs not named, or scale not *within* the graph paper given (to zero, no minus mark). See Unit 22.7
 (b) (i) increases
  (ii) increases O_2/food; for respiration/ increased muscle contraction; increases removal of CO_2/lactic acid/heat from muscle (any 2)
 (c) (i) increases
  (ii) heat from muscles/exercise; can be lost
 (d) brain's activity not greatly changed/maintains essential functions/if blood reduced (diverted) would faint (any 1)

28 A

29 D

30 B

Chapter 9

31 (a) oxygen; water
 (b) (i) limewater; hydrogencarbonate indicator
  (ii) Tube 1: animal respiring; producing CO_2
   Tube 2: plant respiring too; but photosynthesizing more; therefore no CO_2
  (iii) give plant (and also insect) no light/put opaque cover over them both

32 (a)

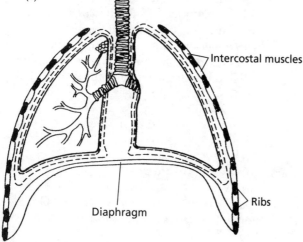

Intercostal muscles

Diaphragm

Ribs

 (b) intercostal muscles contract; ribs pulled upward and outward; diaphragm muscle contracts; becomes less domed/flatter; volume of chest/thorax increases; this drops pressure in chest/thorax/lungs; so air enters lungs (any 6)

33 (a) arteriole's blood contains 10.6 cm³ oxygen per 100 cm³

(b)

CO_2 O_2 → Blood

 (c) greater concentration of O_2 in air than in blood/greater concentration of CO_2 in blood than in air
 (d) large surface area; thin lining; permeable; wet; rich capillary supply (any 4)
 (e) (i) damage to alveolus wall/reduced surface area/smaller
  (ii) slower/reduced/less

34 (a) (i) thickened rings (of chitin)/tubular/ divides to finer tubes (any 1)
  (ii) filled with fluid (not empty), tubular (not spherical)/next to muscle cells (not capillaries) (any 2)
 (b) insect: air direct to cells; humans: air via blood

Chapter 10

35 (a) removal of waste products; of metabolism
 (b) (i) A: cortex; B: medulla; C: ureter
  (ii) urine
  (iii) bladder
  (iv) (renal artery labelled – the horizontal tube)
 (c) protein; molecules too large to pass through filter OR glucose; filtered but reabsorbed into blood

36 proteins broken down to amino acids; deamination in liver; produces ammonia; forms urea; passes to blood; in solution/in plasma; to kidneys; filtration of blood; urine formed; goes in ureter; to bladder; out of body via urethra (any 8) (N.B. logical sequence needed and good English) (2)

37 (a) filters blood; reabsorbs useful substances; and much water, leaving urine
 (b) (i) more water/no protein/no urea
  (ii) same glucose/temperature/osmotic or water potential value (any 2)
 (c) don't have to be hooked up to a machine

38 (a) (i) G
  (ii) A
 (b) (i) sweat gland secretes sweat; erector muscle relaxes
  (ii) water of sweat evaporates; using excess body heat to supply energy to do so; muscle allows hair to lie flatter; so reducing the layer of air which it traps (insulation)
 (c) capillaries just below surface; receive much blood carrying heat; heat radiates away

(d) (i) sea water on skin evaporates or cold sea; taking heat from skin

(ii) shivering = muscle contraction; this generates heat

Chapter 11

39

Stimulus	Sensitive part
Light	Eye/retina
Sound	Cochlea
Temperature (external)	Skin
Blood temperature/CO_2/ water concentration	Hypothalamus
Glucose concentration	Pancreas (islet tissue)
Chemicals in air	Nose

40
(i) A: lens; B: retina; C: optic nerve
(ii) F and A
(iii) F → G → A → D → B
(iv) B to inner part of C; to 4 o'clock out of C

Chapter 12

41 (a) A: cell membrane; B: nucleus; C: cytoplasm
(b) insulation
(c) (i) (grey matter of) spinal cord
(ii) impulse passes to terminal branches

42 C

43 (a) 1: pituitary, 2: adrenal, 3: islet tissue (of pancreas), 4: ovary
(b) (i) glucose level too low/too little energy to cells/faint
(ii) glucose level too high/kidney cannot reabsorb all glucose in nephron/diabetes

44

Comparison	Nervous	Hormonal
Nature of message	electrical	chemical;
Speed of message	fast	slow;
Duration of effect	very short	longer;
Accuracy of message	precise	more diffuse;
Speed of response	very fast	slower

45 (a) light/temperature/water/mineral salts/soil pH/CO_2 in air/O_2 in soil/genes (any 3)
(b) (i) part just behind tip grows most
(ii) grows/bends/curves towards light
(c) (i) positive phototropism
(ii) it must get light to photosynthesize/ grow
(d) tip alone is sensitive to light
(e) (i) substance/hormone that promotes growth; auxin; IAA (any 1)
(ii) (from the data, may not be auxin); if auxin, produced at tip and migrates down – more to unlit side; where it causes greater vacuolation/enlargement of cells

Chapter 13

46 (a) ulna

(b) biceps relaxes; triceps contracts
(c) muscles can only contract – requires a second one to lengthen them again/one muscle reverses the effect of the other

47 (a) X–Y relaxed = 100 mm; contracted = 73 mm; 27%; actin and myosin slide into each other; makes myofibrils shorter; and so shortens muscle
(b) larger curvature above; aerofoil shape; air travels faster (further) over upper surface; causing lower pressure on upper surface, and therefore causes lift

Chapter 14

48 (a) Stage 2: reduce leaf area; Stage 4: keep humidity high – both reduce water loss from cutting
(b) (i) sexual
(ii) asexual
(c) produce identical plants (a clone)/cheaper

49 (a) (i) N.B. on Fig. 1, *open* flower: ring at base, next to stalk (cf. Fig. 2 – lowest 1 cm)
(ii) fruit/pericarp
(iii) cf. Fig. 2: seeds (not ovules)
(iv) 1 sepals
2 four
3 open out to reveal petals; later bent right back when in flower; fall off when fruit formed
(b) (i) stigma
(ii) produce pollen
(c) many flowers leads to many seeds; over long time period – more chance of successful pollination; and survival of seeds (any 2)
(d) wind-pollinated flower has no large petals; no nectaries; has feathery stigma; exposed stigma; large anthers; exposed anthers (any 3)

50 (a) A: anther; B: stigma
(b) feathery stigma; exposed/large anthers; small petals (any 2)
(c) pollen of own species; of another plant, trapped on stigma from air

51 1: A, 2: D, 3: E, 4: B, 5: C

Chapter 15

52 B

53 D

54 (a) (i) food/O_2 pass to embryo; CO_2/waste chemicals pass to mother; a barrier between mother's and embryo's blood, which are kept separate; acts as life support system for embryo; passes antibodies to embryo (any 2)
(ii) acts as life-line/connects embryo to placenta; has blood vessel carrying air/food/O_2 from mother to embryo; has blood vessel carrying chemical

wastes/CO_2 from embryo to mother (any 2)

(b) protects embryo from knocks/from temp. change/supports embryo (any 1)

55 (a) FSH: **growth of follicle in ovary**
LH: **pituitary**
Oestrogen
Progesterone: **corpus luteum**

(b) feedback mechanism; oestrogen inhibits production of FSH/stimulates production of LH; progesterone inhibits production of FSH (any 2)

56 C

57 (a) eggs/ova cannot get through so sperm cannot fertilize them

(b) sperm penetrates ovum; and their nuclei fuse

(c) benefit, e.g. gives her a child; drawback, e.g. embryo could be damaged/multiple births

Chapter 16

58 (a) (i) A: plumule; B: radicle (root)
(ii) C: stores food; D: protects seed/embryo

(b) B longer, outside seed coat – technically germination complete; A just protruding

(c) (i) hypogeal
(ii) mass reduced; owing to respiration; energy needed for growth
(iii) dry at 100 °C in oven; weigh; heat more and reweigh to check mass is constant
(iv) water; warmth; air; live seed (any 2)

(d) (i) correct plots; joined by lines (1 mark off for each incorrect plot)
(ii) between day 10 and day 15 (20 germinate)

59 D (4.0 − 1.5 = 2.5%)

Chapter 17

60 (a) phenotype: visible or measurable characteristic; result of interaction of gene(s) and environment
heterozygous: genotype where 2 alleles (genes) for a particular characteristic/are different

(b) e.g. human blood group AB

(c) XY

(d) (i) **bb**   (BB also a possible genotype)
(ii)

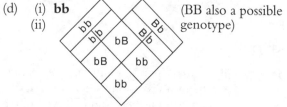

61 (a) only males affected

(b) female 9 must carry 1 haemophilia gene; to have a haemophiliac son (inherited through X); female 12 must carry 2 normal Xs; to have a normal daughter (whose other X carries the haemophilia gene from father)

(c) 9 × 10 marriage could give haemophiliac daughter;
(9) $XX^h \times X^hY$ (10);

gametes X^h X^h
\   /
$X^h X^h$ (haemophiliac)

62 B

63 (a) 1: chromosome/chromatid;
2: cell/plasma membrane

(b) 4

(c) chromosome *pairs* line up at equator/ chromosomes already divided (into chromatids)

(d) testis/ovary/gonads

(e) chromosome pairs split and go to either pole; spindle fibres disappear; cytoplasm constricts (to form 2 cells)

Chapter 18

64 (a) (i) mutation
(ii) coloration similar to toxic species; resulting in less predation; therefore preservation/increase in number of swallowtails
(iii) *different* variants; each may be better adapted to survive *different* selective pressures when they arise; so some always survive

(b) (i) C versus A: strong stem/earlier harvest/ greater number of seeds/yield of oil higher (975 versus 967.5 kg/hectare) (any 3)
C versus B: earlier maturity/yield of oil higher (975 versus 882)/greater number of seeds (any 3)
(ii) artificial/not forces of nature (natural selection); Man selects

65 (a) different number of chromosomes; egg cell is haploid/has half number of chromosomes

(b) easier to obtain (laid externally); large numbers; larger cells to work on (any 2)

(c) (i) B
(ii) genes of B; control characteristics/ phenotype

(d) stage 2: nucleus of egg removed
stage 3: liver/body cell removed
stage 4: liver cell nucleus put into ovum
stage 5: 'engineered' egg put into womb/uterus (of A)

(e) advantage: offspring identical to parent; with a desirable characteristic, e.g. high milk yield
disadvantage: offspring identical; so carry harmful characteristics of parent, e.g. susceptibility to disease OR loss of variety/other useful genes

(f) (i) evolution/mutation/natural selection
(ii) genes for longer necks arise by mutation; gives advantage; e.g. reaching higher

foliage for food; e.g. seeing predators easily; survive better; to breed; shorter-necked giraffes eliminated; offspring of mutants multiply (any 6)
(N.B. 3 marks for good logical English and correct use of scientific terms)

66 Breeding by Man for characteristics that he chooses (1 mark); 5 marks for plants *or* animals
Plants: name of method; e.g. cross-breeding of peas; for colour/scent/disease resistance; method (see Mendel's experiments, Unit 17.4)/use of vegetative propagation/of cloning of a selected variety; must relate to food production
Animals: named method; could include cross-breeding or artificial insemination (AI) or storage of sperm/eggs/embryos and surrogate mothers; must relate to food production

Chapter 19

67 (a) sycamore tree; lacewing larva
(b) secondary consumer
(c) energy/food flow or relationship/lower is fed on by higher organism
(d) sunlight
(e) increase
(f) loss in energy at each link; through respiration/not eating food species totally/e.g. lacewing exoskeleton indigestible; biomass of lacewing much smaller than tit/hawk therefore more lacewings/tits needed to sustain 1 hawk (any 3)

68 (a) squid; krill; sperm whale/seal
(b) krill provide energy for the rest of the food web
(c) whale/seal; top of food chain; pollutant concentrated up food chain
(d) (i) increase; predator gone
(ii) (A) bacteria/fungi
(B) colder; rate of decay slower/decay organisms reproduce slowly
(C) recycles elements; organic food to inorganic for plants
(e) more food from a krill individual; reproduce faster

69 (a) (i) A: transpiration/evaporation; B: urination/(defecation)
(ii) condenses; to rain/hail/snow/run off
(iii) camouflage
(iv) genes/chromosomes/inheritance
(b) (i) X: photosynthesis; Y: respiration
(ii) rabbit eats grass; fox eats rabbit
(iii) less CO_2 removed from air
(iv) nitrogen (or any other *element*)

Chapter 20

70 (a) (i) samples of equal volume/mass; remove large stones; weigh container (Wc), then weigh container + soil (W1); heat in oven; to $100\,°C$; cool in desiccator; if constant

mass; reweigh container + soil (W2);
$$\frac{W1 - W2}{W1} \times 100 = \% \text{ loss in mass (any 8)}$$
(ii) clay has higher % of water than sand
(iii) clay has colloidal (water-retentive) particles; tiny particles (more capillarity); less air, more water between particles (poorer drainage)
(b) For: replaces salts taken up by crops; in targetable amounts; easy to apply; quick acting; increase yield of crop (any 2)
Against: run-off can cause eutrophication; or nitrates in drinking water; can harm soil animals; expensive; can affect soil structure (any 2)

71 (a) (i) felling of American temperate rain forests
(ii) less CO_2 absorbed/O_2 given out/ burning wood adds CO_2 (any 2)
(b) (i) increase in population; needing building wood/land for cultivation or buildings or sport
(ii) increase in population; needing more wood/energy for heating or electricity or cars or chemicals from fossil fuels
(c) (i) gases such as CO_2/CH_4/SO_2; released from burning fuel or anaerobic decay (CH_4/methane); allow light in but not IR (heat) out
(ii) increase global temperature; disrupt weather; rise in sea level/melting of polar ice caps

72 Go to a number of sites; around the town; at varying distances from centre; sample lichens using table; make map of different levels joining sites of like pollution with lines (5) (N.B. plus 2 marks for English)

73 (a) 1981
(b) increasing catches; leads to decreased breeding stock/to unsustainable catches for the future

Chapter 21

74 (a) organism dependent on a host organism; for its food; causing host some harm
(b) female can fly up to 200 km to succeed in gaining a host; maggots difficult to kill; flies lay many eggs, so good chance of survival
(c) makes them sterile
(d) sterile males have high chance of mating with females; so a large number of matings result in eggs laid that do not hatch, which reduces population

75 (a) ladybird
(b) found to eat the cottony cushion
(c) reduction of numbers of a pest; by a natural predator/parasite
(d) e.g. guppy fish; eat mosquito larvae
(e) natural controlling agents present in Australia; absent in America

Index